BIRTH TO OLD AGE
Health in Transition

prepared by the U205 Course Team

THE OPEN UNIVERSITY
Health and Disease U205 Book V
A Second Level Course

THE OPEN UNIVERSITY PRESS

The U205 Course Team

U205 is a course whose writing and production has been the joint effort of many hands, a 'core course team', and colleagues who have written on specific aspects of the course but have not been involved throughout; together with editors, designers, and the BBC team.

Core Course Team

The following people have written or commented extensively on the whole course, been involved in all phases of its production and accept collective responsibility for its overall academic and teaching content.

Steven Rose (neurobiologist; course team chair; academic editor; Book VI coordinator)
Nick Black (community physician; Book IV and Book VIII coordinator)
Basiro Davey (immunologist; course manager; Book V coordinator)
Alastair Gray (health economist; Book III and Book VII coordinator)
Kevin McConway (statistician; Book I coordinator)
Jennie Popay (social policy analyst)
Jacqueline Stewart (managing editor)
Phil Strong (medical sociologist; academic editor; Book II coordinator)

Other authors

The following authors have contributed to the overall development of the course and have taken responsibility for writing specific sections of it.

Lynda Birke (ethologist; author, Book V)
Eric Bowers (parasitologist; staff tutor)
David Boswell (sociologist; author, Book II)
Eva Chapman (psychotherapist; author, Book V)
Andrew Learmonth (geographer; course team chair 1983; author, Book III)
Rosemary Lennard (medical practitioner; author, Books IV and V)
Jim Moore (historian of science; author, Book II)
Sean Murphy (neurobiologist; author, Book VI)
Rob Ransom (developmental biologist; author, Book IV)
George Watts (historian; author, Book II)

The following people have assisted with particular aspects or parts of the course.

Sylvia Bentley (course secretary)
Steve Best (illustrator)
Sheila Constantinou (BBC production assistant)
Debbie Crouch (designer)
Ann Hall (indexer)
Rachel Hardman (designer)
Mark Kesby (illustrator)
Liz Lane (editor)
Vic Lockwood (BBC producer)
Laurie Melton (librarian)
Sue Walker (editor)
Peter Wright (editor)

External consultant

Pamela M. Zinkin (paediatrician) Tropical Child Health Unit, The Institute of Child Health, London.

External assessors

Course assessor

Alwyn Smith President, Faculty of Community Medicine of the Royal Colleges of Physicians; Professor of Epidemiology and Social Oncology, University of Manchester.

Book V assessor

Anne Murcott Lecturer in Sociology of Medicine, Department of Psychological Medicine, Welsh National School of Medicine; Department of Sociology, University College, Cardiff.

Acknowledgements

The Course Team wishes to thank the following for their advice and contributions:

Sheila Adam (community physician) North West Thames Regional Health Authority.
John Ashton (community physician) Department of Community Health, University of Liverpool.
Graham Burchell (philosopher) Westminster College, Oxford University.
Dave Gee (National Health and Safety Officer) General, Municipal, Boilermakers and Associated Trades Union.
Hilary Graham (sociologist) Department of Applied Social Studies, University of Bradford.
Barbara Harrison (medical sociologist) Department of Social Science, South Bank Polytechnic.
Hilary Rose (sociologist) Department of Applied Social Studies, University of Bradford.

The Open University Press, Walton Hall, Milton Keynes MK7 6AA.

First published 1985.

Designed by the Graphic Design Group of the Open University.

Typeset and Printed by the Pindar Group of Companies, Scarborough, North Yorkshire.

ISBN 0335 15054 3

This text forms part of an Open University course. The complete list of books in the course is printed on the back cover.

For general availability of supporting material referred to in this book please write to: Open University Educational Enterprises Limited, 12 Cofferidge Close, Stony Stratford, Milton Keynes, MK11 1BY, Great Britain.

Further information on Open University courses may be obtained from the Admissions Office, The Open University, P.O. Box 48, Walton Hall, Milton Keynes, MK7 6AB.

About this book

A note for the general reader

Birth to Old Age: Health in Transition is the fifth in a series of eight books on the subject of health and disease. The book is designed so that it can be read on its own, like any other textbook, or studied as part of U205 *Health and Disease*, a second level course for Open University students. As well as the eight main textbooks and a Course Reader, *Health and Disease: A Reader**, the course consists of eleven TV programmes and five audiocassettes, plus various supplementary materials.

Open University students will receive an *Introduction and Guide* to the course, which sets out a study plan for the year's work. This is supplemented where appropriate in the text by more detailed directions for OU students; these study comments at the beginning of chapters are boxed for ease of reference. Also, in the text you will find instructions to refer to the Course Reader and to the associated audiotape sequences. However, it is quite possible to follow the argument without these, though your understanding will be enriched if you can do so. Major learning objectives are listed at the end of each chapter along with questions that allow students to assess how well they are achieving those objectives. The index allows key words (in bold type) to be looked up easily as an aid to revision as the course proceeds. There is also a further reading list for those who wish to pursue certain aspects of study beyond the limits of this book.

* Black, Nick *et al.* (eds) (1984) *Health and Disease: A Reader*, Open University Press.

A guide for OU students

Birth to Old Age: Health in Transition is a book about the changing experience of health throughout a lifetime in the United Kingdom in the twentieth century, and the biological, social, personal and historical influences on health during each phase of life.

Book V contains twenty chapters. The first four chapters provide a basic framework for the discussion of health from conception to death that follows in Chapters 5 to 20. In Chapter 1, we set out the principle themes that will emerge repeatedly as we discuss each phase of the lifespan in detail. Chapter 1 also serves as an introduction to Chapters 2 to 4, by explaining why we must focus first on three aspects of contemporary British life that have a profound influence on health experience *throughout* a lifetime: first, age itself and the ways in which our expectations about health and the need for medical surveillance vary across the lifespan (Chapter 2); then, economic circumstances, their variation with age and their effects on birth rates and hence on the requirement for health care in each generation (Chapter 3); and finally, the type of family unit we live in during different phases of life (Chapter 4).

We begin the sequential discussion of the lifespan in Chapter 5 with pregnancy and antenatal care. Chapter 6 focuses on birth and in Chapters 7 and 8 we examine the evolution of our ideas about childhood and discuss the normal course of growth and development during this period of rapid change. Factors influencing children's health are the subject of Chapter 9, including a re-examination of common assumptions about the detrimental effects of parental divorce and maternal employment.

In Chapter 10 we consider the health of adolescents and the effects of gender, through case studies on anorexia and motorcycle accidents.

Adulthood is discussed in Chapters 11 to 13, but it is important to emphasise that patterns of behaviour, biological development and social circumstances occuring in childhood have a profound effect on health in the years of maturity. From many possible aspects of adult life we have chosen to focus on sex and reproduction (Chapter 11), work and health (Chapter 12), and the menopause and the 'crisis' of mid-life (Chapter 13).

Ageing is the subject of Chapters 14 to 16 — what it feels like to grow older, the biological and social changes that accompany old age, and the need for help when physical or economic strength declines. In Chapters 17 to 19 we turn to the end of life — death and dying; the attitudes towards death prevalent in our culture today and in previous times; the contrast between our response to the death of a young person or a suicide and the death of someone in old age; and ethical questions raised by the medical management of dying. Finally, in Chapter 20 we look back over the lifespan and re-consider the fluctuating, transitory nature of health from birth to old age, and the ability to cope with change as an essential aspect of health.

Book V is the longest book in the course, spanning 6 weeks of your study calendar and requiring approximately 55 hours of work, including two TV programmes, several audiotapes and articles in the Course Reader, and a tutor marked assignment (TMA). The table below gives a more detailed breakdown to help you to pace your study. You need not follow it slavishly, but do not allow yourself to fall behind. As a rough guide, we suggest that you tackle Chapters 1–5 in the first week; Chapters 6–7 in the second week; Chapters 8–10 in the third; Chapters 11–14 in the fourth; Chapters 15–18 in the fifth; and Chapters 19–20 in the sixth and final week. If you find a section of the work difficult, do what you can at this stage, and return to rework the material at the end of your study of the book. We have allowed about 5 hours in the final week for revision and 3 hours for completing the TMA on Book V.

Study time for Book V (total 55 hours)

Chapter	Time/ hours		Course Reader	Time/ hours	TV/audio tapes	Time/ hours	Total per week/hours
1	$\frac{3}{4}$	$8\frac{3}{4}$					$10\frac{3}{4}$
2							
3	$1\frac{3}{4}$			1			
4	$1\frac{3}{4}$		Titmuss (1958)	$\frac{3}{4}$			
5	$2\frac{1}{2}$		Oakley (1981)		audio: *Antenatal care — women's views* (AC804)	$\frac{1}{4}$	
6	$2\frac{3}{4}$	5	Pillsbury (1978)	1	TV 5: *A suitable place to have a baby?* and related audio (AC804)	$1\frac{1}{4}$	9
7	$2\frac{1}{4}$		Blaxter (1983)	1	audio: *Children's perceptions of health and illness* (AC805)	$\frac{3}{4}$	
8	$2\frac{1}{4}$	$8\frac{3}{4}$					$7\frac{1}{4}$
9	$2\frac{1}{2}$						
10	4				audio: *'You just live for your bike'* (AC805)	$\frac{1}{2}$	
11	$3\frac{3}{4}$	9					$9\frac{1}{2}$
12	$1\frac{3}{4}$						
13	$1\frac{1}{4}$						
14	$2\frac{1}{4}$				audio: *When you get old* (AC805)	$\frac{1}{2}$	
15	$1\frac{1}{4}$	$6\frac{1}{4}$					$8\frac{1}{4}$
16	$1\frac{1}{2}$		Newton (1980)	$\frac{1}{4}$	TV 6: *Growing older*	$1\frac{1}{4}$	
17	2				audio: *Facing death* (AC805)	$\frac{1}{2}$	
18	$1\frac{1}{2}$						
19	$1\frac{1}{4}$	$2\frac{3}{4}$	Bowling and Cartwright (1982)	1	audio: *Ethical dilemmas* (AC805 and 806)	$\frac{3}{4}$	8
20	$1\frac{1}{2}$				audio: *Reactions to loss* (AC806)	$\frac{1}{2}$	
TMA	3						
Revision	5						

Contents

(Photo: Maria Bartha)

1 Health in transition

This book is about life from birth to old age in the United Kingdom and the fluctuating health experience of individuals at different points in this trajectory. In this endeavour, we shall take a more intimate look at the causes and consequences of health and disease than in earlier books in this course, emphasising that a human life is not simply a subject for quantitative analysis but also an individual experience on which people reflect and communicate. Thus, in addition to the theoretical and experimental dimensions, we have included personal accounts, extracts from interviews, diaries, poetry and other literary sources, either in the text or on audiotape, to bring alive the subjects of our inquiry — the men, women and children who share with the authors of this book the same historical period and geographical location.

A lifetime may span a century or more and in the UK currently averages 70–75 years. In such a long period an enormous diversity of experiences occur, dependent on numerous factors such as the date at which a given life began, the current age of the individual under study, their sex, social class, ethnic group, marital status, whether they have children, a job, a physical handicap, and so on. We have not attempted to discuss all these variations at every stage of the lifespan, but have chosen those health issues that ensure attention is paid to each of these aspects of diversity at some point in the book.

Against this background of variation, three organising principles emerge. The first is the importance of *life-course transitions* — those turning points in a person's life that are experienced as significant by the individual and at least some other members of his or her social world. A transition may be rapidly accomplished, for example a birth usually takes less than 24 hours and a wedding may be over in a few minutes, or it may take years of gradual change, as in puberty. Whatever the timescale over which change occurs, the person feels different afterwards and is treated differently by others in subtle or profound ways. Some rights and expectations associated with their previous state must be relinquished and a new set assumed; their status in the family or wider social world undergoes a shift, and a reappraisal of their self-image, roles and relationships takes place.

For example, during a pregnancy the baby exists as a growing, moving organism, distinctly human, since a foot or elbow may be felt through the mother's abdomen, but not yet fully a *person*. Suddenly, at birth, an individual male or female infant emerges with a unique face, fingerprints, personality. Not only has the baby made an irreversible transition from womb to world, but the parents and other family members undergo important changes too — from childlessness to parenthood perhaps, or grandparenthood; from being the only child to being an older brother or sister. Transitions can have significant consequences for the health of those affected by change, and these form the focus of several chapters in this book.

The second theme which runs throughout our discussion is the interaction of three important influences on health during a person's lifetime — their *biological state*, the *society* in which they live, and their *personal history*. Look at Table 1.1, which sets out the most common turning points in a lifetime.

□ Which transitions are predominately (i) biological, (ii) social and (iii) personal aspects of a lifetime?

■ (i) Birth, puberty, menstruation, menopause and death are transitions that are biologically determined, even though they also have social and personal connotations.

(ii) Attendance at school, criminal responsibility, the ages of sexual or marital consent, eligibility for armed service, voting age, rights of tenancy or mortgage, and retirement from work, are all socially determined transitions, enforced not only by custom but often by law.

(iii) In addition to the influence of social and biological pressures, marriage, parenthood and starting

Table 1.1 Birth to death: the principal biological, social and personal transitions of an average lifetime in the UK in the 1980s (optional transitions are shown in square brackets)

Age/years	Women	Both sexes	Men
0.5		registration of birth	
3		[playgroup]	
5		compulsory schooling begins	
10		can be held responsible for a crime	
		physical changes of puberty may begin	
12	menarche (39% of girls menstruating)*		
16		age of heterosexual consent	puberty complete (only 0.6% of boys have testicles still undescended)*
		minimum school-leaving age	
		minimum age of marriage (requires parental consent)	
		[parenthood may commence]	
		[full-time employment may commence]	
17		eligible for armed services	
18		voting age	
		can marry without parental consent	
		eligible for council-house tenancy/ mortgage	
21			age of homosexual consent
50	menopause (average age)		
55			compulsory retirement from selected occupations, e.g. airline pilots
60	retirement/eligible for State pension		
65			retirement/eligible for State pension
70			death (average age); registration of death
75	death (average age); registration of death		

* Percentages relating to menstruation and testicular development from National Child Development Study, 1958.

a job are also experienced as personal transitions, in the sense that they are neither an inevitable consequence of biological development, nor, on the face of it, socially prescribed acts in which everyone *must* participate.

Note that biological transitions are shared by all members of the human species, whatever their ethnic group or geographical location. However, the *meaning* attached to these biological changes varies greatly between societies. In one, the onset of menstruation may be a cause for public celebration, in another, a private mystery or a source of embarrassment.

Transitions that are determined by society tend to have a rather weak correspondence with the biological state of the individual. For example, reproductive fertility usually occurs several years before sexual relationships inside or outside marriage are permitted by law in the UK. Compulsory entry into formal education, the right to vote or bear arms and retirement from work occur on a particular *day*, regardless of the physical or emotional state of the individual. However, all these transitions may affect the health and well-being of the person undergoing change, though not in a rigidly predictable way. Retirement, for example, may result in better health, more relaxation and freedom to pursue personal interests, or boredom, depression and a sense of life being a downhill slide to the grave.

Society shapes the experience of life, and hence the experience of health and disease, in numerous ways. Some of these flow from cultural values, moral judgements and traditional practices — would some elderly people still feel on the scrapheap for example, if society placed more value on old age? Would depression and anxiety be as common as they are for women undergoing the menopause or following the birth of a baby, if the view of a woman's role in society was different? And the experience of any transition is also greatly influenced by another social dimension — one's economic circumstances. Retiring to a seaside bungalow on a company pension does not have the same health consequences as living in an inner-city tenement on State benefits.

Superimposed on these biological and social influences are the effects of events in our personal life history. Most people go to school, but for some the experience was liberatory, for others brutalising. Serious loss or disruption in childhood, for example, through the death of a parent or several changes of school seems to have consequences for health in later life. Personal transitions such as these go on occurring in adulthood, with only tenuous regard to biological state or the socially-determined transitions enacted on a particular date.

□ Can you suggest examples?

■ Marriage, divorce, bereavement, promotion at work, redundancy, moving house, winning the pools, becoming a grandparent, suffering a burglary, accidental injury, and many others, both planned for and totally unexpected.

Whatever the interaction of biology, society and personal history in a given transition, change tends to be viewed with a certain amount of apprehension. Anthropologists interpret the rituals and practices of cultures at times of transition as defences against contamination of the whole culture by change — as though the person in transition opens a window to instability which could flood in and disrupt not only their own life, but that of the culture as a whole. Similar models have been applied to the 'rites of passage' common in the UK. According to this analysis, christenings, 'coming of age' parties, weddings, the 'golden handshake' and the funeral ceremony, can be seen partly as expressions of cultural anxiety showered on the individuals in transition as a propitiating gesture by those afraid of change. You may not agree with this view entirely, but you can probably empathise with the flood of relief when a birth or wedding is accomplished without mishap, or, possibly, that the retirement collection just contributed to was not your own.

The way in which each person copes with change is itself shaped by their biological state, social circumstances and personal history. Some people thrive on changes, where others find them threatening. Transitions require people to let go their attachments to old identities and to gradually build up new ones that incorporate new circumstances. Most people feel a bit at sea while the process of reassessment and reconstruction is underway — vulnerable and uneasy until the new roles settle down and relationships feel familiar once more. Sometimes the adjustment proves very difficult to make and health may suffer as a consequence. And ill-health or disablement is *itself* an important transition through which everyone passes at sometime in life. This is all too obvious when a person suffers the permanent loss of a faculty, but even a common cold can rattle the self-image of people who feel relentlessly robust and 'above' illness.

However, we must not push the importance of transitions too far — the health of a person who is not undergoing any perceptible change is still being influenced by their biological, social and personal worlds. And there is a limit to how much we can disentangle these influences.

Do some adolescents have a difficult time, for example, because their biology is in uproar, or because authority figures such as parents, teachers, police, and potential employers have an expectation that adolescents are difficult? Obviously there is no definitive answer, but by analysing health through the lifetime from these three perspectives, we believe that a better understanding will emerge.

Finally we must consider the third organising principle of this book — that of history. Not the personal history of individuals, but the national and international history which underlies the shape of modern society. In order to understand contemporary views of the lifespan, we must stand back and ask 'has it always been thus?' An *historical perspective* enables us to step outside the largely unquestioned assumptions about what is normal or natural in the health experience of a lifetime, and uncover some surprising realisations. Sometimes elements of the social organisation of daily life that seem to be fixed and unchanging turn out not to be: for example, the image of childhood held today and the notion of housewives who do not work outside the home, are relatively recent inventions. Conversely, ideas about the 'good old days' when extended families took care of their members, young and old, turn out to be largely fictional. Despite the advances of the twentieth century, people are not as different from their ancestors as they may have thought.

The major part of this book deals with the lifespan in chronological sequence from conception to death, viewed through the prism of the three organising principles that we have just described: the importance of transitions; the interaction of biology, society and personal history in the causes and experience of ill-health; and the need for a broad historical perspective in order to make sense of modern concepts about each phase of life.

However, before we can begin discussing the sequential features of health through a lifetime, some important foundations must be laid. There are several critical aspects of life in the UK in the 1980s that shape each person's experience of growing up and growing old. The first is perhaps the most obvious and therefore the easiest to overlook — that of age itself.

The type of childhood experienced by children in the 1980s is very different from that of their parents, and in turn of their grandparents. As a consequence, the *image* of childhood and the rights, roles and health expectations of children have changed very significantly, even in this century. The same could be argued for each of the 'phases of life' now distinguished in a lifetime. The meaning attached to terms such as *child*, *adolescent*, *adult*, or *elderly person* in British society today, reflects a complex set of expectations about the appropriate behaviour, lifestyle and health of each of these '*age-grades*' — as they are known by sociologists. These expectations extend to the amount of attention people receive from health services at different ages. In this century, some age-groups have seen a spectacular increase in the extent to which their health is monitored and researched, and in the allocation of resources to the prevention of ill-health and its treatment — while other age-groups suffer from apparent neglect. Therefore, we have prepared an overview of the lifespan in terms of the categorisation of people into clearly defined age-groups, and the medical surveillance that each receives.

Another important influence on health throughout a lifetime is the fluctuation of economic circumstances, for example, when a person enters or leaves paid employment. For some occupations, income grows fairly steadily with age — for others, it reaches a peak well before midlife, and may decline in later years. Economic influences on health are far-reaching: for example, family income seems to be related to the timing and number of births. But the total number of births in any year can vary considerably and this in turn may partly determine whether there will be a shortage or excess of school places, jobs, health services, and provision for the elderly or disabled for people in that *birth cohort*. So your health experience may not only be affected by the social class into which you were born, but also precisely when you were born, how many others were born in that year, and what social policies came and went during each phase of your life. Moreover, changes in the *demographic structure* of a society (that is the relative proportion of people of different ages) can create new social issues, such as the 'ageing population'.

Finally, there is the influence of the type of family unit a person lives in at different times in their life. Health care begins at home, and family life (or lack of it) has consequences for health in all age groups. Families do not remain static for most people — periods of living with one or more others are usually interspersed with periods of living alone, and the number of people a person shares their home with also fluctuates. There have been significant shifts in the composition of families during this century: for example, the divorce rate has risen, but fewer marriages are broken by death, and remarriage is now more common than ever before. As a result, fewer families conform to the 'nuclear family' image than is often imagined.

These three fundamental influences on health throughout life — age-grading, economics, and family structure — are discussed in depth in the next three chapters. They form an essential basis from which to launch into the detailed chronological account of a lifetime of health and disease.

2 Age and surveillance

This chapter reintroduces some terms and concepts that were first discussed in Book I, *Studying Health and Disease*; notably, conflict and functionalist models of explanation (Chapter 11), and problems in defining 'normal' health and making a medical diagnosis (Chapter 2).

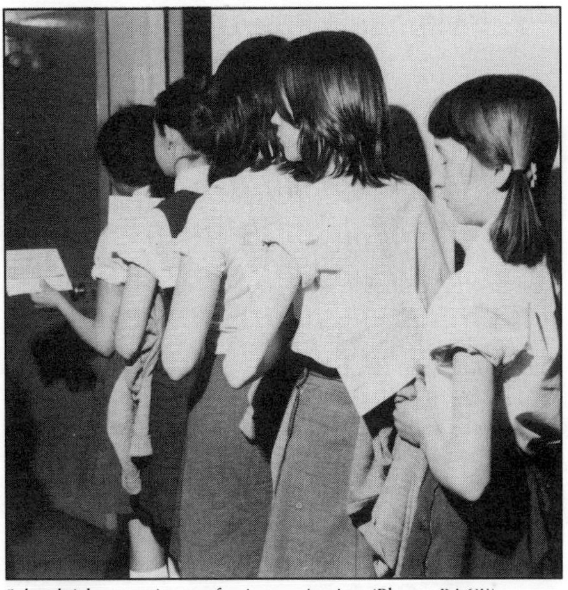

Schoolgirls queueing up for immunisation (Photo: PACE)

All the world's a stage,
And all the men and women merely players;
They have their exits and their entrances,
And one man in his time plays many parts,
His acts being seven ages. At first the infant,
Mewling and puking in the nurse's arms.
And then the whining schoolboy, with his satchel
And shining, morning face, creeping like a snail
Unwillingly to school. And then the lover,
Sighing like a furnace, with a woeful ballad
Made to his mistress' eyebrow. Then a soldier,
Full of strange oaths and bearded like the pard,
Jealous in honour, sudden and quick in quarrel,
Seeking the bubble reputation,
Even in the cannon's mouth. And then the justice,
In fair round belly with good capon lin'd,
With eyes severe and beard of formal cut,
Full of wise saws and modern instances;
And so he plays his part. The sixth age
Shifts into the lean and slippered pantaloon,
With spectacles on nose and pouch on side,
His youthful hose, well sav'd, a world too wide
For his shrunk shank, and his big manly voice,
Turning again toward childish treble, pipes
And whistles in his sound. Last scene of all,
That ends this strange eventful history,
Is second childishness, and mere oblivion,
Sans teeth, sans eyes, sans taste, sans everything.

(Jacques, in William Shakespeare, *As You Like It*, II. vii. 139–166, *c.*1599)

This speech from Shakespeare's play *As You Like It*, though written in the sixteenth century, describes a person's life passing through seven 'ages' that are still recognisable to British men and women four centuries later. People from other ethnic groups within the UK, or from other cultures around the world do not always partition a lifetime into precisely the same phases, but all use age as an important indicator of the status of one individual relative to another. Grading people according to their age permeates every aspect of life. For example, age is central to health, both in terms of the biological state of the cells and organs that maintain life, and the amount of help and attention people attract from family and professional health care services.

□ Go through the extract from *As You Like It*, and list all the ways in which, from a modern perspective, health or issues related to health care could be involved, even if only indirectly.

■ Some things are fairly obvious. Both mewling and puking infants and those experiencing second childishness need special care. Shakespeare points graphically to the physical degeneration that we experience as we grow older. But there are hints of other things too. Perhaps the whining schoolboy is eventually sent to a child guidance clinic; the sighing lover gets some valium from his GP; the soldier, seeking the 'bubble reputation even in the cannon's mouth' ends up a quadriplegic; the JP with the 'fair round belly' has a heart attack. And so on.

In this chapter we shall be looking at the social aspects of age, particularly in the UK, and discussing the consequences for our health. One important element in this is the extent to which a person's health is monitored at different times in life. We shall examine this surveillance of health in the second half of the chapter.

All the parts we play in life have their own health problems. Some of these are biologically given — for example, the common infectious diseases of childhood to which British adults develop immunity. Others are more social in origin: indeed some derive from the way a particular culture thinks about people in a certain age-group. An obvious example here is the sanction given to adults to smoke cigarettes and drink alcohol — an aspect of 'grown up' behaviour that is frowned upon when children mimic it. Age is a social as well as biological phenomenon.

A social analysis of age

All societies are characterised by hierarchy (stratification), and a classic way to start a *social* analysis is to look at these power relationships.*

□ Go back to the speech from Shakespeare and describe which age holds the power, which ages do not, and consider the images used to depict this.

■ In this little picture of the world, it is the age of the 'justice' that holds the power. To decide what counts as justice is power indeed. And the justice looks and behaves like a man with power. His eyes are severe, he dresses formally, he pronounces freely on what the world is like (full of wise saws and modern sayings), and he seems to be doing well out of life — he's comfortably fat and he also takes bribes ('capon lin'd' refers to this). Every other age is either complaining or incompetent. The infant and the geriatric have to be looked after by others. The schoolboy is whining, the lover is sighing, the ambitious soldier is obliged to risk his life in the pursuit of power, and the slippered pantaloon is past it.

In social science jargon, what Shakespeare is describing is the Elizabethan *age-grading system*. Age is a fundamental dimension on which people in every society are stratified. In Shakespeare's England, this stratification seems to result in elements of conflict between different age-groups, as well as in harmony and mutual benefit.† Both themes will crop up repeatedly throughout this book. People of different ages both need and aid one another and yet, at the same time, are also fundamentally in conflict with one another, and each of these factors has major consequences for health. Shakespeare's character Jacques gives most emphasis to conflict, and his view is shared by many social analysts of age-grading systems. Conversely, the rhetoric of politicians, for example, tends to emphasise harmony — adults caring for their children and old folk.

So different ages hold different amounts of power. Is this biologically or socially determined? One way to examine this is to compare our own system with those of other societies. If every culture has the same system, then a largely biological account begins to look plausible. If, however, there are major differences as well as some similarities, we shall need social explanations too.

A classic study was conducted in pre-war rural Ireland by two American anthropologists, Conrad Arensburg and Solon Kimball. In this peasant society, only the eldest son could inherit the farm, but he was not allowed to marry until he had inherited. Until then, he was in some ways a child, even though he might be in his fifties. 'You can be a boy forever as long as your old fellow's alive.' (Arensburg and Kimball, 1968, first published 1940.

What this suggests is that, in different cultures, people of the same chronological age can hold very different amounts of power, depending on their economic and social circumstances. As these change, so does the age-grading system. When Ireland was visited in the late eighteenth century by the English economist and traveller, Arthur Young, at a time when its economy was booming, he commented instead on the extraordinarily early age at which people married and the great independence of Irish youth.

For all this change, however, at any one point there are

*This is discussed in *The Health of Nations*, Chapter 6, The Open University (1985), U205 *Health and Disease*, Book III.

†Conflict and functionalist models of explanation in the social sciences are discussed in *Studying Health and Disease*, Chapter 11, The Open University (1985), U205 *Health and Disease*, Book I.

relatively settled rules concerning *age-appropriate behaviour*. Not only are there often laws concerning the ages at which one may or may not undertake various activities, but there is a whole host of informal sanctions and expectations for those who break other, less serious age-related rules. The following phrases are typical of our own society: 'That's childish'. 'He's always been forty', 'It's about time he got married and settled down', 'Mutton dressed as lamb', 'She's far too young for that sort of thing', and so on.

□ Think back to the Shakespeare quotation — would its description of different ages fit everyone in the UK?

■ No — the most obvious omission is that it says nothing about women. But on closer analysis you'll see that the description is of a middle-class Englishman who goes to school, joins the army, and ends up as a magistrate. It says nothing about the 'seven ages' of a peasant or other working men.

Shakespeare's analysis of the Elizabethan age-grading system leaves out women altogether perhaps because the systems for men and women typically differ. Since men are socially the more powerful gender, male mutton is allowed to pass for lamb rather longer — indeed, grey hair and wrinkles may be considered 'distinguished' whereas women's power is often linked to the dominant cultural association of sexual attractiveness with youthful appearance. Thus in most societies, it is sometimes more appropriate to talk of two age-grading systems, one for women and one for men. Many of the key age terms in English are also gender terms, 'boys' and 'girls', 'men' and 'women' function as both. Moreover, just as you could be a 'boy' forever in pre-war rural Ireland and excluded from the adult world, so in contemporary British society, women may be referred to and treated as 'girls', if not forever, then still into their forties and fifties.

Yet the two systems are not entirely separate. Terms like 'adult' and 'young people' refer to either sex, while at each end of the life-cycle, there is a distinct tendency to minimise some of the standard gender differences. Babies are often just babies rather than boys or girls. More surprisingly, at first, some older women, particularly after the menopause, may take on some of the social characteristics and the authority usually accorded to men. Ena Sharples in the television series *Coronation Street* was a classic British example, but the same phenomenon is found in many different cultures — the 'wise woman' venerated for her age and experience.

Health, disease and age-grading

Let us examine the conflict of interests between age-groups and the consequences of this for health. This conflict is illustrated most starkly by the different value placed on youth and age. The following extract is from a study of death by the American sociologist, David Sudnow:

> Two persons in similar physical condition may be differentially designated dead or not. For example, a young child was brought into the emergency room with no registering heartbeat, respiration, or pulse — the standard 'signs of death' — and was, through a rather dramatic stimulation procedure involving the co-ordinated work of a large team of doctors and nurses, revived for a period of eleven hours. On the same evening, shortly after the child's arrival, an elderly person who presented the same physical signs, with — as one physician later stated in conversation — no discernible differences from the child in skin color, warmth, etc, arrived in the emergency room and was almost immediately pronounced dead, with no attempts at stimulation instituted. A nurse remarked, later in the evening, 'They (the doctors) would never have done that to the old lady (attempt heart stimulation) even though I've seen it work on them too'. During the period when emergency resuscitation equipment was being readied for the child, an intern instituted mouth-to-mouth resuscitation. This same intern was shortly relieved by oxygen machinery, and when the woman arrived, he was the one who pronounced her dead. He reported shortly afterwards that he could never bring himself to put his mouth to 'an old lady's like that'. (David Sudnow, 'Dead on Arrival' quoted in Strauss, 1970, pp.113–14)

In other words, not only are the young, unlike the elderly, put through a highly elaborate system of formal education, but very considerable efforts are made to ensure their health; incidents such as the one recorded above are not uncommon in the social science literature. There is also, as we shall see later, an enormously elaborate system for monitoring children's health in industrialised countries; something that does not exist for the elderly.

□ Why should so much effort be expended on the health of the very young and so relatively little on that of the very old, when both may be equally dependent on others?

■ One of the most powerful tendencies in social life is for people to be valued according to their present or potential contribution to that life. Very young children may sometimes be a burden now as they 'mewl and puke' but they are fascinating in their own right because they are growing and developing. They represent the future of the society, and they are a source of potential support and pride for their parents. Children also have many years of life before them. None of this is normally true for the elderly. If the past is highly valued this may increase the status of the old, but industrialised societies tend to look to the future, not the past. Only if the old control the inheritance — as in pre-war Ireland — do they usually inspire veneration.

No other conflict of interest between the ages has such major health effects. Nonetheless, there are many other struggles which are of some potential importance; though not all their effects are easy to measure. Those designated young may be persuaded to do dangerous things to prove their worth; seeking the bubble reputation even in the cannon's mouth. The very fact of exclusion from power may also have effects upon one's health. To be a 'boy' or a 'girl' enforces both a distinctive lifestyle and a characteristic way of viewing oneself in the world. This seems to influence behaviours that have consequences for health, for example, the preponderance of motor-cycle accidents among adolescent boys and young men, and anorexia nervosa (the 'slimmer's disease') among girls, as you will see in Chapter 10. The 'rules' governing age-appropriate behaviour for this age-group interact with those shaping appropriate *gender roles* for each sex. (*Gender* refers to learned, socially-conditioned behaviour as distinct from sex differences, which are biologically determined.)

Finally, behaviour that is considered acceptable at one age may be felt to be 'sick' at another. The young teenage girl who gets pregnant may be viewed by some as both immoral and disturbed. What counts as 'healthy' is therefore partly a matter of what is considered appropriate of a particular age.

Age and industrialisation

The fact that we know our ages with chronological accuracy is a recent development linked to industrialisation. In industrial societies, our exact age is one of the most important parts of our biography. Not only do most of us celebrate the anniversary of the day we were born, but all kinds of routine bureaucratic transactions require the precise date of our birth. At different ages we can vote, be called up, be held responsible for crime, be sent to school, claim cheap forms of travel, get different life-insurance rates, join or leave particular clubs, or have to retire. But in most non-literate societies, there is no need for precision in this particular matter, and dating may be carried out on a purely local time-scale. Thus, in a peasant society, if a doctor is to take an adequate history from a patient he or she might need to know the year of the big famine; when the river overflowed its banks; when the army came; and so on. The advent of complex bureaucratic methods of organisation and control enforces different means of quantifying individual age, with an objective meaning to those who live beyond that particular village or province. This parallels the development of mechanisms for accurately telling the time of day, which enabled communities to act in a synchronised way, as in the organisation of collective labour.

Industrialisation also has significant effects on the different stages into which societies divide the life span and on the transition from one stage to another. Two features here deserve special attention, childhood and the transition to old age. Commenting on the latter, a young Chinese man remarked, 'In the new society, everyone has a job, and everyone has to retire'. This puts the matter precisely. Retirement at an officially given age, whether 60 or 65, is a phenomenon principally of industrial societies. In pre-industrial societies, whether in China or the UK, most people carried on working until illness or the demands of a younger generation forced them to go.

This formalisation of age-grading in industrial societies is also found at the other end of the life span. Just as older adults are now formally excluded from the workforce, so too are children; indeed, there is now a 'cult' of childhood in modern industrial societies that once destroyed children's health as cheap labour in mines and factories. Whereas the elderly are left largely to their own devices, children are protected and watched over. The key aspect of this is the compulsory provision of schools — organisations that typically operate a rigid internal age-grading system. Each child belongs to a separate 'year' or 'class', and by informal consent each year possesses a special status in a hierarchy of prestige.

Let us summarise the argument so far. We have argued, first, that every age has its own infirmities; second, that age is a form of *stratification* — age-groups have different powers and there can be a conflict of interests between them; third, that different cultures have different age-grading systems shaped by particular social and economic circumstances; fourth, that stratification by age overlaps with that by gender; and, fifth, that industrial societies use elaborate, formal methods to regulate certain aspects of age. In the remainder of this chapter we shall examine a further aspect of both age-grading and industrialisation that has profound medical consequences — formal surveillance of the nation's health.

Health and surveillance

The Unknown Citizen

(To JS/07/M/378
This Marble Monument
is erected by the State)

He was found by the Bureau of Statistics to be
One against whom there was no official complaint,
And all the reports on his conduct agree
That in the modern sense of an old-fashioned word he
was a saint

For in everything he did he served the Greater
Community.
Except for the War till the day he retired
He worked in a factory and never got fired,
But satisfied his employers, Fudge Motors Inc.
Yet he wasn't a scab or odd in his views,
For his Union reports that he paid his dues,
(Our report on his Union shows it was sound)
And our Social Psychology workers found
That he was popular with his mates and liked a drink.
The press are convinced that he bought a paper every
day
And that his reactions to advertisements were normal
in every way.
Policies taken out in his name prove that he was fully
insured
And his Health-card shows he was once in hospital
but left it cured.
Both Producers Research and High-Grade Living
declare
He was fully sensible to the advantages of the
Instalment Plan
And had everything necessary to the Modern Man,
A phonograph, a radio, a car and a frigidaire.
Our researchers into Public Opinion are content
That he held the proper opinions for the time of year;
When there was peace, he was for peace; when there
was war he went.
He was married and added five children to the
population,
Which our Eugenist says was the right number for a
parent of his generation.
And our teachers report that he never interfered with
their education.
Was he free? Was he happy? The question is absurd:
Had anything been wrong we surely would have heard.

(W.H. Auden, written in the 1940s, 1969 edn, pp.146–47)

□ What similarities and differences do you notice in the subject of Auden's poem compared with the speech from Shakespeare's play?

■ Once again the focus of attention is male but this time the subject is more working class.

□ Both Auden and Shakespeare reveal a certain ironic cynicism in these writings, but are they being cynical about the same things?

■ Shakespeare is drawing attention to the posturing of individual men living up to society's expectations of appropriate behaviour as they pass through life; Auden aims his irony not at the individual but at the State and the other organisations involved in watching, measuring and recording every aspect of life.

Auden's poem makes a number of important points about *surveillance*. For a start, there is an awful lot of it. All kinds of organisations, employers, unions and hospitals, are keeping records on those with whom they come into contact. Moreover, in addition to these organisations, there are entire professions that specialise in assessing people — social psychologists, public opinion researchers and demographers. Some disciplines in particular, such as economics, psychology and medicine make a good deal of their living from the promise of better surveillance. Indeed, this course could not have been written without the mountain of official statistics collected by Government Departments, research institutes, GPs, the school health service, and so forth.

In itself surveillance is nothing new. All of us watch each other, and sometimes report to third parties what we observe — 'gossip' is one form of this. And more bureaucratic forms of observation have a long history. In medieval Europe, for example, the Church oversaw many areas of personal life. What is new about the surveillance on which Auden reports is its sheer volume and the number of different organisations and occupations engaged in it.

Surveillance of *health* has obvious advantages for the person under observation. A visit to the doctor may involve blood pressure being measured, likewise pulse rate, temperature, perhaps a blood or urine test — indeed, unless certain measurements are made, the doctor cannot intervene when help is needed. Similarly, unless governments know (for example) how many women of childbearing age the population contains, or how many people are over 70, planning maternity services or health care for the elderly would be impossible. The information gleaned from such data is central to our health and to the conduct of our daily lives.

Surveillance is, however, a rather unpleasant word, normally associated with the activities of the police or secret service — someone under surveillance is defined as 'not trusted to go about unwatched' (Concise Oxford Dictionary, 3rd edition). Why choose it to describe a form of observation that is apparently beneficial to our well-being? The term has come into fashion because, although there are undoubtedly many major advantages to such monitoring, there are also some disadvantages; some aspects to the process that themselves need watching. In reviewing the forms of surveillance that occur throughout an individual's lifetime in the UK, we must consider the costs as well as the benefits. In Auden's poem, the monitoring of health is only a small part of a much wider social surveillance.

□ Can you offer any suggestions as to why JS/07/M/378 had not been of much interest to those professions who collect and interpret data related to health?

■ The most obvious answer is that he hadn't suffered much ill-health — one hospital visit from which he was discharged 'cured'. Had he been chronically ill, or disabled, or afflicted by an unusual disease, more attention would have been paid to him. You might also have pondered on whether we would know more about his health if the poem had been written about a *child* rather than an adult, or even if JS/07/M/378 had been a *woman*, rather than a man.

This raises a related theme that will emerge strongly in the remaining chapters of this book — the concept of 'normality' in health, and the ways in which the definition of what is normal is affected by the age and often the sex of the person under surveillance.

Normality

In Auden's poem, no one complained about the deceased during his lifetime because he was considered *normal* in every possible way: he wasn't 'odd in his views', he held the proper opinions for the time of year and he had the right number of children for a parent of his generation. The concept of *normality* is central to *medical surveillance*.

□ What instances have you experienced so far in your life of being assessed for evidence of normal health?

■ When you or any children you may have were born you would have been checked carefully against a rating scale that assesses whether vital functions (such as breathing and heart rate) are normal. At school you are bound to have been measured and weighed at regular health checks and had your eyesight and hearing tested and your teeth inspected, to assess whether your growth and development were normal for your age. Pregnant women are also monitored closely, for example, by routine sampling of their blood and urine. You may have undergone a medical check-up for insurance purposes or before starting a new job.

Even at the end of life, a doctor will check to see if you are showing the 'normal' signs of death before filling in the appropriate certificate.

□ Are these 'signs of death' objective scientific measurements, which are the same for everyone?

■ As you saw from David Sudnow's account earlier, very similar signs may be interpreted differently if the patient is young or old.

The method by which 'normal' parameters of health are defined depends ideally upon *systematic measurement* of a large number of people who are showing no overt signs of disease. Significant deviations from these norms are then considered indicative of pathology. However, this method has its pitfalls. For example, a diagnostic sign for diabetes is the presence of sugar above a certain concentration in the urine, but a significant number of people who are not apparently diabetic, could be classified as such on the basis of the amount of sugar they excrete.*

This points up one criticism of medical surveillance: the limits of what is considered normal are usually defined by measurements taken on people with *disease* rather than with *health*. Where the measurements *have* been taken on a very large sample of healthy people, the definition of normal has had to be stretched to cover a very wide range. For example, children's height and weight are measured routinely by school health officers at regular intervals and compared with normal growth charts; only 3 out of every one hundred children are considered to be shorter than normal, and 3 per hundred abnormally tall. On investigation, few of these 'abnormal' children prove to have a medical problem that affects their growth (this subject is discussed fully in Chapter 8). This raises the question of whether all forms of medical surveillance are equally useful or effective. New and expensive methods for measuring this or that aspect of health are continually being devised. Do they actually work? And even if they do, are they worth the money? And what are the consequences for those people designated as 'abnormal'?

Given that the definition of abnormality is open to question, we must consider the consequences of attaching a medical label to individuals who fall outside the agreed norms. At one level, *medical labelling* is a perfectly reasonable, indeed, an essential activity. In order to treat patients appropriately, nurses and doctors need to know whether this patient is a diabetic, or that patient is deaf. So, too, do those who administer pensions and special allowances. However, there are two problems that can make the use of medical labels harmful rather than helpful. We have already mentioned the often considerable problem of the accuracy with which a label is applied: some diagnoses are based on the fairly arbitrary selection of a single cut-off point on what is in fact a continuum.

□ Can you suggest another problem of medical labelling?

■ Some diagnoses are themselves highly controversial, and may sometimes be based on dubious assumptions about the origin of the patient's 'symptoms'.†

In other words, given the uncertainty that surrounds so many medical labels, there is a real possibility that some people will be 'treated' for 'problems' that they may not necessarily have, will be cast as sick rather than healthy,

*This diagnostic problem with diabetes is discussed more fully in Book I, *Studying Health and Disease*, Chapter 2.

†This is discussed in the context of hysteria in *Medical Knowledge: Doubt and Certainty*, Chapter 8, The Open University (1985) U205 *Health and Disease*, Book II.

and will occupy resources that might have been better spent elsewhere.

The expansion of medical surveillance

One side-effect of the growing attention to health monitoring is that the relevant professions have extended their scope to cover more and more aspects of daily life. However, there simply are not the adequate resources to keep everyone's health under constant professional observation throughout their lifetime. In consequence, the 'laity' (particularly parents) have been increasingly co-opted into collecting data on behalf of the 'professions'. In some Health Districts, extremely detailed record books are issued to parents who are instructed to measure numerous aspects of the growth and development of their offspring — for example, the dates on which the baby started eating solid foods, dates of immunisations, and the age at which each tooth emerged. Table 2.1 shows the 'parents observation record' from one such record book.

On the one hand, co-opting parents onto the surveillance team can be seen as giving them greater autonomy and involvement with their child's health care. On the other, parents may become needlessly anxious about their child's progress — 'is it normal, and how can I tell?' These judgements are seen to be within the domain of the professional health-care specialist: parents cannot interpret the data they collect, but must rely on the verdict of 'experts'. This may lead to non-professional people belittling their own skills and coming to depend increasingly on expert advice. Thus some writers assert that a 'professionalisation of motherhood' has taken place among the middle classes, with a paperback child-psychology book on every shelf. On this account, the professions have co-opted (critics would say seduced) those whom they cannot directly control. But who 'watches the watchers'?

Table 2.1 Parent's observation record
(From the Child Health Record booklet compiled by the Society of Nurse Advisors (Child Health), 1983)

My child first:	Age	Date
smiled		
reached for a toy		
slept through the night		
crawled		
stood up		
used a spoon		
said the first word		
walked unaided		
put 2 to 3 words together		
pointed to parts of body when asked		
used a knife and fork		
was dry during the day		
was dry day and night		
placed 3 bricks in a tower		
drew a circle		
bounced a ball		
caught a ball		
recognised and named 3 colours		
pedalled a tricycle		
learned to swim		

The distribution of surveillance

This brings us to the next question — precisely *who* is surveyed, and why? We have already hinted, in relation to Auden's poem, that men in full employment with no obvious health problems are not prime targets for medical surveillance. The monitoring of health is not equally distributed across all ages or between the sexes.

□ Where are the 'peaks and troughs' of medical surveillance during an ordinary lifetime in the UK today?

■ All babies and children are systematically investigated, but the extent of state administered checks on their health gradually declines as they grow older. Adolescents and adults are given little attention unless they qualify as members of a 'special group' — for example, pregnant women, disabled people, the very elderly, employees at significant risk of industrially-related diseases (e.g. health checks on coal miners), and professions where lives depend on the health of the employee (e.g. pilots).

You may already have noted differences in the extent to which women's health is subject to greater surveillance than that of men. The wife of JS/07/M/378 would have been the source of a mass of data relating to her reproductive physiology: the age she began menstruating, the regularity and painfulness of her menstrual periods, the incidence of pregnancies, miscarriages or abortions, the birthweight of her babies and any complications in labour, and finally the duration and severity of her menopause (we return to this subject in Chapter 13). Critics have argued that this attention is not for the well-being of the woman herself, but to ensure that she is in the best possible breeding condition. The extent to which babies and young children are monitored by the state seems to support the idea that concern for maternal health might be one aspect of preserving our stake in the next generation.

In summary, we can say two things: first, that age is a social as well as a biological phenomenon with influences on health that vary across cultures and across time; second, the official monitoring of health and the distribution of health care reflect society's attitudes towards the relative importance of individuals at different ages. This raises numerous subsidiary questions. Is the age-grading system in the UK a 'good thing' as it stands, or are there aspects of it that might be changed with benefit for certain age-groups? Does surveillance mean that people may come to be seen as numbers rather than individuals? And there are questions of privacy too — once the data has been collected, who has access to it and for what purpose? These are issues that we shall not tackle here, though some of them will be raised in later chapters.

Objectives for Chapter 2

When you have studied this chapter, you should be able to:

2.1 Illustrate that age is a social as well as biological phenomenon.

2.2 Discuss some of the problems associated with the surveillance of health under the headings: (i) defining normality; (ii) medical labelling; (iii) the expansion of professional scrutiny, and (iv) the distribution of surveillance across different ages.

Questions for Chapter 2

1 (*Objective 2.1*) In South Africa, a black servant may be called a 'boy' or a 'girl' whatever his or her chronological age.

(a) Can you think of any parallel use of such names in our own or other societies?

(b) What does this suggest about the nature of the terms used to describe people of different ages?

2 (*Objective 2.2*) Which of the problems of surveillance discussed in this chapter are illustrated by this woman's account of antenatal care during her first pregnancy?

I can get thrown off balance very easy, by someone, say, just playing around with my blood pressure and there's a machine there, and they're reading the numbers and they're saying, 'ooh, ah', and I begin to doubt that *my* sense that I'm feeling healthy is alright. Maybe I'm not healthy? That happens with tests for anaemia. The midwife told me, 'you must be anaemic, you must be feeling tired' — I haven't been feeling tired at all, but because they've taken away some of my blood to somewhere secret, and analysed it, and brought it back and counted it, and deduced from that that I'm tired - sometimes I think well, maybe I'm deluding myself, and I *am* tired when actually I'm not . . . When you're confronted with experts telling you something, you do lose track of what you feel in yourself is right.

(From an interview recorded during the filming of TV5, 'A Suitable Place to Have a Baby?'.)

3

Changing fortunes: the economic life cycle

This chapter assumes that you are familiar with the meaning of the terms 'demography', 'demographic structure', 'birth cohort', 'longitudinal and cross-sectional data', which are defined in Book I, *Studying Health and Disease*, Chapters 4 and 5. There are also references to the association of poverty, unemployment and occupation with health, discussed in Book III, *The Health of Nations*, Chapters 10 and 11, and the population theories of Malthus in Chapter 6 of that book.

A theme running through this book is that the significant transitions which occur during a lifetime have different dimensions: personal, biological and social, and all these must be seen within their historical context.

This chapter focuses on a key aspect of the social dimension, that of the economic circumstances of individuals, and how these vary during a lifetime. Economic factors influence our experience of life in numerous ways; here we shall concentrate on two areas — first, the transitions relating to work, and second, those of birth, marriage and death. We must also consider how these major life events in an individual lifetime reflect, and are influenced by, the wider economic and demographic trends in society.

□ In what ways are economic factors relating to work likely to affect births, marriages and deaths?

■ Employment and the level of earnings influence many people when deciding whether or when to marry, and when to 'start a family'. Unemployment and the relative poverty resulting from a lifetime of low wages seems to be associated with poorer health, and hence with reduced life expectancy.*

So these two areas interact in significant ways. Bear this in mind as we focus on each in turn.

The life cycle and work

Paid employment is a central feature of our society, though not everyone who works gets paid for doing so. We often ask people what they 'do', and 'doing' has become so synonymous with paid employment that many people not paid for their work tend to answer that they 'don't work', or that they are 'just' a housewife. Of course, the reason why the question is so frequently asked is that a great deal about a person can be discovered or guessed from the answer: their background, education, status, power,

*The association of poverty and unemployment with health is discussed in Book III, *The Health of Nations*, Chapter 11.

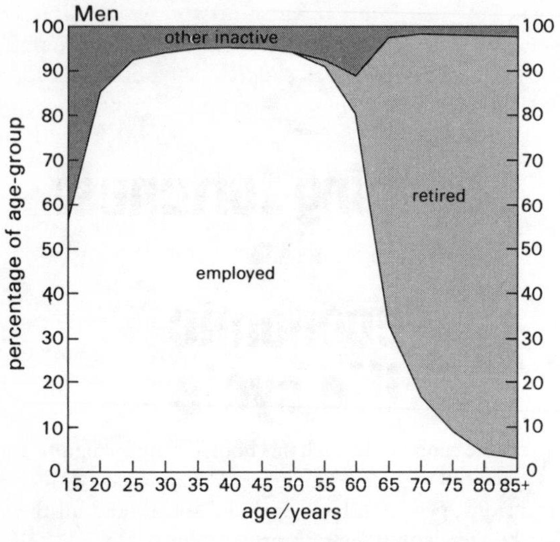

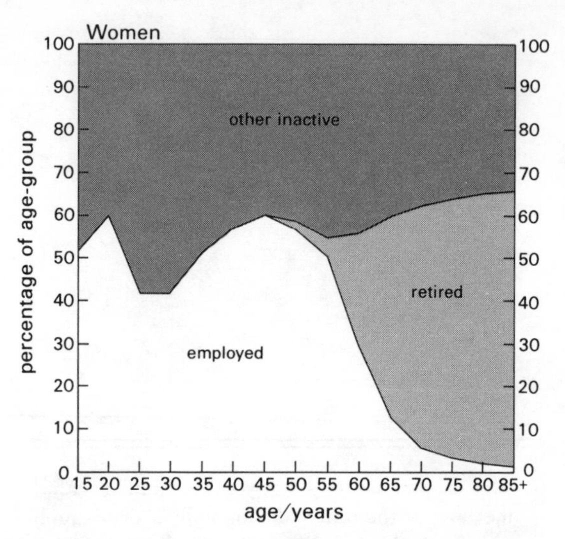

Figure 3.1 Participation rates of men and women, UK, 1971–75. (Fox and Goldblatt, 1982, p.25)

earnings, and so on. A person's health can also depend on their work: people in different occupations are exposed to very different levels of risk or health hazard, and their income and *occupational class** has an important influence on such things as life expectancy or infant mortality.

But occupations, earnings and other health related factors do not simply vary across the population: they also vary with age. Figure 3.1 shows the proportion of males and females in the UK at different ages from 15 onwards who are either employed, retired, or '*economically inactive*'. The term 'inactive' is an official and rather inaccurate way of describing not only the unemployed and those off work through sickness, but also students and housewives.

□ What strikes you first about the different patterns for women and men?

■ The proportion of women in the employed category is much lower than that of men.

The proportion of the population in formal employment is normally called the *participation rate* (sometimes referred to as the 'activity rate'). As Figure 3.1 shows, the participation rate for men rises above 90 per cent for some age-groups, but, for women, barely reaches 60 per cent at around age 45. The average participation rate of married women of all working ages in the UK is in fact less than 50 per cent. This compares with less than 30 per cent in Japan, for example, and over 60 per cent in Sweden. Despite these variations, the participation rate of women has been rising quite steeply since the Second World War in most industrialised countries (it was around 20 per cent in the UK in 1950). Because income is associated with health in so many different ways, rising female participation rates have made it more important to consider *family income* rather than the single income of the husband when studying these associations with health.

□ What reasons can you think of for the decline in the female participation rate between ages 20 and 30 shown in Figure 3.1?

■ There are two main reasons. First, many women leave the labour market in order to have children, and subsequently find employment again once children are going to school. Second, some women stop work when they get married and thereafter depend on their husbands for financial support.

The ages at which employment begins and ends have varied considerably over time and across different societies. At present in the UK the beginning of '*working age*' — that period from when full-time paid employment is legally allowed to when a specified retirement age is reached — is 16, and the end is 65 for men and 60 for women. The trend in industrialised countries is for the starting age to be pushed up and the retirement age to be drawn down. These very clearly defined ages of transition both into and out of working life are a very recent phenomenon — they have nothing to do with biological changes. Take for example, the issue of *child labour* and minimum working age. In non-industrial societies it is the norm for all members of the family to contribute labour from the earliest to the oldest practicable age. This was true of Britain before the Industrial Revolution and is true today in the Third World. In these societies, most of the population is involved in agricultural activity, and production of other goods tends to be domestic, that is, based in the home. In these

*Occupation as a measure of social class is discussed in Book I, *Studying Health and Disease*, Chapter 10.

circumstances the labour of children is often used in or around the home, is supervised by parents, and is likely to change almost imperceptibly into adult work without a set age of transition.

However, the Industrial Revolution involved a move away from rural agricultural life towards urban life, away from domestic production to factory production regulated by the clock, and wage labour. As this system developed in England, children were increasingly drawn into factory employment by the need for money to supplement family income, or were pushed into it by Poor Law Officials anxious to avoid supporting them under the Poor Law. As is well known, the result was a rapid growth of child employment in conditions which were governed solely by employers or managers, and often in particularly dangerous or unhealthy occupations such as mining, machine-minding, or chimney-sweeping. Brutality, ill-treatment, exploitation and fear became commonplace. The dread of punishment for lateness felt by a young mill-worker in eighteenth-century Derby is graphically conveyed in the following recollection:

> I did not awake ... till daylight seemed to appear. I rose in tears for fear of punishment, and went to my father's bedside to ask what was o'clock? 'He believed six'; I darted out in agonies, and from the bottom of Full Street to the top of Silkmill Lane, not 200 yards, I fell nine times! Observing no lights in the mill, I knew it was an early hour and the reflection of the snow had deceived me. Returning, it struck two. (William Hutton, quoted in Challis and Elliman, 1979, p.23)

Throughout the nineteenth century, controls over the kinds of work children were permitted to do and over their conditions of employment were gradually tightened. By the end of the century, full-time factory work had been replaced by full-time compulsory education, and the idea of what a normal, healthy child could do had radically changed — a subject to which we return in Chapter 7.

Our assumptions and images concerning child labour still tend to be influenced by this episode of British history. But how relevant are these to a consideration of child labour in the present world? The first point to note is that child labour is still common in the world. In Third World countries children are employed in heavy industry, construction work, factories, service trades and domestic services, and agriculture. The International Labour Office (ILO) has suggested that these children fall into three main groups: those working under the supervision of their families; those in factory or other employment; and those who have been thrown out or run away from their family home, or who are lost or orphaned (ILO, 1971). In industrial countries, full-time factory work is usually illegal, but other forms of part-time work seem still to be common. A DHSS-sponsored report in 1977, for example, found that 75 per cent of all children between 13 and 15 in the UK had some form of part-time employment, a third of them in paid work such as delivery rounds or work in shops, the remainder in domestic or voluntary work.

A survey conducted in 1970 in the USA found that children were extensively used in agriculture, representing no fewer than one quarter of paid farm workers in California. No concrete information exists on the proportion of such child labourers exposed to health risks, or how serious these risks might be. However, one study showed that the Californian child farm workers were exposed to heat stroke, chemical and food poisoning, and skin diseases (R.B. Taylor, *Sweatshops in the Sun*, 1973, quoted in Challis and Elliman, 1979, p.71). In the Third World, it is likely that the conditions of children in factories are often similar to those that prevailed in Victorian Britain. Prostitution, drug-pushing, begging, the sale of children as domestic chattels or their employment in debt bondage (being bound over to work for creditors) are just some of the many examples of child abuse and exploitation that have been reported in many Third World countries. The Anti-Slavery Society and the ILO have documented the conditions of child labourers around the world (Anti-Slavery Society, 1980). One reason why data on health consequences are hard to obtain is, of course, that many of these activities are illegal.

Why should the working conditions of children be of particular concern? First, developing children may be particularly susceptible to chemical, radiological or other hazards, and may be in need of longer hours of sleep etc. Second, they may be given jobs which are particularly dangerous, but which only they could do because of their size: climbing into machines, along pipes, up chimneys, for example. Third, because they are relatively powerless they need the protection of the law. At the same time, however, it is important to ask if the bad conditions sometimes experienced by labouring children are a problem of *age*. In many instances, the occupations that children were eventually prevented from doing in Victorian Britain were taken over by adults, who nevertheless experienced the same conditions. It seems reasonable to suggest that the problem was related to the working conditions, rather than the age of the person doing the job.

It is also important to note that not all types of child labour are likely to be injurious to health, and that obtaining even a small income may be an important source of independence and freedom. The gradual abolition of many forms of child labour in industrialised countries such as the UK, and the rise of compulsory and supervised education, brought freedom from some forms of exploitation, but also created new forms of regulation and control.

At the other end of working life, having a *fixed age of retirement* is also fairly recent. This again is largely confined to industrialised countries that can afford to make provision for pensions. Although, as Figure 3.1 shows, substantial numbers of men and women in the UK do continue in employment beyond the official retirement ages (in some occupations, including politics, the law, and general medical practice there is no compulsory retirement age), most people have stopped working by the official retirement age. In fact, the participation rates of men in the pre-retirement age-group (60–65) in the UK have been falling in recent years. This may be because of more widespread occupational pensions, early retirement schemes and redundancy, and may also be due to the prevailing high rate of unemployment which presents particular difficulties for older people in obtaining work.

This contrasts markedly with the reported situation in the Soviet Union. There, the labour shortages which are endemic in the economy seem to have been exacerbated by the introduction of extended pension coverage in 1956, resulting in a fall in the percentage of working pensioners from almost 60 per cent in 1956 to under 11 per cent in 1960. In recent years attempts have been made to encourage those reaching pension age to continue working. These have had limited success, but two interesting pieces of information have emerged from the policy. First, health surveys found that management fears of higher absenteeism and sickness among working pensioners were not borne out:

> ... it was found that sickness involving temporary loss of working capacity was significantly rarer among working pensioners than among persons of non-pensionable age; in fact only half as many cases occurred, and days off work amounted to no more than two-thirds of those required by younger people. (Smirnov, 1977, p.90)

Second, the measured fall in the productivity of these older workers was less than expected. This is shown in Figure 3.2.

□ Compare the output of the oldest and youngest age-groups in Figure 3.2. What pattern emerges?

■ Output among all age-groups over 60 is still higher than among 15–19 year olds, and in the age-groups 60–69 is almost the same as in the age-group 20–24.

As with the official beginning of working age, then, there is a good deal of evidence that the end of working age is relative to time and place, and has little direct association with the biological capacity to sustain work effort.

During the years of working age in countries like the UK, there are a number of ways in which certain economic and social factors influence health and disease. There are marked occupational-class differences in the patterns of mortality, and there seems to be an association between

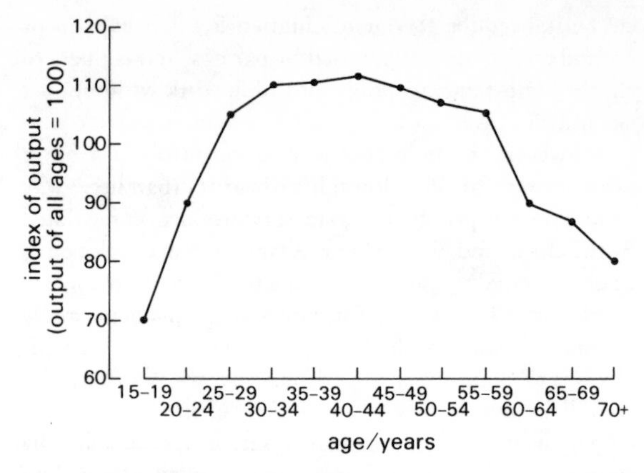

Figure 3.2 Output by age-group, Soviet Union, 1971. (Data from Smirnov, 1977, p.88)

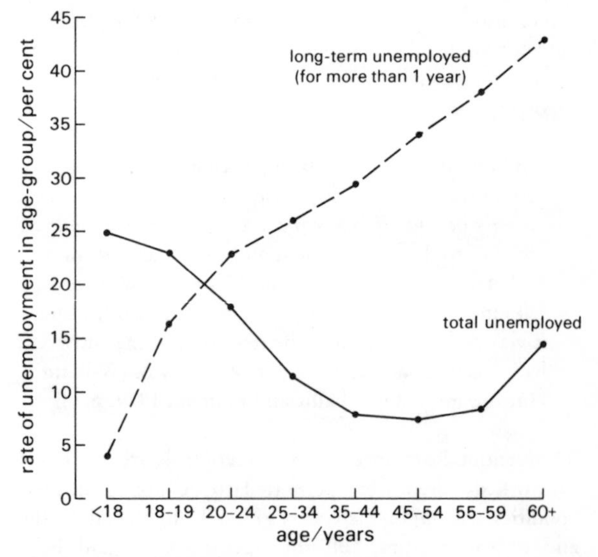

Figure 3.3 Unemployment by age-group, Britain, 1981. (Data from Employment Gazette, November 1981, Table 2.6)

unemployment and health.* Factors such as unemployment and income are also associated strongly with age, however, and this must be remembered when considering patterns of health and disease at different stages in the lifespan.

Figure 3.3 for example, shows two aspects of unemployment in the UK in 1981: the rate of unemployment in each age-group, and the proportion of the unemployed in each age-group who have been out of work for more than a year.

□ What do the two lines on the graph reveal?

*This is discussed in Book III, *The Health of Nations*, Chapter 11.

■ The unemployment rate forms a 'U-shape' with increase in age: that is, it is high among young people, then falls to a low point for the age groups 35–44 and 45–54, then starts to rise again as people get towards the end of their working life. The pattern of long-term unemployment for one year or longer is different — this proportion starts low with younger age-groups then climbs steadily. Almost half the unemployed aged 60 or more have been out of work for over one year.

The likelihood and consequences of losing work depends quite heavily on what age an individual has reached.

Let us now look more closely at those who are employed during their working years. Not only do the earnings of people in employment vary widely depending on occupation, sex, and ethnicity, but also vary considerably according to age. These patterns of earnings at different ages are normally called *lifetime earnings profiles*. Figure 3.4 shows a typical set of such earnings profiles for six different classes of employees in France, and the situation is much the same in the UK. The absolute value of earnings (on the vertical axis) is less important than the shape and relative position of the profiles. The top profile in the figure is for those in higher management occupations. From around age 20 their earnings increase quite rapidly, continue to increase at a slow rate right up to age 60, then decline slightly. The same broad pattern is true of middle management, except that the increase is less steep and the tailing off at the end of the working life is more pronounced.

□ Compared with the top two profiles, what most strikes you about the profiles for the manual groups shown in Figure 3.4?

■ Their earnings at all stages are much lower, and their earnings flatten out at quite an early age rather than keep on rising.

Salaried white-collar and management jobs tend to be accompanied by a whole package of inducements, promotions, and increments that ensure a fairly steady increase in earnings throughout most of the working life. This is not the case in most manual jobs, where there is little or no scope for promotion after the first few years. In Figure 3.4, for example, the unskilled manual worker has reached the top of the lifetime earnings profile between the ages of 20 and 30. In Japan, however, wages of manual workers are tied to age so that earnings gradually increase during a lifetime.

□ Why might you expect the earnings of manual workers in the UK to decline towards the end of the working life?

■ By their nature, many manual jobs are physically demanding and it can become progressively more difficult for older workers to sustain them.

One of the most frequently quoted examples of this is coalmining, where coalface workers frequently have to move to surface jobs in their late 40s or early 50s. As a result, the earnings profile of miners tends to peak fairly early and then decline. This example shows the complexity of health and disease changes over the lifespan: because of their health at a particular age, coalface miners may move to another job with a lower income, and this may, in turn, influence their health.

At this point it is important to note something about the figures we have been looking at that is relevant to many

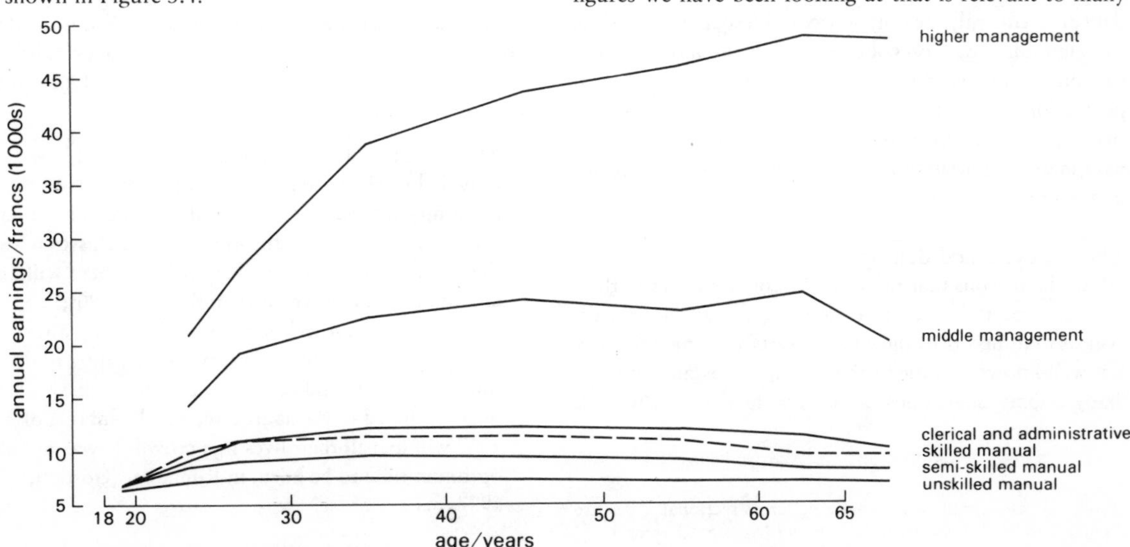

Figure 3.4 Annual earnings of French employees at different ages. (Phelps Brown, 1979, p.263)

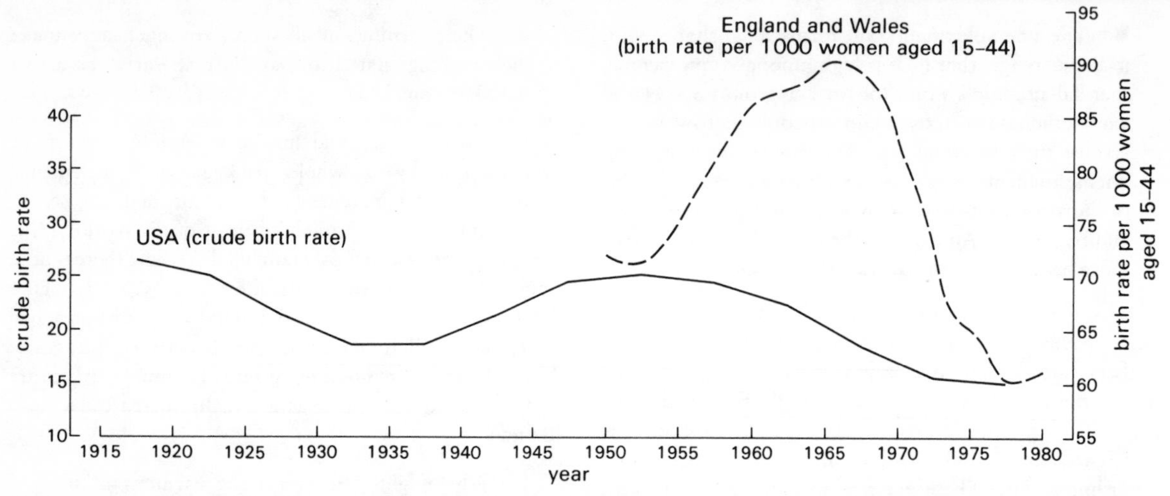

Figure 3.5 Fluctuations in birth rates over time, England and Wales, USA. (The crude birth rate is the number of live births per 1 000 population.) (Data from Easterlin, 1980, p.167, and Becker, 1981, p.253)

aspects of the lifespan examined in this book.

□ Why might the earnings profile in Figure 3.4 be misleading as a description of the lifetime experience of an *individual*?

■ Because it is based on *cross-sectional* rather than *longitudinal data*.* That is, it is illustrating the earnings of one group of people aged 30 with *another* group aged 40, rather than the same group 10 years later.

Because the cohort currently aged 40 has a particular rate of earnings, it does not necessarily follow that the cohort aged 30 will have the same rate of earnings 10 years later: an age-cohort can have its own characteristics that make it different from older or younger cohorts.† Cross-sectional data are frequently the only source of lifespan information, as longitudinal data on cohorts are difficult and expensive to obtain, involving the monitoring of large groups of people for long periods. The crucial point to remember is that a generalised lifespan constructed from cross-sectional data might not accurately describe the lifetime experience of any one individual.

The life cycle and demography

Of all the reasons that might make cohorts differ in their lifetime experiences, one of the more interesting suggestions is that the *size* of the cohort exerts a strong influence. It is well-known that the birth rate is not constant, and that 'baby booms' sometimes occur. The first person to note that the *birth rate* and *population growth rate* seem to fluctuate in *long-term* cycles was the American economist Simon Kuznets, and in consequence these are referred to as '*Kuznets cycles*'. Figure 3.5 shows clearly the changes in the birth rate in the USA and in England and Wales over time.

□ From Figure 3.5, how might you expect the size of the cohort born in or around 1965 in England and Wales to vary from that born in the early 1950s?

■ In 1965 the birth rate was significantly higher than in the early 1950s, suggesting that the mid-1960s cohort would be substantially bigger in relation to the rest of the population than the early 1950s cohort.

A graphic comparison of the life experience of those born at the peak of such a wave compared with those born at the trough is made in the following two passages. The first refers to a cohort born in Rumania in the late 1960s, at the peak of a birth-rate wave:

> These poor souls came into a crowded world — crowded by themselves. There was crowding in the maternity wards, when they first saw the light of day; there was crowding in the kindergarten classes when they entered the school system in 1971; there will be crowding in the universities in the mid-1980s; crowding in the search for jobs and housing a few years later; and so on until there is crowding in the funeral parlours and cemeteries. Rumania may not be overpopulated in the aggregate, but the infants of 1967 will live all their lives in a crowd. It was not an optimum time to be born, in Rumania. (Gordon, 1977, p.4.)

The second passage describes someone born in the trough of a low birth rate period:

*Problems associated with analysing cross-sectional data are discussed in Book I, *Studying Health and Disease*, Chapter 4.
†An example of a *cohort effect* in the incidence of lung cancer is described in Book III, *The Health of Nations*, Chapter 9.

> When he opens his eyes for the first time it is in a spacious hospital, well-appointed to serve the wave that has preceded him ... When he comes to school age, the magnificent buildings are already there to receive him; the ample staff of teachers welcomes him with open arms. In high school the basketball team is not as good as it was but there is no problem of getting time on the gymnasium floor. The university is a delightful place ... and the professors are solicitious. Then he hits the job market ... His parents tell him how tough things were when they entered the job market, but he has many offers, and good ones, so perhaps he takes a year or two off to go backpacking in Europe ... He is truly demographically lucky. (Gordon, 1977, pp.7–8)

The argument which Gordon sets out in these two passages has been taken even further by another American economist, Richard Easterlin. Easterlin has suggested that a large generation — that is, a cohort born at the peak of the birth-rate cycle — will experience a high degree of stress from 'crowding' at different stages of life, leading to higher rates of suicide, murder, drinking, and other drug use, longer-term higher mortality rates, and even higher levels of 'political alienation' and general dissatisfaction.

Easterlin notes that among the largest post-Second World War American cohort there has been a rise in violent deaths (suicides, homicides, and accidents) producing a '... change in overall mortality for this group that contrasts noticeably with that for other age groups in the population. ... We have dramatic testimony to the growth in mental stress among young adults' (Easterlin, 1980, p.107).

□ Is this the only conclusion you could draw from the rise in violent deaths among young adults? Think about the main cause of death in these age-groups.

■ The largest single cause of death among young adults in the USA as in the UK is from motor vehicle accidents.* The increased mortality might simply be because the greater prosperity of the post-war period gave more young adults access to vehicless.

There are many similar criticisms which can be levelled at these '*cohort size*' *theories*. For example, the number of school places available and the degree of classroom crowding is clearly influenced by such things as public expenditure and social policy decisions, irrespective of changes in cohort size. Similarly, the number of jobs available to a cohort reaching employment age is strongly influenced by the state of the national and international economy, the economic policies being pursued, and many other factors. Moreover, we do not have a very big sample size of birth-rate cycles on which to build elaborate theories: between 1950 and 1980, as Figure 3.5 shows, there was only one upswing and one downswing, hardly a sufficient number from which to generalise. So cohort size alone cannot be used to explain the life-experience of its members as it may itself be a product of other factors.

Cohort-size theories have concentrated on the consequences of birth-rate changes, but there is still a great deal of uncertainty about why the birth rate should vary so much, as in Figure 3.5. Since the eighteenth century when Malthus expounded his influential theories about population growth, it has been argued that the *fertility rate* and *nuptiality* (marriage) *rate* are associated with real income levels.† Thus, not only might economic conditions affect the life experience of different cohorts but the birth rate itself might be related to economic cycles. Perhaps these are long-term cycles in economic activity, stretching over decades, which are related to the 'Kuznets cycles' via birth rates? The suggestion that long economic cycles do exist was made by a Soviet social scientist called Kondratieff, who vanished into the labour camps in the 1920s. But there is still no agreement about the existence of these so-called *Kondratieff waves*, let alone their effect on birth rates. It has also been argued that the number of children that families have is influenced by the 'cost' of children. The cost will include food, clothing, housing, and the mother's time, after any contributions children can make to the family income by working in the home or elsewhere have been deducted. Thus, it is argued, when costs are low, the fertility rate will rise, and vice versa. Food and housing, for example, have traditionally been cheaper in rural than urban areas and the productive contribution children can make has often been greater on farms than in cities.

□ What would these facts lead you to suggest about the birth rate in rural compared to urban areas?

■ That in rural areas the birth rate would be higher.

If we look at the United States in 1800, we find that this was indeed the case. In fact the rural birth rate was one-and a half times that in urban areas (Becker 1981, p.96).

□ By the twentieth century, however, the birth rate in rural areas was about that in urban areas in the USA. Why might this have happened? (*Hint* Think back to the discussion of child labour, and the effect compulsory schooling might have on the productive contribution of farm children.)

*This is discussed in Book III, *The Health of Nations*, Chapter 9, and is given further attention in Chapters 9 and 10 of this book.

†Book III, *The Health of Nations*, Chapter 6.

■ Compulsory schooling would have greatly reduced the time which children could spend working on the farm, thus increasing their net 'cost' and reducing the birth rate.

Clearly if such economic factors falling unequally across the population can influence the birth rates of different population groups, it could also be expected that changes in these economic factors over time could influence trends in birth rates over time. Table 3.1 lists five instances of birth rate changes in different countries at different periods.

Table 3.1 Changes in the birth rate in different countries

Country	Period	Percentage change in birth rate
USA	1920–30	−24
USA	1960–72	−38
Japan	1950–60	−45
Taiwan	1960–75	−51
England and Wales	1871–1901	−26

(Data from Becker, 1981, p. 106, Table 5.1)

Some of these changes were remarkably rapid: in Taiwan, for example, the birth rate halved in 15 years. In 1920–30 in the USA, when the birth rate fell by 24 per cent, was there an increase in the cost of children? Yes: education was spreading rapidly, and secondary enrolment increased by 81 per cent over the same period. In the period 1960–72, when the birth rate in the USA fell by one third, the cost of having children was also rising, but in a different way: the participation rate of women was rising rapidly, and because more women had jobs or job opportunities, the cost of the time required to bring up children was rising.

Another important transition that is related to the birth rate and that seems to be influenced in some way by economic factors is the *age of marriage*. In early nineteenth-century England, for example, the average age of marriage seems to have been affected by the 'copiousness of the harvest, because of its importance for the income of the farming community', (Checkland, 1969, p.2a). Michael Drake, in an Open University course on historical demography, provides the story of herring shoal movements as a vivid example of economic influence on marriage:

> There is evidence ... from Norway in the mid-nineteenth century, of dramatic surges in the number of marriages and falls in the age at marriage in coastal areas that happened to be visited — usually for only a matter of a few years — by shoals of herring. The atmosphere created seems to have been rather like that of a gold rush. Thus, in the 1840s, herring shoals appeared quite suddenly off the south-west coast of Norway. In the decade 1835–1845, the deanery of Stavanger, which lies in this area, increased its population by 14 per cent through immigration alone. The rise in the number of marriages between the 1830s and 1840s in this same deanery was 49 per cent: whilst in the neighbouring deanery of Karmsund it was 51 per cent. This was a higher rate of increase than anywhere in the country. Age at marriage, too, would appear to have been low ... (Open University, 1982, p.37)

Such are the strange ways in which life events can be influenced by economic factors!

Birth-rate changes affect the proportions of the population in different age-groups: a 'bulge' caused by a 'baby boom' will move up the *population pyramid* as that cohort gets older, and so on. In one particular respect, the distribution of the population across the different age-groups has become a subject of increasing interest: more and more is heard about the '*ageing population*' and its implications for society. The demographic structure of industrialised countries such as the UK is currently characterised by having a much higher proportion of the

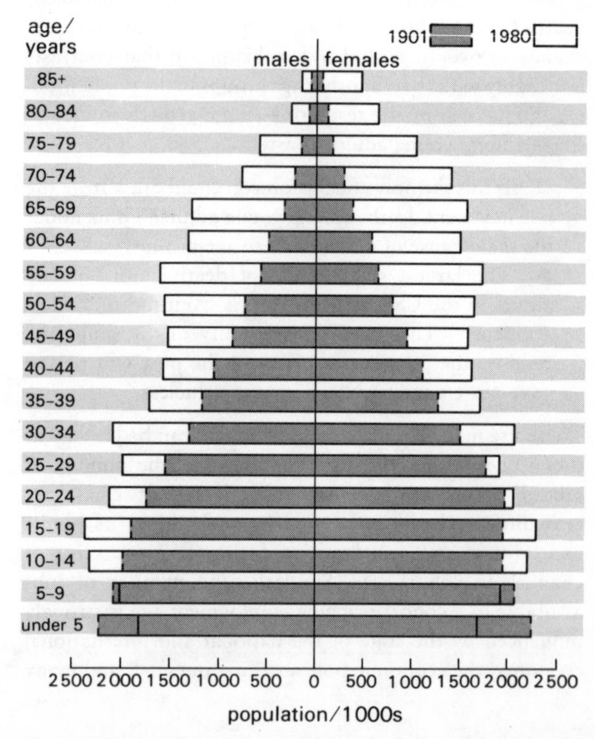

Figure 3.6 Sex and age structure of the population of the UK, 1901 and 1980. (Donaldson, 1983, p.428)

Table 3.2 Percentage of different age groups in the population from 1901 to 2001

	Percentage of total population in that age-group in specified years				
Age/years	1901	1951	1971	1981	2001 (projection)
65 and over	4·7	11·1	13·4	15·1	14·2
75 and over	1·2	3·6	4·8	5·8	6·5
85 and over	0·2	0·5	0·9	1·0	1·5

(Data from Donaldson, 1983)

population in older age-groups than is the case in Third World countries.*

□ What demographic changes have given rise to this characteristic structure?

■ Lower birth rates have reduced the proportion of the population at the base of the 'pyramid', while lower mortality rates have increased the proportions at the top of the 'pyramid'.

The extent of the change which has occurred is shown in Figure 3.6, which compares the age structure of the UK population in 1901 and 1980.

□ Is the change in the age structure the same for men and women?

■ Both men and women show an absolute increase in numbers of old people, and a relative increase compared to the rest of the population, but these changes are greater for women.

Table 3.2 shows the proportion of the elderly in the UK population from 1901 up to 1981, with an estimate of what these figures will be by the year 2001.

□ What was the percentage of over-65s in 1981 and was this expected to rise?

■ In 1981 it was 15.1 per cent, having risen from 4.7 per cent at the beginning of the century, but the projection was that this increase will have dropped a little by 2001.

□ Is this also the case for over-75s and over-85s?

■ No. Although these numbers are smaller, they are expected to continue to rise relative to the rest of the population.

This is the picture in most industrialised countries. The proportion of old people has risen for the last 80 years, more so for women, and now seems to be relatively steady. The proportion of very old people is still increasing.

*Book III, *The Health of Nations*, Chapter 3.

This would seem to be good news — fewer people are dying in childhood; and more are reaching a 'green old-age'. The rising proportions of elderly people in the world has, however, caused considerable panic in those responsible for planning health-care and pensions in the next few decades — we shall address this 'problem' in Chapter 16.

There is one point, however, that is frequently overlooked in the discussion of this issue: there is a tendency to think that only the industrialised countries are faced with the issues arising from large elderly populations. In fact, a number of Third World countries are rapidly approaching the same situation, the most important of which is likely to be China. Since 1979, China has been pursuing a policy of drastic restrictions on fertility, by limiting each couple to one child. What happens when time elapses until each single child is an adult with two ageing parents to support?

> For the next twenty-five to thirty years, not much is likely to happen, and the campaigners have taken comfort from this fact. Thereafter, the proportion of the elderly will begin to grow, as it did in Britain between 1940 and 1980 — slowly at first, but at a gathering pace, which might soon become faster than the most rapid such development known to demographers. By the third or fourth decade of the 2000s a quarter or even a third of the population would be over 60. One more unknown and unique demographic situation in the largest population of the world. (Laslett, 1984, p.5)

An ageing population, therefore, may shortly be a typical and characteristic feature of all world societies.

In this chapter you have seen that the various events and transitions that occur during a lifetime, such as the beginning of working age, age of marriage, having children, and retirement are associated with a variety of economic factors. In addition, levels of income and likelihood of redundancy are strongly associated with different ages, and different demographic conditions such as cohort size. These associations will be encountered again at many points in this book, as we explore in greater detail the lifetime experience of health and disease.

Objectives for Chapter 3

When you have studied this chapter, you should be able to:

3.1 Outline the main lifetime characteristics of employment and earnings.

3.2 Discuss examples of economic influences on birth rates, and their implications for demographic structure.

Questions for Chapter 3

1 (*Objective 3.1*) (a) Summarise the main points of difference in the participation rates of women and men, according to recent UK data.

(b) For what reason might such data be a poor guide to the lifetime experience of individuals?

2 (*Objective* 3.2)

'The lesson of what a baby boom can do to an economy may not have been well learned by Europeans, but it is one that Americans have now taken very much to heart. Now that the disruption of the first baby boom is almost over — the pig having passed through the python, as the saying goes — US demographers are warning of the 'echo effect' that will produce a second baby boom there around the turn of the century.' (Merritt, 1982, p.28.)

(a) What kind of disruptions have been attributed to this 'pig in the python' phenomenon?

(b) What suggested reasons have been given for such fluctuations in the birth rate occurring in the first place?

4

Family images, social change and health

This chapter builds on the discussion of health in the UK in Book III, *The Health of Nations*, especially explanations for the diversity of health experience and life expectancy between people of different social classes, marital status, and between men and women contained in Chapters 9 and 10. The effect of poverty on health and the relative poverty of one-parent families (Chapter 10) is also referred to. You will be asked to read an article by Richard Titmuss, 'The position of women: some vital statistics', in the Course Reader (Part 2, Section 2.3) during your study of this chapter.

The wedding of Minnie Banfield and Thomas Harrison on 10 September 1919. (Photo: Courtesy of A. Biles)

In the previous chapter we considered in some detail a few important economic aspects of a person's lifetime experience. In this chapter we are concerned with another key social aspect — living in a family unit. The *family* is possibly one of the oldest but certainly one of the most ubiquitous of all social institutions. Though the definitions of a family may vary over time and between places, all societies have some such concept and membership of one or more family unit is something most people experience over their lifetime.

But what has that got to do with health and disease? A great deal. As people move through life they will leave, join or create family units, and these represent major points of transition in their lives with social, economic and even biological dimensions. The relationships with other family members, and the social and economic circumstances of the families of which they are a part can also exert a powerful influence on the experience of health and disease and that experience may in turn affect family life. The family is widely seen as a source of nursing care; a source of information about health and disease; adult members decide when to seek professional help in caring for the health of children and the aged; and the family is a site for the nurture and socialisation of children. As such it is the focus of a greal deal of surveillance within the health and social services. For all these reasons and more, the family will be a recurring theme in future chapters of this book.

There are deeply held beliefs in our society about what is normal and abnormal in family life, both in terms of the composition of families, and in terms of the roles and relationships within them. There are also strong assumptions about an idealised past when families were more stable and more caring than they are today. The quotations below, taken from various sources in recent years, reflect the range of these concerns and their pervasiveness over the political spectrum and over time.

> The duty of supporting parents and children in old age or infirmity is so strongly enforced by our natural

feelings, that it is well performed even among savages and almost always so in a nation deserving the name of civilised. We believe that England is the only European country in which it is neglected. (Report of the Poor Law Commissioners of 1832, 1905 edn, p.43)

It is striking that the widespread disintegration of the concept of the family as the nucleus of society, the increasing instability in family relationships reflected by the spread of cohabitation and divorces, the new position of women in society and their wish to work, the crisis in traditional moral values, the falling birth rate, which is now approaching or even falling below the rate required for the population to renew itself, are trends common to all the countries of Europe, even if they vary in intensity. Thus the future and the very survival of these countries are at risk ... the concept of the family as the basic nucleus of society has reached crisis point. (European Parliament, Committee on Social Affairs and Employment, Working Document: 70, 147 Family Policy in the EEC, 18 December 1980, paras 14–15)

They [the family and civilised values] are the foundations on which the nation is built; they are being undermined. If we cannot restore them to health, our nation can be utterly ruined ... Parents are being divest of their duty to provide for their family economically, of their responsibility for education, health, upbringing, morality, advice and guidance ... (Keith Joseph, 'Britain: A decadent new Utopia', *Guardian* 21 October 1974)

The socialist concept of the family is based on the fundamental consideration that it constitutes an entity in which social and personal interests are present and closely linked in view of the fact that it is the elementary cell of society and, as such, contributes to its development and plays an important role in the upbringing of the new generations. (Family Code, Law No. 1289, 14 February 1975; Official Publication of the Ministry of Justice, Havana, Cuba)

The family is not a static entity. Over centuries, in the UK as elsewhere, there have been changes in the types of families people live in and in the relationships between individual family members. Some of these developments have implications for health and disease. But in order to unravel what these implications might be, contemporary family patterns must be seen within an historical perspective. This will help us to clarify exactly what is new about families today.

However, a somewhat technical point of definition needs to be made first. Social scientists usually reserve the word 'family' to refer precisely to groups of people related by blood or marriage, whether or not they live together — that is, kinship groups. A '*nuclear family*', for example, consists of mother, father and children, whereas the '*extended family*' includes other kin, such as uncles, aunts, cousins and grandparents. The term '*household*' is used to refer to people's living arrangements whether in families or not. In popular usage, 'family' refers to both kinship groups and living arrangements. In this chapter we are primarily concerned with the family situation *in which people live* and we will be using the word 'family' in this somewhat broader sense most of the time.

The family in history

During the past century there have been significant changes in the birth rate and in *life expectancy*, which have had profound effects on the age structure of the population today and on patterns of health and disease in society. These trends have also had quite dramatic effects at the level of the individual and the family. Writing in 1952, Richard Titmuss discussed some of these effects and the impact they have had on the health and wider experience of women in the family, and in society at large. You should now read his article 'The position of women: some vital statistics', which is in the Course Reader (Part 2, Section 2.3).*

□ What does Titmuss describe as 'one of the dominating biological facts of the twentieth century' and how has this affected family size?

■ Titmuss was referring to the rapid fall in the birth rate in the fifty years preceding 1952, which had led to a fall in the *average completed family size* from six or more children in mid-Victorian England, to just under two and a half children for marriages contracted in 1925–29.

□ What consequences for health does Titmuss attribute to falling family size and why?

■ He suggests that these changes made a major contribution to the increased life expectancy experienced by women in the fifty years after 1900. This was primarily because both the hazards of childbirth and the frequency of confinement were greatly reduced. He also suggests that the reduction in the number and the proportion of women worn out by excessive childbearing meant fewer succumbed to diseases such as tuberculosis and pneumonia. Finally, he argues that the decline in family size led to a rise in the standard of living of women through its effects on 'family economics' and this would also be expected to have implications for their health (and, of course, for the

*Nick Black *et al.* (eds) (1984) *Health and Disease: A Reader*, The Open University Press.

health of other family members, although Titmuss does not discuss this).

□ According to Titmuss, how did the reduction in family size and increased life expectancy affect the experience of women during an 'average' lifetime?

■ He argues that, together, these two factors have had a dramatic effect on the length of time women spend tied to the wheels of childrearing. From around one third of a woman's life at the beginning of this century, this period had fallen to 7 per cent by 1952. As Titmuss puts it, 'by the time the typical mother of today has virtually completed the cycle of motherhood, she still has practically half her total life expectancy to live'.

□ Titmuss also points to changes in marriage patterns as an important dimension of the changes affecting the position of women, and, by implication, family life. What changes does he discuss?

■ Titmuss points to four separate but related changes:

(i) a 'remarkable' increase in the amount of marriage in the community;

(ii) more and more youthful marriages, especially among women;

(iii) a concentration of 'family-building habits' (child-rearing) in the earlier years of married life;

(iv) a substantial increase in the number of years of married life experienced by couples.

□ Titmuss suggests that changes in the patterns of birth, death and marriage present new problems and issues to consider. Which ones does he focus on?

■ Titmuss is concerned particularly with the dual role of women with 'the apparent conflict between motherhood and wage earning'. He also points, however, to the increase in the years of exposure to the strains and stresses of married life, which he feels must be relevant to the trends in divorce that were emerging in 1952 and to the fact that increased marriage rates meant that 'a wider range of personality and character variations may now be drawn into the orbit of married life and childrearing'.

The data presented in Richard Titmuss's paper illustrate how changes in the patterns of health and disease and in the patterns of family life have influenced each other. Many of the trends he identifies are still evident today. Average family size, for example, has continued to decline, and for couples marrying in the period 1961–1965 the average was two children after ten years of marriage. Childrearing is therefore condensed into an even shorter time span. There are, however, differences in family size among the different ethnic groups in the UK. Women born in the Indian subcontinent for example are more likely to have larger families than are those born in either the UK or the West Indies, though there has been a decline in the frequency of births of three or more children in all the minority ethnic groups in recent years. However, trends in *divorce* and *maternal employment* — both stressed by Titmuss — are also subjects of considerable debate in the 1980s.

'Till death us do part'?

Ten years after Titmuss wrote his paper, the *divorce rate* stood at two divorces per 1 000 married couples. Twenty years later, in 1981, it had increased by over 500 per cent and stood at twelve divorces per 1 000 couples — a trend which, if continued, means that one in every three marriages taking place while you are reading this book can be expected to end in divorce. This may have profound implications for the health of the adults and children involved. Mortality and morbidity rates among separated, divorced or widowed people are higher than among married people and these differences appear to be greater for men. These data suggest that the personal experience of divorce or bereavement and the loss of social support it can entail, may be very detrimental to health though there may be other explanations.

□ How might these higher mortality and morbidity rates be explained?*

■ A number of explanations contribute to the overall picture:

(i) bereaved and divorced people in poor health might be more likely to remain unmarried than people enjoying good health;

(ii) the material circumstances of divorced, separated and bereaved people will tend to be poorer than other groups;

(iii) divorced, separated and widowed people may experience discrimination, with adverse effects on their health;

(iv) there may be important lifestyle differences between people who are married and those who are not;

(v) people of different marital statuses may use health services differently or may be treated differently by health professionals.

Developments in psychology and changing attitudes to childhood have brought with them a strong belief that a stable family life is of crucial importance to the emotional and intellectual development of a child. From this perspective the loss of a parent, through separation or divorce, may have long-term implications for child health. Additionally, a change in material circumstances following divorce or separation may also have an impact on child health. There is, however, little consensus about what may be regarded as a 'stable' family situation.

*There is a discussion of such explanations in Book III, *The Health of Nations*, Chapter 9.

These issues will be discussed in more detail in a later chapter, but both Titmuss and history caution us against any simple interpretation of the trends. As Titmuss suggests, and Figure 4.1 demonstrates, though many marriages now end in divorce, early deaths broke just about as many in the nineteenth century. Indeed, the period between 1920 and 1946 stands out as an exception in relation to the *duration of marriage* rather than the rule. Though accurate estimates are lacking, an historical perspective on *marital 'breakdown'* including death as well as divorce also suggests that a far greater proportion and number of children might have been affected by the loss of a parent in the nineteenth century than they are today.

□ Can you suggest at least one reason why this might be the case?

■ More children might be expected to be involved because family size was greater.

Historical research similarly casts other contemporary debates on the family in a somewhat different light. Nineteenth-century records on illegitimacy, for example, suggest that the extent of pre-marital sexual activity may not be so dramatically different today, at least when compared with the early nineteenth century. Compare, for example, the 67 per cent of women marrying at the ages of 25–29 in the early 1970s, who said they had engaged in premarital sexual activity with their eventual husbands, with the 60 per cent of women bearing their first child in the early nineteenth century, who had apparently conceived that child outside marriage.

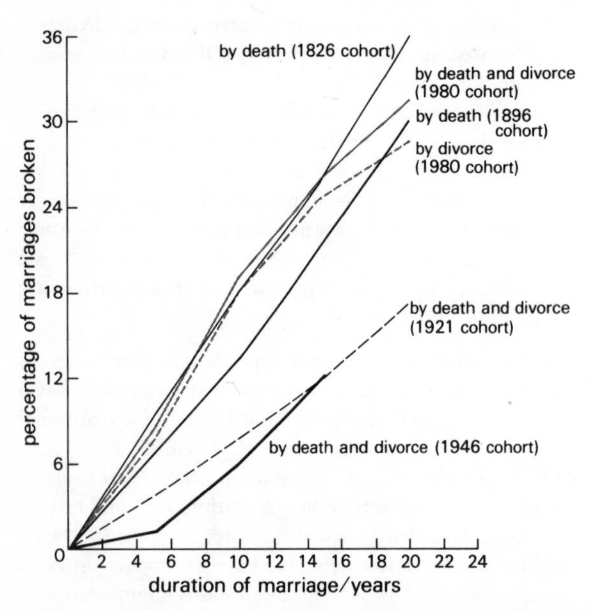

Figure 4.1 Percentages of marriages broken by death or divorce for cohorts of people marrying in 1826, 1896, 1921, 1946 and 1980*. (Anderson, in British Society for Population Studies, 1983, p.5) *For the 1980 cohort, rates of marriage breakdown (divorce) are estimates based on current levels.

A shorter time scale does show births to non-married mothers to have increased from 6 per cent of all births in 1961 to 11 per cent in 1979 but this is partly the result of a fall in births to married mothers, and in any event there is evidence that the nature of illegitimacy itself is changing. Some 55 per cent of births to non-married mothers in 1979 were registered on the joint information of *both* parents compared to 49 per cent five years earlier. This suggests that the children will have contact with both parents and reflects at least in part the increasing popularity of cohabitation before or instead of marriage. In the late 1970s, for instance, 20 per cent of women marrying for the first time had lived with their husband first compared to 3 per cent of those marrying in the 1960s, and another 9 per cent of women aged between 17 and 29 were cohabiting. West-Indian born mothers are more likely than other groups to have children outside formal marriage, but such children appear to have close relationships with both parents and such trends may therefore reflect the multiracial character of contemporary British society rather than 'moral decay'.

The historical context of maternal employment

Richard Titmuss also discussed the changing role of women in the family and in society. Like divorce, this issue is still the focus of debate, particularly the increasing participation of mothers of dependent children in the formal labour market.

As you saw in the previous chapter, almost 50 per cent of married women are now in paid employment, a figure which has increased dramatically in the past few decades. Indeed, in 1921 married women made up less than 4 per cent of the labour force compared with over a quarter today. There is now good evidence that paid employment may protect some women from psychiatric disorders such as depression, while increased family income may also contribute to health. But, on the other hand, work also has its health risks. An increasing number of women are exposed to *occupational health hazards*. Moreover, to the extent that they are combining unpaid work in the home with paid employment, their health may be threatened by the double burden this imposes.

Yet another aspect of women's work raises health issues. Maternal employment may possibly represent a threat to the health and wellbeing of children by reducing the amount of time a woman is able to give to them. We shall consider some of the evidence related to this and the implications of employment for married women's own health in later chapters but, once again, those discussions need to be placed within an historical perspective.

Attitudes towards the employment of married women are often based on the belief that the proper role for a married woman is as mother and housewife. By this account only the man should be the breadwinner. Men's and women's roles in the family were more sharply delineated in the 1920s than they are today, but for how long before that had this been the case? Looking at employment in the past is quite difficult because the very idea of participating in a 'formal' labour market is a relatively recent phenomenon. Much paid work was done in the home in a '*domestic economy*' well into the nineteenth century. However, three quotations from eighteenth- and nineteenth-century sources suggest that very different attitudes towards women's role in the family once prevailed.

> Consider my dear girl that ... you cannot expect to marry in such a manner as neither of you will have occasion to work and none but a fool will take a wife whose bread must be earned solely by his labour and will contribute nothing towards it herself. (*A Present for a Servant Maid*, published 1743, quoted in Hewitt, 1958, pp.2–3)

> What a prodigious difference our machines made in the gains of the females in the family! Formerly the chief support of a poor family arose from the loom. A wife could get comparatively little on her single spindle. But, for some years a good spinner has been able to get as much, or more, than a weaver ... If it were true that the weaver gets less, yet, as his wife gets more his family does not suffer. (1780, quoted in Pinchbeck, 1977, p.150)

> One of the greatest advantages resulting from the progress of manufacturing industry ... is its tendency to raise the condition of women. Education only is wanting to place the women of Lancashire higher in the social scale than in any other part of the world. The great drawback to female happiness among the middle and working class is their complete dependence and almost helplessness in securing the means of subsistence. (Government Commissioners, 1840, quoted in Hamilton, 1965, pp.323–4)

Yet even as the Government Commissioners penned their report, industrialisation was having profound effects. The worlds of work and the home were becoming separated. The outlawing of child labour, and an increasing emphasis on the 'nurture' of children was leading to a differentiation of childhood from adulthood (a process which will be discussed further in Chapter 7), and the modern roles of housewife and mother were emerging. According to Ann Oakley, a sociologist:

> ... female employment began to be condemned on moral grounds, on grounds of damage to physical and mental health, on grounds of neglect of home and family and lastly, simply on the grounds that it contravened the 'natural' division of labour between the sexes. (Oakley, 1974, p.45)

As the Earl of Shaftesbury, a prominent social reformer and philanthropist, argued in the 1840s, during the period of factory reform, for which he was a prime mover:

> ... the moral effects of the [factory] system are very bad: but in the female they are infinitely worse, not alone upon themselves, but upon their families, upon society and, I may add, upon the country itself. It is bad enough if you corrupt the man but if you corrupt the woman you poison the waters of life at the very fountain. (quoted in Hill, 1896, p.200)

It should be stressed, however, that condemnation of female employment varied considerably by social class and marital status. Right up until the end of the nineteenth century, women in the labouring classes were considered a breed apart from middle-class women. Legislation was introduced to restrict their hours of work in factories and to bar them from certain spheres, such as mining, but they continued to be seen as a source of labour, particularly paid domestic labour in middle-class homes, whereas the employment of middle-class women — whether married or single — was relatively abnormal. When this attitude did spread to the labouring classes, the condemnation of female employment was restricted to the employment of married women.

The First and Second World Wars, however, saw a considerable change in social attitudes as the shortage of male workers drew more and more women back into the labour force. Thus began the emergence of the modern trend for women of all classes to combine the roles of housewife, mother, and employee. However, you should note that this situation has been the common experience of working-class women for centuries. The full-time or even part-time housewife/mother is a modern invention, not much more than a century old. Such a historical perspective cautions us against assuming that modern ideas about the 'proper' roles of housewife/mother and breadwinner/father are in some sense determined by the 'natural laws' of biology.

The significance of diversity in family life

Of course important changes are still occurring in family life in contemporary Britain. But an historical perspective does suggest that the time scale one adopts to consider change can have an important influence on the picture that emerges. More particularly, it means that we need to consider the processes that are at work in generating change (divorce, separation or bereavement, for example) rather than focusing simply on family composition, such as the absence of a parent.

On a shorter time scale, for example over one or two decades, it is clearly the case that the increasing divorce rate has led to a growing proportion of children living for some of their childhood in a *one-parent family*, compared to the experience of children born say in the 1940s or 1950s. In 1971–73 for example, around 8 per cent of all families with dependent children were headed by a lone parent, and around one million children were involved. By 1979–81, these figures had increased to 12 per cent and 1.5 million. Both of these figures are also underestimates of the number of children who have ever lived in a one-parent family, for they are cross-sectional. A great deal of concern has been focused on the circumstances of parents and children in such one-parent families, for they may well face greater hazards to their health than other types of family.

□ Why might this be the case?

■ People in one-parent families tend to have lower incomes and this may adversely affect health. The physical and emotional pressures of caring for children alone may also take their toll of the health of parents (there is some evidence that lone mothers are more susceptible to depression than other mothers).*

Nevertheless life in a one-parent family is not inevitably a greater threat to health than life in any other sort of family. Some lone parents feel that their situation is considerably improved, especially if they had previously had insecure or unhappy marriages.

It is therefore wrong to assume that all one-parent families, or for that matter, all two-parent families, form homogeneous groups. By 1979, for example, 5 per cent of all children were living in step-families. One in every three marriages now involve a remarriage for one or both of the partners, and becoming a step-parent or step-child may also be a difficult transition for all concerned. There is also considerable variation in the material circumstances of people in two-parent families, and these variations are associated with considerable differences in the health of the people involved. Further aspects of diversity are revealed in Table 4.1.

□ What are these aspects of diversity?

■ Though the majority of lone parents are women, almost a quarter are men. It is also clear from the table that the marital status of lone mothers varies. Almost half are divorced and a further 23 per cent separated. There are as many single mothers as widowed mothers.

*The material circumstances of one-parent families and the effects of poverty on health are discussed in Book III, *The Health of Nations*, Chapter 10.

Table 4.1 Marital status of lone parents, 1981

	per cent
lone parents	*100*
lone fathers	23
lone mothers	77
lone mothers	*100*
single	14
widowed	14
divorced	48
separated	23

(Data from National Council for One-Parent Families calculated from 1981 census, *Household and Family Composition, England and Wales* 1984, Table 32.)

As we have already suggested, the actual experience of divorce, separation, single parenthood and bereavement may differ significantly, but these elements of diversity are also associated with other important differences, in income level, for instance, and housing circumstances — issues which are discussed further in Chapter 9.

The impact of smaller families

One final aspect of changing family relationships should be commented on for it has important implications for contemporary discussions about the family's role as a source of 'nursing care'. We have already suggested that the reduction in family size that has occurred since the end of the nineteenth century has had a dramatic effect on the role of women. There have also been no less dramatic effects on the nature of *kinship ties*, such as the number of relatives a person has. Look at the quotation below, for example, taken from a study of patterns of family and kinship ties in a South Wales town by two anthropologists in the 1960s.

> Trevor Jones was 69 and was thus born in 1891. He was the last but one of thirteen children (two of whom died in infancy), covering an age span of twenty-two years. His wife, Maud, whom he married in 1917, was one of eleven children covering a span of nineteen years. Two very large families. Trevor was the son of a blacksmith, and his wife the daughter of a collier. Trevor and Maud had just two daughters (now in their thirties) and have three grandchildren. Not one of the twenty uncles and aunts of these two daughters (that is, the brothers and sisters of Trevor and Maud) had more than three children. Five of them remained unmarried into old age, and four more had just one child each. The familial experience of these three generations — that of Trevor Jones's own generation, and of his grandchildren — within a single Swansea family is markedly different. His own generation was thickly peopled with relatives; his grandchildren in comparison have remarkably few. (Rosser and Harris, 1965, p.117–118)

Much has been written about the significance of such extensive *kinship networks*. In contemporary debates and media coverage there is a tendency to refer to an idealised past when families were more caring and more enduring and kinship ties were strong. Does this necessarily mean, however, that because people today may have fewer kin, ties to them are weaker? Once again historical research cautions us against oversimplification. In terms of the stability of communities and the geographical proximity of kin, the picture was little different a century or more ago from that of today. According to an analysis of the 1851 census undertaken by Michael Anderson, a sociologist at Edinburgh University, well under half of the population at that time were living where they had been born, and one child in six had moved to another part of the country by their second birthday. As Michael Anderson comments: '... with these rates of population turnover, the likelihood that people would have had many relatives living in the same village as themselves was quite low right into the twentieth century — even if they had the living relatives to live near.' (British Society for Population Studies, 1983, p.3).

In a society where the major form of transport was by foot even distances which today would be considered relatively short must have been considerable barriers to communication. Similarly, as Anderson also notes: '... no mail service in the past was in any way a substitute for the telephone on which so many longer distant migrants today rely for much of their kin contact.' (ibid, p.3).

The rapid period of industrialisation during the nineteenth century is often argued to have begun the disruption of extended family and kinship networks. Historical research, however, suggests that quite the opposite might have been the case. According to Michael Anderson, mass migration, female employment outside the home in textiles, shortage of housing and rising wage levels, in the absence of any effective public welfare system, may have *increased* the importance of kinship relationships, especially those between married children and their parents. Nevertheless, Anderson cautions against assuming that this provides support for the popular myth that families in the past were much more likely to care for their elderly relatives. In 1906, for example, almost 6 per cent of the population over 65 were living in Poor Law institutions — today the proportion in institutional or hospital care still stands at around 6 per cent.

In fact, with the ageing of the population, an increasing number of families are providing care and support for elderly and infirm relatives. In 1979, for example, 38 per cent of women aged over 85 were living without a spouse but with other people, most of them relatives. One small-scale study in 1980 found that there were more people caring for handicapped or elderly relatives than there were caring for children under 16. It has recently been estimated that there may be as many as 1.25 million people providing such care, and the vast majority of them are women.*

The family life cycle

Individuals are born, age and die, but families go on through generations, producing new but related families, each progressing through a fairly uniform sequence of developmental stages. Each stage is marked by a major transition as it begins and ends, so that the family is a radically different structure before and after these turning points. The complete sequence has been termed the *family life cycle*, a title that denotes the continuous cyclic nature of the process compared with the finite *lifespan* of individual family members.

□ What are the key transition points in an 'average' family life cycle, starting from the decision of a young adult to leave the parental home and begin a new family?

■ A simplified sequence of transitions might be: (i) finding a partner — marriage or cohabitation; (ii) birth of the first child; (iii) births of second and subsequent children; (iv) youngest child goes to school; (v) first child leaves home; (vi) last child leaves home; (vii) retirement from work; (viii) death of spouse.

This sequence takes no account of several sources of disruption — childlessness (chosen or involuntary), divorce, children who do not leave home, premature death of a spouse, and so on — but every family passes through at least some of these transitions. In the 1980s, for example, about a third of women in the UK will fail to pass through this simplified family life cycle, and, if present trends continue, this figure is likely to reach 50 per cent of those in their 20s today. The main reason for failing to complete this progression is, as we have seen, marital breakdown due to divorce, but the family life cycle is also made more complex by other trends such as the propensity of divorced people to remarry, and by the increasing number of women starting childbearing before, or, in a much smaller proportion of cases, without, subsequent marriage.

Such experiences are not, however, unique to the late twentieth century: for example, 15 per cent of women born around 1900 had not been married by 50 years of age, and the higher mortality rates prevailing then resulted in many families being 'fractured' by the death of a parent. At the beginning and ending of each family unit there is often a period of living alone, before a partner has been chosen and after his or her death or separation, and some people live alone for most of their adult lives. The shift between living

*The implications of this for the health of the people involved, and the nature of this care are discussed more fully in *Caring for Health: History and Diversity*, The Open University (1985) U205 *Health and Disease*, Book VII.

in a family and living alone is an important transition that has significant consequences for health. For example, widowed or divorced people on average suffer more ill-health than their married counterparts; married men live longer than men who remain single, whereas marriage has less effect on the length of women's lives.*

Although men can now expect to live almost 90 per cent of their lives in a family, and women, 82 per cent, the periods of living alone represent a significant strain on health, particularly in later life. At any one point in time, almost a quarter of all households consist of someone living alone, as Table 4.2 shows, and the majority of these people are over retirement age.

You will see in later chapters that many elderly people do not have family members that they can call on for help and support and they depend on friends, neighbours and statutory or voluntary services such as home helps or meals on wheels. Many young people living alone, particularly in large cities, may also experience considerable loneliness.

Historical research has shown that there has been both continuity and change in family life over the past century and beyond. The absence of a parent, for example, or maternal employment are not unique to the late twentieth century. But what has changed is the social, cultural and economic environment within which mothers work, parents bring up children, marriages dissolve and people grow old. Some of the processes involved in these have themselves changed: for example, while there have always been marriages that have dissolved, they are now more likely to do so through divorce rather than death. If we are to understand the implications of such family changes for the health of the individuals involved, we therefore need to look carefully at the processes contributing to change, as well as the wider environment within which it occurs.

Table 4.2 Households by type, Great Britain, 1981

Household	Percentage
No family	
one person	
—under retirement age	7
—over retirement age	15
two or more people	
—one or more over retirement age	2
—all under retirement age	2
One family	
married couple only	26
married couple with 1 or 2 dependent children	26
married couple with 3 or more dependent children	6
married couple with independent child(ren) only	8
lone-parent with at least one dependent child	4
lone-parent with independent child(ren) only	4
Two or more families	1
total households	100
average household size (number of people)	2.71

(Kiernan, 1983, Table 2, p. 18)

Objectives for Chapter 4

When you have studied this chapter, you should be able to:

4.1 Describe the demographic trends that have contributed to changes in family life in the past century, and discuss the health implications of these changes.

4.2 Comment on the need to take account of diversity in family life when considering issues of health and the family.

4.3 Discuss the importance of taking an historical perspective on such aspects of social life as the family.

Questions for Chapter 4

1 (*Objective 4.1*) 'The fall in the birth rate in Western Societies is one of the dominating biological facts of the twentieth century.' (Titmuss, Course Reader, Part 2, Section 2.3).

What were the health consequences of this demographic trend for the UK population as a whole?

2 (*Objective 4.2*) The following quotation is taken from a text book of medical sociology:

> In such dysmorphic families an enduring set of relations between parents and children cannot be established. A syndrome characterized by shallowness of affect, psychopathic behaviour, immature personality and even retardation of growth, speech and intellect occurs, particularly in children who have been deprived of their mothers in infancy. (Susser and Watson, 1971, p.335)

The authors were referring to families with only one parent (*dysmorphic* means 'the wrong shape'). Comment on the assumptions underlying this statement.

3 (*Objective 4.3*) 'If disintegration (of the family) continues at its present rate, we should run out of families about a year or two before we run out of oil.' (Amitai Etzioni, in Wood, 1978, pp.19–25).

How does an historical perspective help in evaluating the validity of such a statement?

*The effects of marital status on health are discussed in detail in Book III, *The Health of Nations*, Chapter 9.

5
Pregnancy and antenatal care

This chapter is in the first of two devoted to a particular stage of life — the nine months between conception and birth. Relevant background information on the biological aspects of this period can be found in Book IV, *The Biology of Health and Disease*, especially Chapter 10 (the hormonal control of conception and pregnancy), and Chapter 13 (which discusses threats to fetal development from X-rays, drugs, etc.). You will need a cassette player to listen to a short (10 minute) audiotape 'Antenatal care: Women's views', on Cassette AC804, Band 4. You will also be asked to read an article in the Course Reader by Ann Oakley, called 'Doctor Knows Best' (Part 3, Section 3.9).

Doctor knows best? (Cartoon from the quarterly journal of AIMS, Association for Improvements in the Maternity Services, Spring, 1982)

Life begins with the moment of conception. From this moment, the developing child increasingly becomes the focus of attention, from the mother herself, other members of the family and (in industrialised countries) the State. Unless a pregnant woman in the UK actively avoids medical surveillance, she and her baby will be drawn into a highly organised system of *antenatal care*. In 1983, over 5 million antenatal visits were made by pregnant women in the UK and £200 million were spent by the Government on antenatal care. What is the rationale behind this degree of surveillance?

Every culture views pregnancy and birth in particular ways, and even though the biological process is much the same for women the world over, a huge diversity of rituals and attitudes can be found. But the most striking common ground between different cultures is the view of pregnancy as a time of potential danger, or, since the outcome is always uncertain, at least as a cause for anxiety. This is still so in UK culture, despite the very low current risk of damage or death to either mother or baby. Not so long ago this anxiety was totally justified, and recent history has profoundly influenced the modern trend towards medical surveillance during pregnancy and intervention in childbirth.

The history of antenatal care

The professional care and attention received by a pregnant woman in the UK today is elaborate compared with the last century, and with some other contemporary cultures. Antenatal care is a comparatively recent phenomenon. At the turn of the century, there was no State provision in the UK, and specialised surveillance of the health of mother and baby, in order to treat or forestall complications was virtually unknown. If women became ill during pregnancy and needed a doctor's skill and attention, they had to seek it out and pay for it. This was especially difficult for working class women who were at the mercy of low wages and had to work long hard hours, often throughout pregnancy, in order to make ends meet. In addition, lack of contraception and the cultural values of the time meant that women of all social classes embarked upon many more pregnancies than is currently the norm. The following quotations, first published in 1915, come from hundreds of letters by working women who became members of the Women's Cooperative Guild, one of many pressure groups that actively campaigned for State maternity care and provision.

> The first part of my life I spent in a screw factory from six in the morning to five at night; and after tea used to do my washing and cleaning. I only left two weeks before my children were born.
>
> The strain was fearful and one night I felt I must sleep or die — I didn't care which ... A miscarriage followed and the doctor's bills grew like mushrooms.
>
> In my case before these two were born, I had to work harder than usual and the consequences were they were born delicate.
>
> Hard work and worry and insufficient food told on my once robust constitution with the result that I nearly lost my life through want of nourishment and did, after nine months of suffering, lose my child. (Llewellyn Davies, 1978, pp.16, 45, 101 and 23).

The letters are vivid and harrowing, nearly half of the writers having suffered from miscarriage or stillbirths. Although these women are but a small sample of those having babies around 1900, their experiences are a personal testimony to the suffering that was behind the high *maternal* and *perinatal mortality rates* of the time. (A woman's risk of dying during pregnancy around 1900 was 1 in 200, and that of her baby nearly 1 in 10 — in 1983, maternal mortality was 2 in 10 000, and perinatal mortality was just over 1 in 100.*)

Concern for high mortality rates led to antenatal care becoming a public issue after the First World War, especially after the high death toll suffered during the war. The first antenatal clinic opened during the war in Edinburgh in 1915, staffed by State-trained midwives — a relatively new professional group, who had only been registered since 1902. By 1932, there were well over 700 clinics throughout Britain, and when the Departmental Committee on Maternal Mortality and Morbidity (Ministry of Health, 1932) investigated the problems of childbearing in Britain, its unequivocal finding was that the safety of childbirth was directly related to the quality of the mother's general health during pregnancy. This was in turn related to her nutrition and the conditions in which she lived — factors that antenatal care could do little to influence. By 1944, the number of clinics had risen to nearly 2 000, and with the inception of the National Health Service in 1948, free antenatal care rapidly became available to every woman. Within ten years, more than 99 per cent of women were receiving antenatal care, and 64 per cent were being seen at a clinic ten times or more during the pregnancy.

There were, however, areas of tension between midwives, general practitioners and obstetricians who had previously occupied rather separate territories in relation to the care of pregnant women. Before the NHS, all three professional groups received fees for attending women with pregnancy problems and during delivery. Midwives (who charged the least) made their entire living from this practice. When antenatal care became free, there was a significant switch from using midwives to the previously more expensive care available from GPs and hospital clinics. Obstetrics had been a recognised branch of medicine since about 1870, but with the new influx of clients with the NHS in the 1940s and 1950s, the influence of obstetricians rose, and they increasingly stressed the advantages of their specialist attention during pregnancy. With the advent of new technology that required sophisticated equipment and highly specialised skills, antenatal care became increasingly centralised in hospital clinics, and doctors, rather than midwives, came to have most influence. By 1970, nearly two-thirds of pregnant women were attending a hospital clinic, and although the majority were seen by midwives more often than by doctors, their care was officially supervised by the medical rather than the midwifery profession. This trend has gone hand in hand with the switch from delivering babies in the mother's home to almost 100 per cent being delivered in hospital, as you will see in Chapter 6.

Current practice in antenatal care

Today, most women in the UK take it for granted that they will have their pregnancies confirmed and monitored by specialised health-care practitioners. Antenatal care is now provided in three main ways: care by GPs, hospital care, or *shared care* — the most common method, which is a combination of the two. With shared care, women see GPs and midwives for the first part of their pregnancy, then switch to a hospital clinic supervised by an obstetrician later on. The basic pattern of antenatal attendance is a visit once every four weeks for the first 28 weeks, once every two weeks up to 36 weeks and once a week thereafter. Each woman averages about 11–12 visits during pregnancy.

At each visit a routine examination takes place which includes weight measurement, blood pressure and urine tests. The first visit is regarded as especially important: the woman's history is noted and an assessment is made of any risk factors that her pregnancy might involve, for example,

*The perinatal mortality rate (PNMR) is the number of babies dying between the 28th week of pregnancy (that is, stillbirths) and the end of the first week of life, per 1 000 births.

Table 5.1 Perinatal Mortality Rates, Scotland, Wales and England in 1977

	Total PNMR	Legitimate	Illegitimate	Age of mother						Number of previous births (parity)					Social class*				
				16	16-19	20-24	25-29	30-34	35+	0	1	2	3	4+	I	II	III	IV	V
Scotland	18	17	–	20	24	17	16	17	29	19	13	15	25	39	11	14	18	19	23.5
Wales	18	17	28	33	26	18	15	17	22	20	14	15	20	30	16	16	17	17	20
England	17	16	23	34	22	17	15	16	24	18	13	16	19	28	11	13	16	19	22

* England and Wales legitimate births only.
(Data from Office of Health Economics, 1979, Table 1, p. 2)

the incidence of twins in her family or a history of high blood pressure. As pregnancy continues, the fetus is monitored with the help of sophisticated diagnostic aids such as ultrasonic scanners*, which are used to detect poor fetal growth, congenital abnormalities or multiple pregnancy, and to ascertain the age and size of the fetus. Some of these investigations have led to the general categorisation of women as either '*low*' or '*high risk*' on the basis of certain biological or social factors that have been shown to have an association with a higher perinatal mortality rate. The following, broadly 'biological' factors that indicate a 'high risk' are: if the woman is below 5′ 2″ (157 cm) in height; if there is a family history of certain diseases; if previous pregnancies have had complications; and if there is evidence of high blood pressure, diabetes, or several other conditions in the woman herself. Of course, social factors such as diet influence height and susceptibility to certain diseases, so the distinction is not clear-cut. Some social and biological factors associated with higher than average perinatal mortality are shown in Table 5.1.

□ According to Table 5.1, which factors are associated with the highest risks of a perinatal death?

■ Maternal age (but only if she is under 19 or over 35); marital status (illegitimate babies are at greater risk); number of previous births (first time mothers are at a slight increased risk, but the risk rises significantly after three or more previous births); social class (risk increases with lower social class).

Categorising pregnant women as high or low risk raises an issue that we touched on in Chapter 2 — that of medical labelling. Women who have no known factors associated with a higher than average perinatal mortality rate in their case history are categorised not as 'healthy' but as 'low risk', in other words, in terms of potential ill-health rather than present health. Notice also that the term 'high risk' *sounds* as though there is a high probability of perinatal death, whereas all this term means is that the probability is higher than *average*. The emphasis placed on perinatal mortality statistics as a measure of *satisfactory outcome* (i.e. live mother, live baby) is itself a subject for debate.

The highly organised pattern of modern antenatal care certainly provides a striking contrast to the total lack of provision at the turn of the century, and is an obvious advance. However, in recent years anxieties have surfaced about the quality of care available, not only from people utilising the services, but also from some doctors and midwives involved in delivering that care. These anxieties can broadly be summarised under three interrelated questions:

(i) Is antenatal care *effective*? Does it actually improve or sustain the health of mother and baby?

(ii) Is antenatal care *efficient*? Does it make the best possible use both of the time spent on it by the pregnant woman and her professional attendants, and of other resources such as money and health-service facilities?

(iii) Is antenatal care *humane*? Does it meet the personal, emotional needs of those who use or are employed in that service?

Is antenatal care effective?

There has been a widespread assumption that regular antenatal examination has made the major contribution to the steep fall in maternal and perinatal mortality since the 1920s (see Figures 5.1 and 5.2 overleaf).

In the 1920s and 1930s many women and babies died from complications of pregnancy that are now usually lessened or prevented by medical intervention. For example, maternal diabetes, chronic high blood pressure, incompatibility of the mother's blood group with that of her baby (for example, rhesus incompatibility) and haemorrhage from the womb claimed many lives. The rise in obstetric knowledge, medical technology and diagnostic skills, all an integral part of modern antenatal care, have been of crucial importance in reducing the numbers of lives lost through these complications. However, just as the

*High-frequency sound waves are 'bounced' off the fetus and other important structures such as the placenta. The reflected sound can be converted into a 'picture' of these structures, since different tissues reflect the sound to different extents. (See Book I, *Studying Health and Disease*, Chapter 3.)

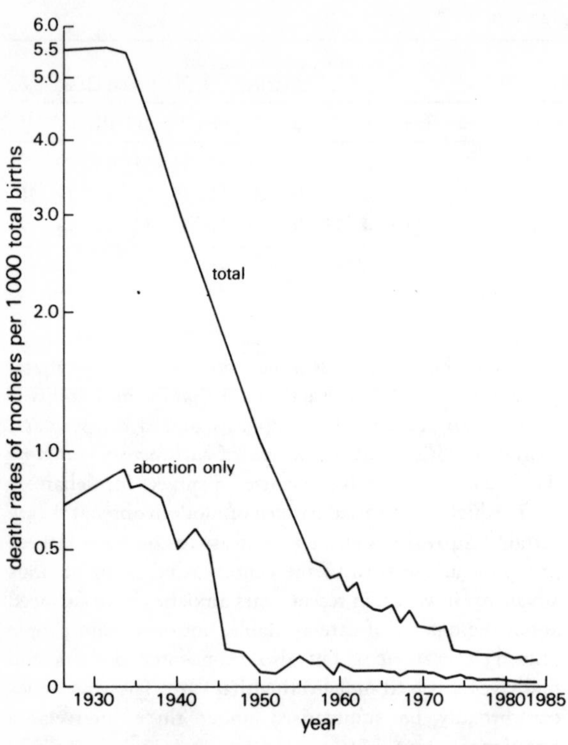

Figure 5.1 Trends in maternal mortality, England and Wales, 1928–84 (using a logarithmic scale*). (Data from Huntingford, 1979, p.236) *Defined in Book I, *Studying Health and Disease*, Chapter 5.

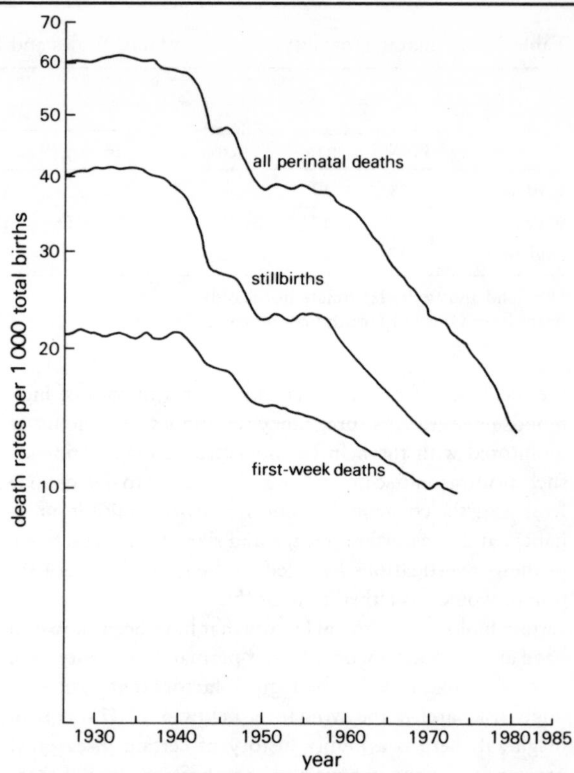

Figure 5.2 Trends in perinatal mortality rates*, England and Wales, 1928†–84. (Data from Huntingford, 1979, p.240) *Stillbirths plus deaths in the 1st week combine to make up the total PNMR of the top line. †PNMR was not measured separately from *infant* mortality (i.e. deaths between 1 week and 1 year of age) before 1928.

contribution of medicine to the decline of infectious diseases has been questioned,* so it is by no means certain that antenatal care has been the most important factor determining the decline in maternal and perinatal deaths.

□ Can you conclude that this fall in perinatal and maternal mortality rates can be attributed to the rise in antenatal care? Can you think of any other contributing factors?

■ Although there may well be an *association* between the level of antenatal care and perinatal and maternal mortality, the data do not prove that there is a *causal* connection. Other factors that you may have considered are: better medical care during labour and delivery; better housing and sanitation; improved nutrition and standard of living; the decline in infectious diseases; increased availability of safe abortions.

No one disputes that all these factors have contributed to falling mortality, but there has been contention about the relative importance of medical surveillance during pregnancy. There is some evidence that socio-economic factors have had at least as much of an impact — some would even argue that they outweigh the beneficial effects of antenatal care. Consider the following example that seems to support this view.

In the early 1930s there were high hopes that the rapid increase in the number of antenatal clinics and in pregnancy care would lower the maternal mortality rate. However, as Figure 5.1 shows, maternal mortality remained high for several years which caused alarm in medical circles. In August 1934, the *British Medical Journal* carried a series of contributions under the collective heading, 'Are we satisfied with the results of antenatal care?' The consensus was 'No'. As well as being self-critical about the lack of success of direct medical intervention, many doctors were aware of the poor social and economic conditions of the severe economic depression at that time.

□ What connection do you think there might have been between the 'Depression' and the maternal mortality rate?

■ As the quotations from the Women's Guild letters

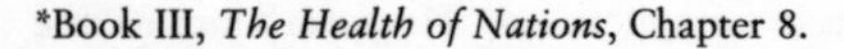

*Book III, *The Health of Nations*, Chapter 8.

illustrated, poor, undernourished women were at greater risk during pregnancy.

A leader in the *The Lancet* in 1934 suggested that 'perhaps the most potent influence tending to counteract the benefit of antenatal care is poverty'. Although the introduction of antibacterial drugs (sulphonamides) contributed to fewer women dying of postnatal infections after 1938, socio-economic factors also had an unexpectedly dramatic effect on both perinatal and maternal mortality rates during the Second World War. During the War, the British government pursued a national food policy that directly affected all pregnant women, who received cheaper milk and had special allocations of high protein foods and vitamins. In 1941, for example, they received four eggs per week instead of the normal allocation of one. Maternal mortality more than halved in the decade 1936–46 (see Figure 5.1).

□ What do you notice about the *stillbirth* rate for the same period?

■ It fell from 39 per 1 000 to 27 per 1 000.

Precisely which factors led to these impressive falls are difficult to ascertain, but it is reasonable to surmise that improvement in diet among poor mothers contributed to them, together with shrinking family size, full employment and relative economic stability. The view that social factors have a profound influence on mortality rates is therefore firmly held in some quarters. For example, in 1979, under the heading 'Poverty — Prime Cause of Baby Deaths', a leading national newspaper maintained that there is 'no evidence' that better maternity care or services would save lives (*Guardian*, 20 October 1979). In contrast, many policy-makers remain convinced about the mitigating factors of clinical intervention throughout pregnancy. For example, a spokesman from the North-Western Regional Health Authority speaking to the government committee investigating perinatal mortality in 1980 said that 'The region firmly believes that intervention by a professional service is able to a significant extent to reverse and counteract the influence of the adverse social and economic environment.' (Short, 1980, Vol.1, para. 314, p.99).

It may thus appear that there is a direct conflict between those who advocate improved antenatal services and those who emphasise the role of socio-economic factors in perinatal mortality. At its centre is the question of belief in the effectiveness of antenatal care to reduce deaths. To examine this in more detail demands a closer inspection of perinatal mortality rate as a measure of outcome. The most potent influence on PNMR is *birthweight*. Figure 5.3 shows that, on average, a baby weighs about 3 300 g at birth, and that most weight is gained in the last three months. In the UK, babies weighing 2 500 g or less at birth account for 60 per cent of the live-born babies who die by the end of the first week. So, to determine the effectiveness of antenatal care, we need to consider the causes of low birthweight, and whether antenatal care has any impact upon them. In 1970 a British national survey on PNMR showed that birthweight is associated with social class (see Table 5.2 overleaf). As you can see, the percentage of *low birthweight babies* (under 2 500 g) in social classes IV and V is consistently greater than in social classes I and II.

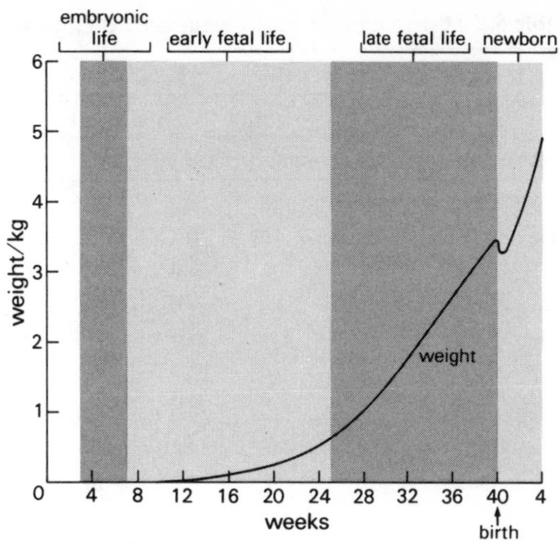

Figure 5.3 Fetal growth. The most rapid growth in weight is in late fetal life. (Smith-Bierman, 1978, p.54)

Premature birth is associated with low birthweight as the baby's weight increases at a faster rate in the last 8 weeks (see Figure 5.3). Surveys have also shown that premature births and *placental insufficiency* (in which inadequate nourishment reaches the baby through the placenta) are also associated with lower social class, and these two conditions are the major factors associated with low birthweight. The effect of prematurity on birthweight can be seen in Figure 5.4 (overleaf).

Antenatal care clearly cannot alter a woman's socio-economic circumstances. However, professional advice during antenatal check-ups could bring about some improvements, for example, improving dietary habits, and some specific medical interventions can be carried out to try and prevent premature delivery. Women who have already had one or more premature deliveries are at significantly greater risk of another. In such cases, the doctor may decide to insert a knot or a stitch in the cervix (neck of the womb). This practice is based on the belief that a 'weak' cervix can lead to premature delivery. Although thousands of such operations are performed every year, there is little published research data available that supports the effectiveness of this procedure. However, you will see later that this practice seems to have reduced premature births (and hence low birthweight and PNMR) in the example of

Table 5.2 Distribution of birthweight according to social class

	Social class					
	I, II		III		IV, V	
Birthweight	number	%	number	%	number	%
1 000 g and under	5	0.2	26	0.3	11	0.4
1 001 g–1 500 g	9	0.4	36	0.5	18	0.7
1 501 g–2 000g	23	1.0	72	1.0	37	1.4
2 001 g–2 500 g	68	2.9	284	3.8	145	5.7
2 501 g–3 000 g	337	14.5	1 367	18.1	491	19.1
3 001 g–3 500 g	929	40.1	2 955	39.1	993	38.7
3 501 g–4 000 g	710	30.6	2 148	28.4	652	25.4
over 4 000 g	236	10.2	655	8.7	217	8.5
no information	2	0.1	14	0.2	—	—
total	2 319	100.0	7 557	100.1	2 564	99.9

(Chamberlain, Chamberlain and Howlett, 1975, Appendix, Table 3.3, p. 85)

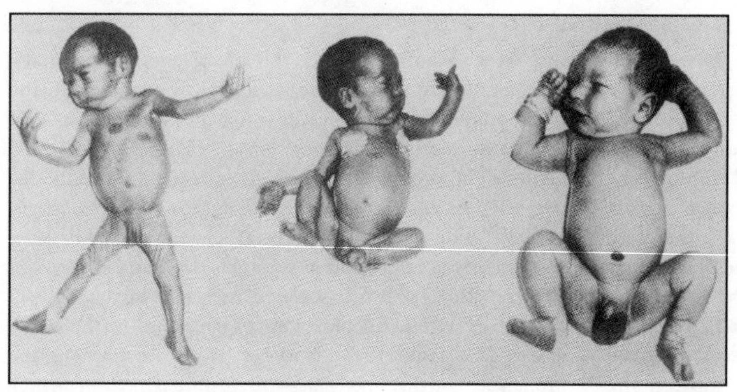

Figure 5.4 Infants (left to right) born at 28, 33 and 40 weeks of pregnancy. (Smith-Bierman, 1978, p.103). Notice how the premature babies are fully formed but very much smaller than the full-term baby.

an innovative antenatal care scheme at Sighthill in Edinburgh.

It is certain that some interventions and diagnostic medical skills can be effective in providing expert management of serious specific pregnancy complications or that problems can be detected early by the use of ultrasonic scanners. However, it remains very difficult to gauge the effectiveness of antenatal care. Not even the most elaborate of statistical techniques can take into account all the variety of socio-economic and biological factors that may affect a fetus adversely and then relate this to the number of antenatal visits and tests that its mother receives.

Several studies have attempted to prove that an increased number of antenatal visits will lower the PNMR; however, they are fraught with pitfalls. An Aberdeen obstetrician, Marion Hall, and her colleagues have questioned these studies on two main grounds. First, those women who attend early and regularly and therefore tend to clock up more visits, are often those who are healthier and better off financially and socially; they would have a lower risk of losing their baby anyway, irrespective of the care they received.

□ Secondly, what effect might the length of pregnancy have on the relationship between the number of visits and PNMR?

■ Those women whose babies are premature have both a higher risk of the baby dying and less time in which to make routine antenatal visits, giving support to the hypothesis that a high PNMR and a lower number of visits are linked.

Nevertheless, for all these uncertainties as to its effectiveness, antenatal care undoubtedly does some good. So why do some women only start attending late on in pregnancy or attend irregularly? The Short Committee, for example, found that in Leicestershire, over 40 per cent of mothers whose babies had died had not been in contact with a doctor or midwife until after 16 weeks of pregnancy. This lack of attendance has often been attributed to carelessness and irresponsibility on the part of these women.

□ Can you suggest other explanations?

■ Low attendance is more likely among working-class women with other small children, who cannot find or afford childminders, who have to travel long distances, are less able to afford bus fares or take time off work.

Thus it seems that the women who may need antenatal care the most attend the least, and the ones who need it least attend the most. This obviously has implications for the efficiency of antenatal care.

Is antenatal care efficient?

Whereas the effectiveness of antenatal care is evaluated in terms of *outcome* (for example, perinatal and maternal mortality rates), its efficiency is evaluated in terms of how the resources put into it are utilised. Many people are now concerned whether the pattern of antenatal care established fifty years ago with its repeated visits and attention to mortality rates is appropriate and meets the needs of pregnant women today. Iain Chalmers, an obstetrician and director of the National Perinatal Epidemiology Unit, and Murray Enkin, Associate Professor of Obstetrics and Gynaecology at McMaster Medical School in Canada, have voiced this concern in no uncertain terms:

> The compulsion to shave a further fraction of a percentage off perinatal mortality rates, combined with interprofessional rivalries, have produced the current bizarre approach to antenatal care in which a bulldozer is used to unearth pathology whatever the cost. (Enkin and Chalmers, 1982, p.283).

This 'cost' refers to the resources, time and effort expended in the antenatal care system. Because of the way in which the National Health Service collects financial information, it is not always easy to find out how much it costs to provide a particular set of services, and antenatal care is no exception. However, it is known that maternity services as a whole absorb about 4 per cent of all NHS spending, and that about 30 per cent of the maternity budget goes towards antenatal care. In 1983, therefore, it cost around £200 million to provide these antenatal services. How effectively are these resources used? What evidence exists on the outcome of antenatal care?

In 1981, Marion Hall and Pang K. Chng, in a study of antenatal care provided for more than 2000 women in Aberdeen, came to the conclusion that the mass approach to antenatal screening involving 12 visits, not only ignores a woman's individual needs, but is also inefficient, costly and often results in a diagnosis of conditions that do not exist.

> Overdiagnosis is another major problem. For every case of sustained hypertension [high blood pressure], at least one case of transient hypertension of no clinical importance was diagnosed. For every woman correctly diagnosed by the physician as having a growth-retarded baby, another 2.5 were so predicted without having the condition. (Hall and Chng, in Enkin and Chalmers, 1982, pp.66–67)

Hall suggests that 'low risk' women should attend for only 6 antenatal visits, thus releasing more time and resources for 'high risk' women.

□ Would more time and resources for antenatal care reduce problem pregnancies?

■ Not necessarily, for social factors such as nutrition and living conditions must still be taken into account.

However, some women may experience anxiety or lack of confidence, which could be exacerbated by so few visits in the early months of pregnancy.* Nevertheless, in the proposed scheme, 'high risk' women visiting a hospital clinic would get much more time with an obstetrician. Many obstetricians agree that discussions with healthy women about minor ailments are not an efficient use of their expensive training. In 1982, a working party on antenatal care for the Royal Society of Obstetricians recommended that healthy women should visit hospital clinics less frequently, and there should be an increased use of midwives in looking after them. (However, the definition of what is 'normal' and 'healthy' is in itself problematic, as you saw in Chapter 2 when surveillance was discussed, and we will return to a fuller discussion of this in the next chapter.)

In addition, centralised hospital clinics are very costly in terms of the expectant mother's time when compared with antenatal care available from her local GP's surgery. Table 5.3 (overleaf) shows the amount of time spent on antenatal visits in a national survey of more than 3000 randomly selected pregnant women in 1981.

Notice that the women spent about twice as long in travelling to the hospital than to their local GP's surgery, and three times as long in the waiting room. The fact that examinations and tests took twice as long in the hospital does not mean that more procedures were carried out, but that there are concealed 'waiting times' between one test and the next. Some duplication also occurred when more

*This point is illustrated by the first-time mother in TV programme 5, who says that until she could feel the baby moving for herself, she had needed repeated reassurances that it was still alive.

Table 5.3 Time spent on antenatal visits to hospital and GP surgery

	Average time/minutes	
	hospital	GP
time spent travelling to and from place where care received	57	30
time spent waiting	62	22
time spent being examined and having tests	37	17
time spent on whole visit (from time left home or work to time got back)	156	69
number of women	1589	1774

(Quoted by Zander in Enkin and Chalmers, 1982, p. 248)

than one person examined a woman during a single visit. It was also found that the longest and most inconvenient way to get to the hospital clinic was by public transport, the use of which had a marked social-class difference (44 per cent of women in social class V used it as compared with 18 per cent in social class I).

It seems from this evidence that the efficiency and effectiveness of the present system of antenatal care could be improved by taking more consideration of the best use of expensive professional resources and the differing needs of women. This brings us to the final question. Is current antenatal care humane?

Is antenatal care humane?

The best answer to this question is likely to come from women themselves. It is to them that we now turn, for even though antenatal care revolves around the pregnant woman, it is often *she* who is ignored as an individual.

> We need to get our antenatal work into focus, remembering that the process of childbirth is a continuous one, and it is no good concentrating on antenatal care unless we give attention to other matters. Antenatal care is an essential part of obstetrics, not a specialised stunt by itself, and the expectant mother is not an ambulant pelvis but a woman with human needs, whose soul and body are interlocked. In our zeal, let us not forget the mother. (Dr Letitia Fairfield, letter to *The Lancet*, 1934, p.104).

The quotation encapsulates one of the central dissatisfactions with antenatal care in its early days — that it did not cater for the differing individual needs of pregnant women, who often felt unimportant and ignored. That this is still the case is borne out in the interviews with women contained on the audiotape sequence, 'Antenatal care — women's views' (AC 804, Band 4) to which you should now listen.

The following four main areas of dissatisfaction emerge from the interviews:

(i) that what women experience of antenatal care does not match with their expectations of it;

(ii) that the siting of clinics and the appointment systems are largely inconvenient;

(iii) that communication between pregnant women and staff is in many instances unsatisfactory;

(iv) that there is a lack of *continuity of care*.

Further evidence of this dissatisfaction is contained in several recent sociological studies which investigated what women themselves think of the care they receive, for example, the 1981 'Baby Survey', a study of what 6000 British women thought of their maternity care. It was initiated by a BBC consumer programme and compiled into a book, *The British Way of Birth*, by Catherine Boyd and Lea Sellers. The chief drawback of this survey is that the 6000 women involved were self-selecting in that *they* were interested in taking part and were not chosen at random.

□ Why is this a drawback, and what should you be wary of in interpreting the results?

■ *Self-selection* will *bias* the survey towards women with more interest in the matter, with more time, who are more articulate, or who may wish to express their dissatisfaction. They may not, therefore, fairly represent the views of *all* pregnant women.

The sample was in fact biased towards social classes I and II, in that 36 per cent of the women were from these classes (compared to 25 per cent of the UK population as a whole), and towards older women (only 3 per cent were under 20 and this should have been closer to 10 per cent to be representative of the population). Nevertheless, other studies with a more representative sample have also shown, for example, that there is a lack of créche facilities for small children during antenatal visits and that there can be long distances to travel to hospital clinics.

This general lack of support is not only confined to the organisation of maternity services. Sometimes work conditions for pregnant women are not ideal, as the 'Baby Survey' revealed — for example:

> My manager wasn't pleased when I had to have half a day off to go to the hospital and at first said that I'd have to make the time up. If I hadn't known that I was allowed time to go I would have had to make the time up. (Sales assistant, quoted in Boyd and Sellers, 1982, p.62).

> They would have given me time off to go to the clinic but being a mill it is difficult to get someone to take over the machine. (Millworker, ibid., p.62)

A study carried out by Hilary Graham and Lorna McKee in 1980 on a sample of 200 women in York, collected their views during pregnancy and after their babies were born.

Even though 90 per cent felt that the antenatal check-up was important, only 17 per cent said that they had learned anything about themselves or their babies, and only 31 per cent said that they had enjoyed their visits. In the 'Baby Survey', half the women said they had received no advice at all about diet, travelling, exercise, working hours, work hazards, teeth, the possible dangers of alcohol and smoking, taking pills or medicine or X-rays.

□ Why do you think this may be cause for concern?

■ You may have thought of the possible hazards that a fetus in the womb can be exposed to; for example, the damaging effect of excessive alcohol and some medicinal drugs, and the danger of damage from X-rays.*

On the other hand, some other women felt pressurised by too much advice, especially in relation to giving up smoking. Most antenatal clinics display Health Education Council posters aimed at persuading pregnant women not to smoke (Figure 5.5). However, the evidence for harmful effects of smoking on the fetus is still inconclusive.

The data so far do not support the warning in the poster that smoking can kill babies. Although smoking is associated with a reduction in birthweight, and low birthweight is the strongest indicator of perinatal mortality, it does not necessarily follow that smoking leads to perinatal death.

□ Why do you think it might not be justified to conclude that *smoking* by a pregnant woman increases the chance of the baby's death?

■ The association between smoking and perinatal death may not be *causal*. In fact there is evidence that both are related to social class. In other words, a woman in social class V is both more likely to smoke and more likely to suffer a perinatal death. The common factor, and the 'cause' of perinatal death is her social class, not the fact that she smokes.

Anti-smoking propaganda aimed at pregnant women ignores the problem of physical and psychological addiction, the meaning of the behaviour for the women involved, and the guilt and anxiety felt by those who continue to smoke despite pressure to give it up. In another study by Hilary Graham, some pregnant women were interviewed about their attitudes to smoking during pregnancy. Some women felt guilty and inadequate:

> I know if anything were wrong with her, I'd blame the cigarettes and I'd know I'd done it myself, and my husband would know I'd done it. (Graham, 1977, p.403)

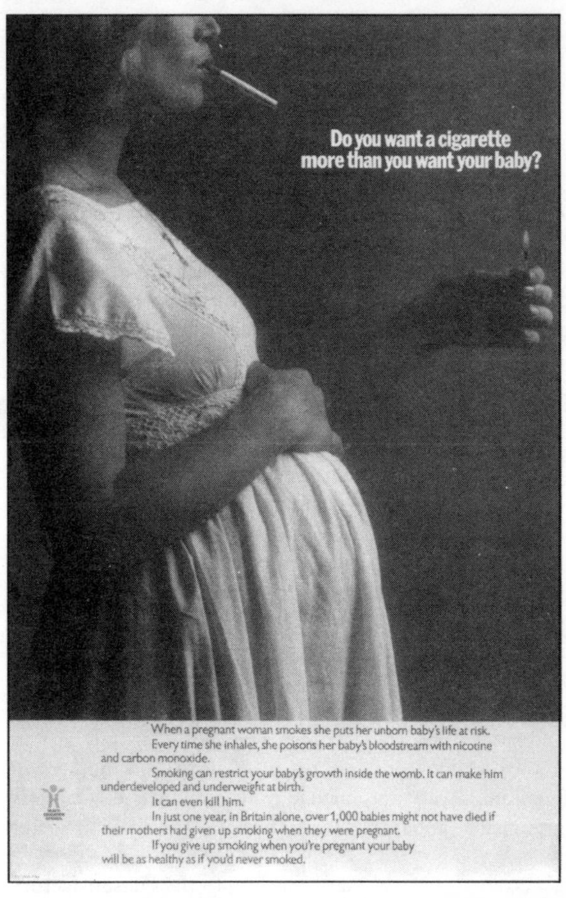

Figure 5.5 Health Education Council poster warning of the dangers of smoking in pregnancy. (Reproduced by kind permission of the Health Education Council, London.)

> I'm worried sick about it. I can't stop and there's an end to it ... every time I open a magazine, I'm told I'm killing my baby, and now it's even on the telly. (ibid, p.403)

Others, however, saw giving up smoking as harmful to other people for whom they are responsible, for example:

> I've cut down ... to 10 a day. If I cut down any more, I take it out on him [her son] which isn't fair on him. So it's one bairn or the other. (Graham, 1977, p.403)

> I gave up smoking for a bit, and I was even more irritable ... I reckon if I get much worse, Dave'll move out! (ibid., p.403)

□ What sentiments expressed in the quote from *The*

*These hazards are described in *The Biology of Health and Disease*, Chapter 13, The Open University (1985) U205 *Health and Disease*, Book IV.

Lancet, 1934 at the beginning of this section do these examples highlight?

■ That antenatal care cannot be given in isolation, without taking into account the *whole* of the woman's life.

Many of the women in the surveys complain of lack of continuity in the care they receive. This results from seeing different doctors and midwives at each hospital visit. In a survey conducted in Glasgow by M.E. Reid and G.H. McIlwaine in 1980, 84 per cent of the women would have preferred to see the same doctor each time, and in the York study by Graham and McKee, the figure was 81 per cent. In practice, the continually changing rota of medical personnel in hospital clinics leaves little possibility of pregnant women forming relationships with their care-givers. This plays a large part in the unsatisfactory communication between staff and pregnant women that is so commonly mentioned in the studies.

The quality of communication between pregnant women and their doctors is discussed in an article in the Course Reader, 'Doctor Knows Best' by the feminist sociologist Ann Oakley.* It is taken from her book *Women Confined* (1980). The extract in the Course Reader includes conversations between women and their doctors during antenatal visits. These women were part of a study carried out by Oakley on a group of 60 first-time mothers in London. Read the article and summarise Oakley's arguments about medical attitudes towards pregnant women.

Oakley argues that much of the unsatisfactory relationship between pregnant women and their doctors is due to discrimination by a male medical profession against female 'patients' — in other words, *gender discrimination*. For example, she asserts that:

(i) Doctors patronise women, and assume they are ignorant, as in the quotation from Family Doctor Publications.

(ii) Doctors sometimes treat women as irresponsible; for example, the doctor not believing that women know or remember their pregnancy dates (as in the last two dialogues).

(iii) Women are sometimes treated as 'children' who cannot cope with technical information, e.g.

DOCTOR I've given the membranes a good sweep over.
PATIENT What does that mean?
DOCTOR I've swept them — not with a brush, with my finger.

(iv) Women are not taken seriously, e.g. the doctor who responds to the discomforts of one pregnant woman with, 'We need to put you in a hammock, don't we?'.

□ What attitudes of the *author* do you notice that you may need to be wary of when interpreting her material?

■ She is very critical of the male medical 'takeover' of women's reproductive processes. This *may* lead her to interpret doctors' statements in a harsher light than is justified.

For example, Oakley suggests that the jokes at the beginning of the dialogues: 'So you're an expert', 'weighed it did they?', and 'Yes, it's a piece of cake, really' indicate the presence of unresolved questions about what Oakley refers to as 'intra-uterine neocolonialism'. This may possibly be true, but there may also be other interpretations.

□ Can you suggest alternatives?

■ Your suggestions may include that the doctors are just insensitive, or engaging in a particular brand of medical humour, or that doctors generally employ this 'patronising' tone with *all* their patients, male or female. (Note that Oakley's research does not include comparative interviews between doctors and male patients.)

It is important to note that not all women are treated by doctors as they are in the article in the Course Reader, and many women talk highly of the care they receive. The point is not to malign doctors, but rather to note that complaints about interactions between pregnant women and their doctors are frequent enough to warrant attention. The attitude that 'Doctor Knows Best' is not restricted to the case of pregnant women and will be discussed again several times in this course, but pregnancy is a particularly clear example of the sometimes troubled relationship between the medical profession and those that it is trained to serve.

These studies strongly suggest that there are measures other than 'live baby — live mother' that we should consider when assessing the outcomes of the current pattern of antenatal care, such as emotional well-being and contentment. It seems that many women feel dissatisfied with the service they get, in ways that are far less easy to measure than mortality rates. But if antenatal care is not felt to be humane, does not this also reduce its effectiveness? The number of missed appointments suggests such a connection. Conversely, it has been argued that we cannot afford to give women the individual attention that many seem to want — in other words, a humane service might be effective, but its efficiency would fall, perhaps prohibitively so. An experiment in Edinburgh sheds some light on this.

The Sighthill antenatal scheme

In recent years there have been several innovative community antenatal schemes that have attempted to be

*Nick Black *et al.* (eds) (1984) *Health and Disease: A Reader*, The Open University Press.

effective, efficient *and* humane. The antenatal scheme at Sighthill in Edinburgh has attempted (quite successfully) to deal with the worst criticisms of antenatal care, and enhance the best aspects (see The Sighthill Maternity Team, 1982).

Sighthill is situated on the western boundaries of Edinburgh. The population comprises all social classes, but has a higher proportion of social classes IV and V than the average for Scotland. In 1975, the Sighthill Health Centre operated a shared-care system in which pregnant women came there for initial visits and were then referred to a large maternity hospital clinic, the nearest being Simpson Memorial Maternity Pavilion, six miles away. For the women this was unsatisfactory as it involved long, expensive bus journeys, long waits and finally a two-minute consultation with an unfamiliar doctor. Morale was low among the Sighthill midwives. All they had to do was administer routine tests, and they felt that their skills were not being used adequately. Attendance at antenatal clinics was poor, and the PNMR for Sighthill residents in 1972 was 27.9 per 1 000.

□ How did this compare with the average for Scotland in 1972? (See Figure 5.6)

■ It was higher. The PNMR for Scotland in 1972 was 23 per 1 000.

Two obstetricians from the Simpson hospital and a community specialist, all of whom were keen to introduce an experimental scheme of community antenatal care, suggested Sighthill for a pilot scheme. They were especially concerned that the women in the lower social classes who were poor attenders were also at the greatest risk of experiencing a perinatal death. They teamed up with the midwives, GPs and health visitors of the area, and worked out a scheme that would take antenatal care into the community and offer close liaison between professionals and parents. The scheme began operating in 1976.

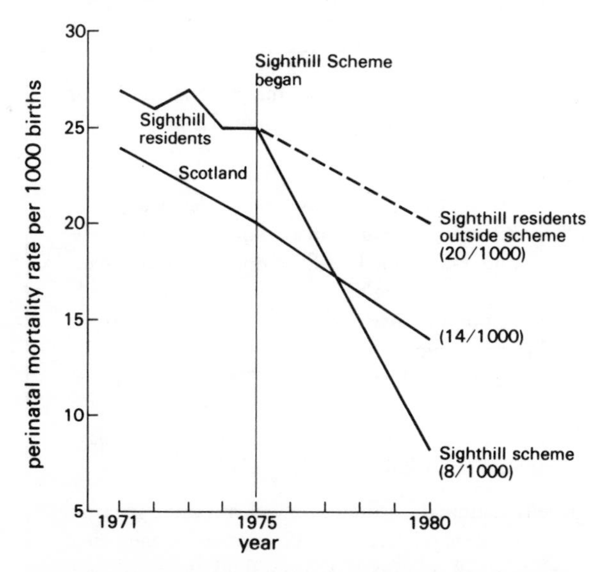

Figure 5.6 Perinatal mortality rates from 1976–80 for women in the Sighthill Scheme compared with that for Scotland as a whole. (The Sighthill Maternity Team, 1982)

All of the women involved attended the local clinic at the Sighthill Health Centre throughout their pregnancy, seeing the same team of GPs and midwives. Women with diabetes, severe heart disease and previous rhesus incompatibility problems were excluded from the scheme as they received their care at the hospital (because of their high risk status). At the first clinic a full medical examination was carried out by the GP, and a detailed history taken by a midwife, who then prepared a risk assessment card. All women underwent a routine blood test to check for signs of possible spina bifida in their babies. The women were introduced to health visitors who gave them welfare rights information, for example about their entitlement to supplementary benefits, free milk, etc. The whole team then discussed the subsequent clinical management of each woman, gave parents the opportunity to discuss with as many people as possible their worries and concerns, and to receive professional advice in an atmosphere that was relaxed and friendly. A hospital consultant visited the local clinic about once a month and was available on standby for advice.

Women attended the more distant hospital clinic usually only once to have an ultrasonic scan. Some antenatal care was done in the home by visiting midwives who assumed a great deal of responsibility and autonomy. Special measures were taken to prevent premature labour, either by inserting a stitch in the cervix of women with a history of previous miscarriage, or by giving drugs to counteract contractions if labour had started too early.

The scheme has used a number of both quantitative and qualitative criteria to assess the 3 000 births which took place up to 1984. The rates of both low birthweight and premature births halved during this period: premature deliveries fell from 15 per cent to 7.8 per cent, and the number of low birthweight babies (less than 2 500 g) fell from 12 per cent to 6.8 per cent.

□ Would you expect the PNMR to be lower as a result?

■ Yes, because the PNMR is associated with the incidence of premature and low birthweight babies.

In fact PNMR in this particular scheme dropped to 8 in the first 1 000 births. This is compared with a control group in the rest of Sighthill where the PNMR had fallen from 28 to 20 per 1 000 in the same timespan. In 1983 there were no perinatal deaths in the scheme. The latest average PNMR based on 3 000 births stands at 4 per 1 000 (1984).

The Sighthill scheme has been successful in other ways as well. The rate of non-attendance at appointments dropped from 16 per cent to 1 per cent suggesting that local antenatal care is much more appealing than hospital-based care. No systematic follow up has been done to find out what parents' reactions were to the scheme, but in conversations with midwives many women said they felt much more relaxed, made new friends and had developed confidence in the team over the pregnancy period. GPs and midwives enjoyed the greater responsibility, and reported vast improvement in job satisfaction. The women were affected by the midwives' enthusiasm for the scheme, and cooperation was very high. In fact, the routine home visit in cases where a women did not attend happened in only 1 per cent of the cases and the number of women coming for early booking (before 10 weeks) rose to 95 per cent (compared to 63 per cent in the period 1971–75). The results are impressive and seem to show that antenatal care can be effective — perhaps *because* the scheme was felt to be both efficient and humane.

□ Can you suggest any areas where criticisms can be made or caution taken in interpreting the results?

■ You may have considered the following:

(i) The focus of the scheme is still oriented to things going wrong and greater surveillance, and might not suit the 'normal healthy' women of the population. For example, as in conventional antenatal care, all women have a test to detect spina bifida. Studies have shown that waiting for results of screening for neural tube defects can cause anxiety.

(ii) The focus of results has been on quantitative measures and no systematic studies (up to 1984) have been made of what the women themselves think of the scheme — we must rely on anecdotal evidence of this.

(iii) Caution should be taken in attributing the falls in PNMR totally to the medical aspects of the antenatal scheme. Certain categories of 'high risk' women were excluded and treated elsewhere. It is also important to note that the fact that health visitors routinely informed all women of social security benefits to which they were entitled, plus free milk and vitamins, would have had an effect on their standard of living during pregnancy, which in turn may have affected the outcome (as during the Second World War). However, there has been no research to ascertain whether families took up more benefits as a result of the scheme.

The Sighthill scheme has demonstrated that systematic antenatal care which combines the latest medical expertise and technology with sensitivity to the individual emotional needs of pregnant women and awareness of socio-economic factors, can be very effective in reducing perinatal mortality *and* increasing satisfaction. However, whether this fall in PNMR has been as a direct result of medical intervention or increased awareness of social benefits remains to be seen.

In the next chapter, we turn to the birth itself and examine the trend towards delivery in hospitals rather than at home, with the concomitant increase in medical procedures that require a hospital setting. The three questions that we have posed about the care of the baby in the womb apply equally strongly to the circumstances of her transition into the world.

Objectives for Chapter 5

When you have studied this chapter, you should be able to:

5.1 Illustrate the interaction of biological, socio-economic and personal factors in determining pregnancy outcome.

5.2 Discuss the relationship between effectiveness and efficiency in antenatal care and their contribution to a humane service.

Questions for Chapter 5

1 *(Objective 5.1)*

> If the mother has smoked heavily, followed an unhealthy diet, or simply comes from a deprived household, it can be too late to save the baby even if the mother changes her lifestyle. (Ann Oakley, quoted in Inch, 1982, p.32)

How does Oakley's statement illustrate the interaction of biological, socio-economic and personal life-history factors in determining the outcome of a pregnancy?

2 *(Objective 5.2)*

> There appears to be a growing tendency to apply as screening measures in all women tests that are of unquestionable benefit to only a few. It is true that the screening tests in current use are by and large non-invasive and free from direct hazard, but this in no way implies that there is no risk associated with their use. Their potential for harm derives primarily from their capacity for erroneously indicating the presence of pathology. (Enkin and Chalmers, 1982, p.270)

Briefly outline the grounds on which routine screening tests in antenatal care could be criticised as inefficient, ineffective or inhumane. Do you think these criticisms are sufficient to justify abandoning routine tests?

6

Birth and the first week of life

In this chapter we assume that you are familiar with the hormonal changes that occur during childbirth (Book IV, *The Biology of Health and Disease*, Chapter 10). Ideally you should watch the TV programme 'A suitable place to have a baby?' close to the period in which you study this chapter, but do not delay work on the chapter if you have not yet seen the programme. There is an audiotape sequence discussing the programme on cassette AC804, and you should play this soon after viewing. You will be asked to study an article in the Course Reader — 'Doing the month' by Barbara Pillsbury (Part 1, Section 1.3) — towards the end of this chapter.

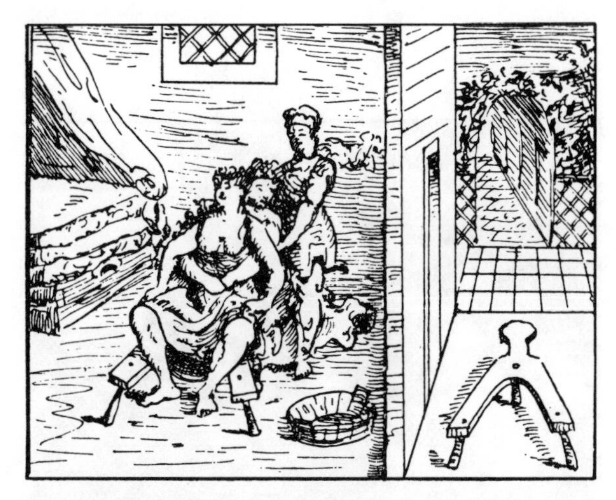

Figure 6.1 'Scientific' posture advocated in Europe in the sixteenth century, with a birthing stool. (From G.J. Engelmann, *Labor Among Primitive Peoples*. J.H. Chambers, St Louis, 1982)

After an average of nine months in the womb, a baby is born in a matter of hours. This is a relatively dangerous time: even in the UK where babies die quite rarely, the risk of death is greater during delivery and in the next 24 hours than during any other 24-hour period in a lifespan.

As we noted in Chapter 1, such major events in life as the transition from the womb into the world are accompanied in every society by certain rituals or customary procedures which are designed to minimise the dangers. Even if they are ineffective in making the transition literally safer, their ritual aspects may still provide a means of coping with the attendant anxiety and uncertainty. Looking at the ways in which other societies, contemporary and historical, have dealt with the event of birth, can thus provide a different perspective from which to evaluate some of the practices current in the UK today (see Figures 6.1–6.6).

□ What can you see as the main differences between the births shown in Figures 6.5 and 6.6 (overleaf)?

■ In Figure 6.6, the woman is in an upright position and has close physical support from female attendants. The technology is rudimentary, in the form of a hanging rope and the birth takes place in a hut. In Figure 6.5, the woman is lying on a delivery table on her back with her legs up in stirrups. The attendants are both male and female. You might recognize some of them as nurses, and the setting as a hospital. The technology is advanced — there is medical equipment in the background.

Over recent years medical intervention in childbirth has increased in industrial countries. Although this has taken place in the attempt to reduce the mortality rates of mothers and babies which remain high in many non-industrialised/Third World countries today, there has been growing concern about the extent of this intervention. Criticisms have come from some parents, the women's movement, and a growing minority of midwives, GPs and obstetricians.

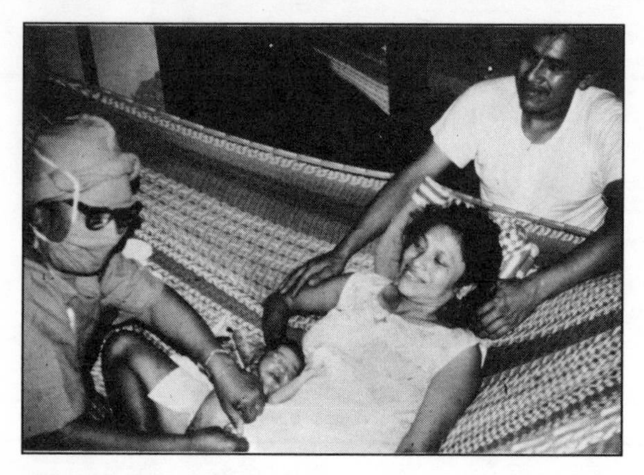

Figure 6.2 Mayan woman in labour with mother as 'head helper', 1970s. (Courtesy Brigitte Jordan, 1980)

Figure 6.3 Birth in New Guinea, 1970s. (From Michel Odent, *Genese de l'Homme Ecologique*, Epic, 1979)

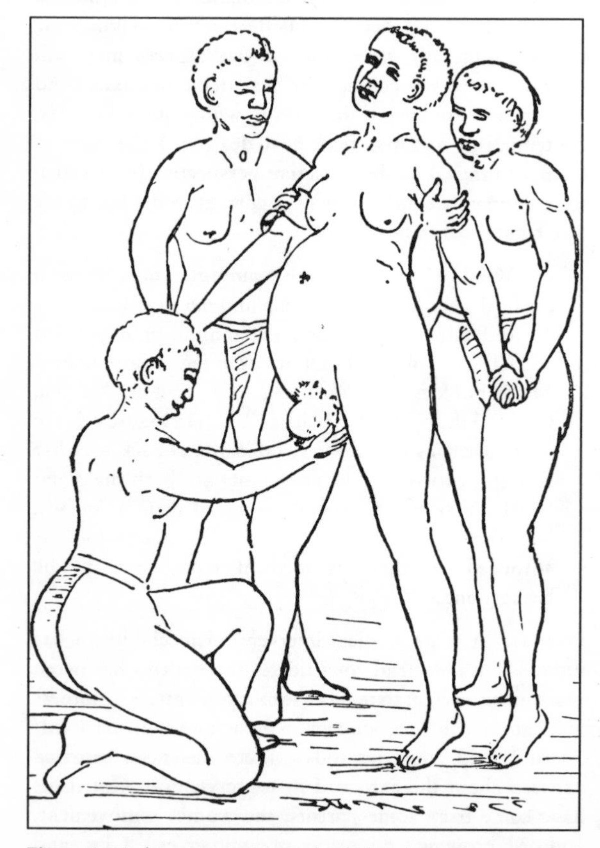

Figure 6.4 Labour scene among the Wakambas (Western part of Central Africa). (From Engelmann, *op. cit.*)

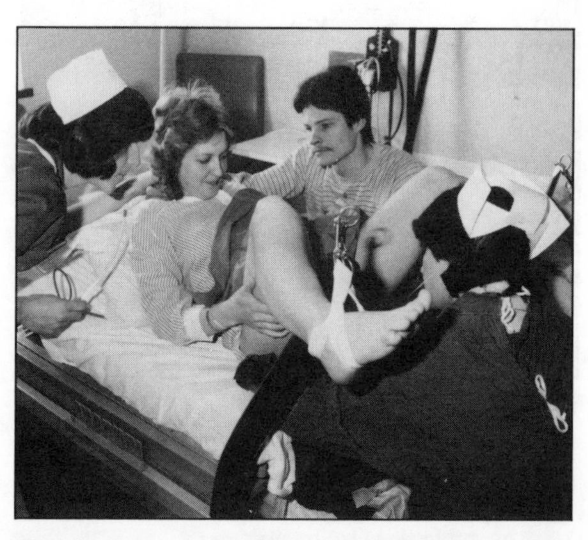

Figure 6.5 Birth in the UK, 1970s. (*Nursing Mirror*)

Figure 6.6 Mexican Indian labour scene. (Engelmann, *op. cit.*)

The current debate about childbirth has tended to polarise between a 'back-to-nature' camp and the advocates of 'high-technology'. The crucial factor in this argument is the way in which 'natural' birth is defined. As Figures 6.1–6.6 show, although the biological process is the same, what is 'natural' is seen very differently by different cultures.

As in the previous chapter we shall be asking how far western medical practices in childbirth are effective, efficient and humane. Do all the common procedures actually improve the health of mother and baby, or are some closer to the magical rituals of primitive cultures? For example, there is already broad agreement that two birth practices routinely used in the UK until recently are of no real value — women no longer have their pubic hair shaved at the onset of labour in many hospitals, and midwives are gradually giving up wearing surgical masks. In this chapter we shall focus on two interconnected trends: first, the *place of birth* — almost 99 per cent of all babies are delivered in hospital or a maternity unit, whereas at the start of this century nearly all were delivered in their mothers' homes. The second trend is referred to as the increasing *medicalisation of childbirth* — a shorthand term meaning the increasing use of equipment and drugs that require the skills of professionally trained medical or nursing personnel. This above all has led to birth becoming a medical rather than a domestic event.

□ Can you see ways in which these two trends are interdependent? (Hint: think back to the discussion of trends in antenatal care in the previous chapter.)

■ Just as antenatal care shifted towards hospital clinics after the free National Health Service began in 1948, so too did childbirth. By having their babies in hospitals, women had access to medical procedures and expertise that were less readily available in their own homes.

Place of birth

The shift in place of delivery from home to hospital is a comparatively recent phenomenon. In 1927, 85 per cent of babies were born in their mothers' homes. In 1961, 32.5 per cent of all births still took place at home, but by 1980 this had fallen to only 1.3 per cent.

The rise of the hospital as the centre for birth has gone hand in hand with the rise of *obstetrics* as a specialist branch of medicine. The training of obstetricians is supervised by the Royal College of Obstetricians and Gynaecologists (RCOG). It is oriented towards teaching surgical skills, and experience is gained exclusively in hospitals. At the start of this century, the specialist skills of obstetricians were directed towards the management of difficult births, but nowadays obstetricians supervise straightforward births and routinely use equipment or procedures that demand their particular expertise, *and* are dependent upon a hospital setting. This century has seen a consistent pattern of State legislation recommending moving birth into hospitals, usually following advice from obstetricians.

Very few consumer views were sought in this change: for example, mothers were not consulted or represented at the Peel Committee in 1970 which investigated *domiciliary midwifery* and recommended 100 per cent hospital confinements. Consequently, women today have little choice as to where to have their babies. This is usually arranged at the first antenatal visit. Most women, whether they are considered 'high risk' or 'low risk', are booked into a *maternity unit* which is part of a large hospital. Here the birth is supervised by a consultant obstetrician, although midwives usually perform routine monitoring and assistance during labour and uncomplicated deliveries. After the birth, women and their babies usually stay in hospital for between 2 and 7 days. Some 'low risk' women also have the option of giving birth in hospital with the help of a community midwife, and then leaving after 6 hours (called the *'domino' scheme* after 'domiciliary-in-out'); or in a local *General Practitioner Unit* (*GPU*), which is a local

Table 6.1 Perinatal mortality rates of different places of delivery, Britain, 1970*

Place of delivery	Number of births	Percentage of total	PNMR
NHS consultant hospital	11 156	66.3	27.8
General Practitioner Unit	2 589	15.3	5.4
home	2 085	12.4	4.3
other	985	6.0	12.0
total	16 815	100.0	21.0

* Survey taken during 1 week, April 1970.
(Data from Tew, 1979, p.1389)

maternity unit with 3 to 25 beds; or more rarely at home. Both in the GPU and at home, babies are delivered by their GPs or community midwives. Local GPUs are being gradually phased out, and, if present trends continue, delivery in a GPU (like home births) will become a rarity.

The period in which the incidence of hospital births rose from 15 per cent in 1927 to 98 per cent in 1980 has also seen spectacular falls in PNMR and maternal mortality rates. This certainly suggests in crude statistical terms that hospital confinement has been beneficial. But, as you saw in the last chapter, these falls in mortality rates are due to a number of factors. As in the case of antenatal care, there has been dispute about the relative contribution of, on the one hand, hospitalisation, and, on the other, social and economic changes during the same period.

□ Can you think of one significant cause of perinatal death that would not be changed by a hospital delivery?

■ Low birthweight. The *incidence* of this is unaffected by the place of delivery, though it may well affect the survival of babies with low birthweight.

Home-birth advocates point to the fact that in the Netherlands nearly half of confinements take place at home, yet that country has the second lowest PNMR in the world (9 per 1 000 in 1982). A leading Dutch obstetrician, Professor G.J. Kloosterman, has argued that with effective selection of 'low risk' pregnant women, many babies may be safely delivered at home. Martin Richards, a social psychologist, has suggested that in the UK this could be 40 per cent of women. However, the effective selection of low-risk women in itself is open to question. In 1976 a study was made of risk factors and complications during and shortly after 155 home births in Hounslow. The authors, paediatricians and obstetricians from the Institute of Child Health in London, estimated that 39 per cent of these mothers had risk factors that should either have prevented them from being allowed a home confinement in the first place, or that should have resulted in a switch to a hospital birth at some stage during pregnancy. Despite these risks, the women gave birth at home. However, the authors concluded:

> In this study half the babies with problems at birth occurred in the obstetric *low risk* group, and although there were no perinatal deaths there were occasional potentially hazardous situations which may have prejudiced the child's optimal development ... Nevertheless, the reasons given by mothers who prefer home confinement are valid and must not be ignored ... The answer to clinical deficiencies and bad social relationships within hospitals will not be found in a 'back to nature' cult jeopardising the safety of mother and child. (Cox, Fox, Zinkin and Matthews, 1976, pp.6–7)

Their solution was to make hospital a more attractive and humane place to give birth, but Marjorie Tew, a British statistician, has consistently challenged the assumption that hospital *is* a safer place to give birth for low risk women (for example, see Tew, 1980). Although PNMR has declined over the years, it has been higher in hospital than at home (see Table 6.1).

□ Does this *prove* that home births are safer than hospital births?

■ No — PNMR in hospitals could be higher because a larger proportion of 'high-risk' mothers give birth there.

Most obstetricians and health planners have consistently held that this is the main reason why PNMR in hospital is higher than at home. In several detailed statistical analyses of UK data collected over the last 25 years, Tew has demonstrated that the increased proportion of high-risk mothers delivering in hospital only explains a small proportion of the higher perinatal mortality that occurs there. She makes the claim that the babies of 'low-risk' mothers are in fact at *greater* risk if they are born in a hospital. Research carried out by an American doctor, Lewis Mehl supports Tew's statistical findings (Mehl, 1976). In a carefully controlled study comparing outcomes between home and hospital deliveries in California, of matched 'low-risk' women, he found higher perinatal mortality and morbidity associated with birth in hospitals. We shall explore some of the reasons for this later when we discuss the greater incidence of certain interventions that take place routinely during birth in a hospital.

Powerful arguments have been advanced for and against hospital deliveries; some from the medical profession, some from parents.

□ Can you see a number of advantages of hospital deliveries compared with home births?

■ You may have thought of some of the following:

(i) There is always the chance that something may go wrong even in a supposedly 'low-risk' delivery;

(ii) Medical and nursing staff might feel less confident away from the hospital setting with its emergency facilities;

(iii) 'Flying squads' to deal with emergencies during home births are expensive to maintain;

(iv) Many women prefer to give birth in hospital because they feel more secure about expert help in an emergency.

This list stresses the *risks* associated with birth, and reflects the general dictum of obstetrics that no labour is considered normal until it is over. Ian Craft, the senior consultant obstetrician at the Royal Free Hospital at the time summed up this view in 1982: '... even of those presumed to be of low risk, five per cent might develop some unforeseen complication requiring life-saving intervention' (*Sunday Times*, 4 April 1982, p.36). And a Milton Keynes doctor says the same thing, but from a more personal perspective: 'If you have ever faced the horror of sudden haemorrhage in the third stage of labour, you would never consent to a home delivery' (in a personal communication to a Course Team member).

But what of the other side of the coin?

□ Can you see any advantages of home deliveries compared with giving birth in hospital?

■ You might have thought of some of the following:

(i) Women in labour are not 'patients', and the risk of something going wrong is very low.

(ii) Some routine interventions that take place in hospital deliveries may actually *increase* the risk to otherwise healthy mothers and babies (according to Tew and others),

(iii) Home births are cheaper overall, even including the cost of 'flying squads',

(iv) Many women would prefer to give birth at home, feeling more confident in familiar surroundings.

Obviously there is no right or wrong answer to all of this; at least, not one that will suit *all* women in labour equally well or provide optimum levels of safety for every single delivery. But the question of *choice* arises here, since, in most parts of the UK, no matter how unproblematic an impending birth seems to be, the only available choice open to women is between one hospital and another. Luke Zander, Senior Lecturer in the Department of General Practice, St. Thomas's Hospital, London, has criticised this situation repeatedly. An editorial in the *British Medical Journal* quotes his view in the following words:

> Just as a society may be judged by its policy on capital punishment so an obstetric service could be assessed by its attitudes to home deliveries. For the services to oppose home deliveries when they could produce no evidence that they were dangerous, was an act of professional bullying. (*British Medical Journal*, 1982, p.1648)

If women *did* have more freedom to choose the place in which to give birth, it is clear that some would prefer their own home, while others would still choose the hospital setting. There are numerous reasons for this, and we have attempted to explore them in the U205 TV programme 'A suitable place to have a baby?'. In this programme three couples talk about their attitudes to giving birth in hospital — two would still have chosen this option had a home birth been available, and one couple (with certain reservations) would have preferred their baby to be born at home. For all three couples, the main attraction of hospital was its safety, but whereas two of them were certain that a hospital must be safer than their own home, the third couple were much less certain. They felt that this would be true only in a real emergency, but that in an otherwise normal labour in hospital they might have drugs or monitoring equipment forced on them unnecessarily. These somewhat different opinions about the risks involved have been echoed in larger surveys. The 'Baby Survey', for example, conducted by BBC television and analysed by the Spastics Society, produced the following statements, the first from a first-time mother in hospital:

> The machine monitoring the baby's heart suddenly showed that she was struggling; it turned out that the cord was wrapped around her and she was getting crushed; they had to do an emergency operation and even then she didn't breathe properly. If they hadn't of acted so quickly, I'm sure she would have been brain damaged or died. I'm so grateful for all their skill. The hospital saved her. Personally I'd never dare have a baby at home seeing how quickly things can go wrong. (From 'That's Life: Having a Baby', BBC TV programme, 18 March 1982)

Compare this with a mother who had had her first baby in hospital which had been a bad experience, and her second baby at home, which was a good experience:

> I think there is a good percentage of women who really would like a home delivery who are able to and

should. But I think it's something you have to come to terms with yourself and think of the consequences. Things can go wrong with births at home and in hospital. Personally, I battled this out in my own mind and I decided I was willing to take the risks of birth as they were and I feel strongly that if something had happened, for example a stillborn birth, I wouldn't have blamed myself personally. I would have accepted it as a statistic — as one of the things that do sometimes go wrong. (as above)

□ Can you think of other possible reasons why some women would prefer to give birth at home?

■ (i) Familiar surroundings are much less threatening than a hospital, which has associations of illness and accidents.

(ii) Much closer contact is possible between the parents during the birth, and especially between the father and his new baby afterwards.

(iii) There may be fears of being isolated in hospital and of the restrictive hospital routine (meal-times, visiting hours, etc.) in the days before going home.

(iv) Parents might prefer the baby to start life as a member of a family in a home, rather than as a 'patient' in a hospital.

These considerations point to the fact that the shift from home to hospital confinement carries with it a considerable social reorganisation, not only for the mother and baby, but also for all other members of the family. The desire for a home birth has been criticised as being restricted to middle-class parents who have modern, comfortable houses and who can afford additional help — for example, a cleaner or a childminder to look after older children. Although this is not the case with the couples in the television programme, of whose views some are given above, there have been few studies of the attitudes of working-class families, and the results are ambiguous. One study in the UK by Eva Chapman in 1983 showed that some working-class women wanted home births, but lacked the confidence to 'fight the system', while another in the USA concluded that working-class women preferred hospital births as they were more concerned about having a healthy baby rather than worrying about where it was born (Nelson, 1983).

□ Can you suggest reasons *other* than safety why a hospital delivery might be preferable to some women?

■ Other reasons given (some of which arise in the television programme):

(i) Childbirth is messy and noisy — bedding can get stained, and it is embarrassing if neighbours hear you in labour.

(ii) Hospital is more restful after the delivery — at home a woman would get sucked back into housework; in hospital, nurses share the task of caring for the baby, especially at night.

(iii) The father can go off to work secure that his family are in expert hands rather than at home alone.

(iv) A first-time mother can get immediate advice and reassurance about breast-feeding, for example, or any worries while she is in hospital.

However, these reasons seem to be secondary to the vexed issue of safety — clearly hospitals can deal with emergencies that might result in deaths or injury at home, but what about 'routine' births? There has been a concerted feminist critique (for example, from Ann Oakley, whose article 'Doctor Knows Best' was referred to in Chapter 5), accusing the medical profession of 'colonising' women's bodies during pregnancy and childbirth. From this perspective, the shift to hospital deliveries is part of the medical takeover which has depersonalised women to the status of reproductive machines, and increased the 'territory' over which doctors preside. The usual justification for the close medical supervision of childbirth is that it increases safety, but data have gradually accumulated on the adverse effects of certain procedures that are routine in most hospital deliveries. These include the positioning of women on their backs in labour, starting labour artificially (induction) or accelerating its course, and the use of analgesics to reduce pain. It is to these detailed issues that we now turn.

Trends in medical intervention in childbirth

Table 6.2 shows trends in certain medical procedures during childbirth over the last thirty years.

□ What do you notice about changes in levels of intervention?

■ The use of induction, instrumental delivery and Caesarean section has more than quadrupled since they were first recorded, and episiotomy rates have increased by a third.

Table 6.2 does not give a comprehensive survey of all interventions that are common in UK obstetric practice. For example, pain during labour is usually reduced by injecting an analgesic drug (pethidine) or inhaling a mixture of nitrous oxide and oxygen ('gas and air'). Over 75 per cent of women in labour have one or other of these painkillers, and many have both. Since the early 1970s, another method of pain control has become increasingly popular — epidural analgesia, which involves the injection of an anaesthetic directly into the area surrounding the nerve cord in the spine. This reduces, or even abolishes, all sensations, including pain in the lower half of the body. The incidence of this procedure varies greatly from one hospital to another, but can be as high as 40 per cent of all births (for example, in St. Mary's Hospital in Manchester in 1982).

Table 6.2 Trends in obstetric intervention, England and Wales, 1953–78 and 1984

Year	Estimated percentage of all deliveries in England and Wales*			
	Induction of labour or artificial rupture of membranes	Caesarean section	Instrumental delivery†	Episiotomy‡
1953	—	2.2	3.7	—
1958	—	2.3	4.4	—
1963	8.9	3.1	5.3	—
1968	18.0	4.0	7.9	—
1973	34.9	5.0	11.0	44.0
1978	36.3	7.3	13.3	53.4
1984	36.0	10.0	15.0	66.0

* Includes women resident outside England and Wales.
† Forceps or vacuum extraction.
‡ A small cut made to enlarge the vaginal opening.
(Data from MacFarlane and Mugford, 1984, Table A7.32(a), p. 575)

Table 6.3 Levels of intervention in a consultant unit (shared care) and a General Practitioner Unit (GPU)

	Nulliparous (first-time mothers)		Multiparous (have had babies before)	
	consultant (shared care)	GPU	consultant (shared care)	GPU
Anaesthesia/analgesia				
epidural	28.6	14.3	4.8	3.2
pethidine (painkilling drug)	61.9	38.1	34.9	12.7
nitrous oxide and oxygen (gas and air)	33.3	30.2	39.7	15.9
none	11.1	36.5	33.3	77.8
Procedure				
electronic fetal monitor	34.9	17.5	19.1	3.2
augmentation (acceleration)	33.3	19.1	12.7	6.4
forceps	20.6	20.6	6.4	1.6

(Data from Kline, Lloyd and Redman, 1983, Tables 4 and 5, p. 125)

In recent years another technological innovation has been widely adopted and is now routine for all deliveries in an increasing number of hospitals. Electronic monitoring devices are used to record the intensity and duration of contractions, and the baby's heartbeat during labour and delivery. Contraction monitors are usually strapped around the woman's abdomen. Electronic *fetal heart monitors* may also be applied in this way but more usually involve an electrode being passed up through the vagina and clipped to the baby's scalp. Wires from these monitors are attached to machines alongside the delivery table, which record and display the information. Note that when a labour is being monitored in this way, the woman cannot move around much and is effectively confined to bed.

Giving birth in a hospital in the UK today usually involves one or more of these interventions — all of which have increased significantly in recent years. While some procedures (such as pethidine injections) can be performed as easily during a home confinement or in a local General Practitioner Unit, the majority are dependent upon the hospital setting. For example, epidural analgesia requires the skill of an anaesthetist. Table 6.3 shows the relative occurrence of several of the interventions we have been discussing, during the labour and delivery of 'low-risk' mothers matched for similar social class, age and health, in a hospital consultant unit and a GPU.

□ What do you notice about the relative occurrence of these interventions between the GPU and the consultant unit?

■ All the interventions listed occurred less often in the GPU than in the consultant unit, and this cannot be totally explained in terms of reduced availability of complex equipment in the GPU. For example, the use of pethidine was significantly lower in the GPU.

What could account for this 'all-round' increase? There have been suggestions that the use of certain interventions during childbirth makes the need for others more likely. This has been called the *'cascade of intervention'* and we will investigate it in detail in a moment. However, one procedure in current Western obstetric practice that has this 'cascade' of consequences is so pervasive that until recently its use was unquestioned — position during labour.

Position during labour

The physical position which women adopt during labour and delivery varies from culture to culture (as you saw in Figures 6.1–6.6), but in the UK the so-called *lithotomy position* (Figure 6.5) has been considered normal and correct for at least the last century. Supporting the woman's legs in stirrups is now mostly used only in complicated deliveries, but the majority of women still give birth lying on their backs (supine), although usually propped up on pillows. The most usual position in other cultures is not supine but vertical. Of 76 non-European countries in a survey, published in 1964, by the anthropologist C.S. Ford, 62 used upright positions.

Women have not, for the most part, questioned the supine position, since it has been customary for generations. Obstetricians and midwives have always reasoned that it allowed them to see what was going on. Critics have argued that the supine position is one consequence of medical staff viewing women in labour as patients, whose correct place is lying in bed. However, this seemingly innocuous practice may have consequences for the health of mother and baby. Dr. Yehudi Gordon, then a consultant obstetrician at the Royal Free Hospital in London, said in 1982:

> If a woman is in the horizontal position, labour will be slower, and if she is positioned on her back there is an increased chance that the pressure of the pregnant uterus on the mother's aorta and inferior vena cava [main blood vessels] reduces foetal blood flow, causing foetal distress. (quoted in *Sunday Times*, 4 April 1982, p.36)

These effects of the supine position lead to the 'cascade of intervention' referred to earlier, in which longer labour and fetal distress make the use of painkillers and electronic monitors more likely. Figure 6.7 depicts a flow-chart of possible consequences of lying down during labour. These consequences have been challenged by some senior obstetricians, including Ian Craft (also a consultant at the Royal Free Hospital in 1982), who fundamentally disagreed with his colleague, Gordon. Craft banned women from giving birth in an upright position until, he said, 'appropriately controlled studies in a cross-section of obstetric patients indicates that it is as safe as current practice' (quoted in *Sunday Times*, 4 April 1982, p.36).

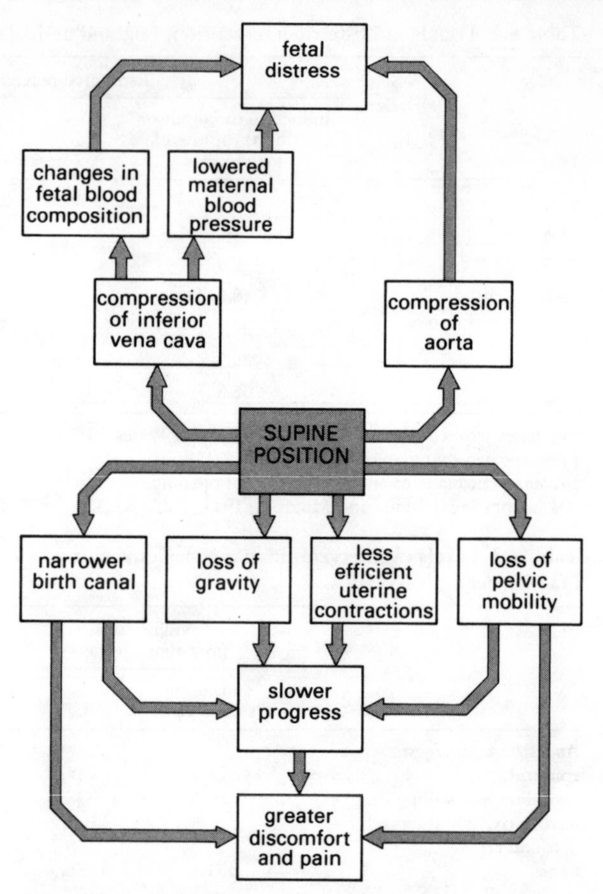

Figure 6.7 Possible consequences of the supine position in labour. (Lean, 1981, p.8)

Although the 'supported squatting' position publicised by the French doctor Michel Odent remains controversial during the actual delivery of a baby, there is sound evidence that remaining upright during the first stage of labour has beneficial consequences. Figure 6.8 shows the results of a randomised controlled trial of the length of the first stage of labour of two groups of normal low-risk Latin-American first-time mothers in either the usual horizontal position or experimental vertical position.

□ What do these data show about the length of labour in the different positions?

■ The first stage of labour was on average 85 minutes shorter for women in the vertical position. The highest proportion of labours in this group lasted 2–3 hours (40 per cent), whereas the highest proportion of labours among women who lay down lasted 3–4 hours (25 per cent).

As a result of evidence like this, attitudes are changing, and

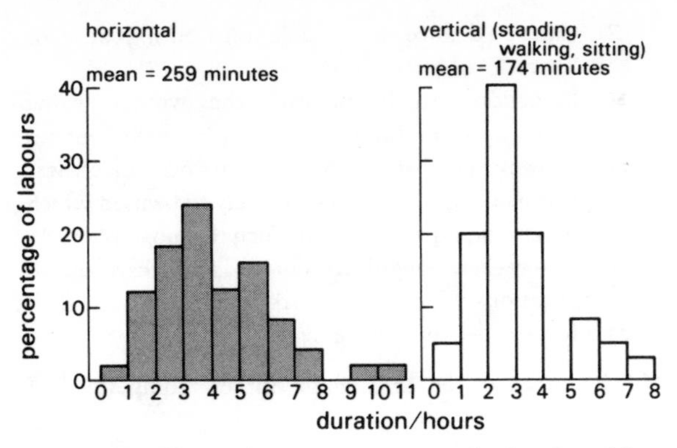

Figure 6.8 Influence of woman's position on the duration of first-stage labour (first-time mothers only). Number of women in 'horizontal' group = 51, and in 'vertical' group = 40. (Caldeyro-Barcia, 1979).

Figure 6.9 Cartoon from Lean (1981). (Courtesy of the Association of Radical Midwives)

many hospitals encourage women to move around in the early stage of labour. Some even provide birthing chairs or bean bags to aid delivery in the vertical position (Annie, from the TV programme, gave birth in hospital squatting against a bean bag on the floor of the delivery room). As the paediatrician Hugh Jolly said in an article in *The Listener*: 'No one would choose to open their bowels lying down; similarly gravity should be harnessed to help delivery.' (Jolly, 1982, p.7).

This view is echoed in the cartoon from the journal, *Radical Midwife*, shown in Figure 6.9. Many women argue that they are more active and more in control of their labour if they can change their position during labour and delivery and this view has found increasing support among some midwives. This is why birth in an upright position is sometimes called *'active' labour*.

You have seen that there are health consequences of the deceptively simple practice of lying down during labour. Are there similar consequences of the more obvious medical interventions that have increased during the last 30 years? There has been rising concern that the routine administration of some procedures during straightforward births may be counterproductive. Peter Huntingford, then a consultant obstetrician at a London teaching hospital, said in 1978:

> There must be a balance between the amount of obstetric interference that is positively beneficial to both mother and baby, and an amount that ceases to reduce mortality and morbidity and may even increase it. I believe that balance has been lost. (quoted in Kitzinger and Davis, 1978, p.248)

All the interventions we have mentioned may be of enormous benefit when mother or child are endangered, and some (for example, epidural analgesia) are actively sought by some women. But these interventions also carry a certain amount of risk which in some cases has not been sufficiently evaluated in clinical trials. In an emergency the risk is no doubt justified, but it becomes an issue when techniques that are of great benefit to the few are used routinely on large numbers of birthing women 'just in case' something goes wrong. The advantages for the 'high-risk' women must be weighed against disadvantages for the majority, but many obstetricians argue that complications during birth cannot be accurately predicted, and hence 'blanket-coverage' is necessary. The classic example of a procedure that was initially performed only in 'high-risk' situations and then used on a much larger group of women routinely, is induction.

Induction

Induction is the artificial initiation of labour before it begins spontaneously. The most common method is first to rupture the bag of membranes (amnion) which enclose the baby, releasing a gush of fluid ('breaking the waters'). Then drugs that closely resemble the hormones which stimulate the uterus to contract during spontaneous labour are administered, usually via an intravenous 'drip'. (The most commonly used drug is related to oxytocin, the hormone that causes uterine contractions during spontaneous labour.*) From the 1950s onwards, induction was found to be effective in reducing perinatal deaths in certain groups of mothers over 35; those with high blood pressure; and those with placental insufficiency (placenta not functioning efficiently).

In 1960, a leading obstetrician, Dugald Baird, recommended routine induction for women whose births were overdue, arguing that diagnosis of placental insufficiency was unreliable, and therefore blanket coverage was justified. In the next few years, as with many other innovations in medical science, the use of induction increased rapidly. Although there had been no randomised,

*The role of hormones in reproduction is discussed in Book IV, *The Biology of Health and Disease*, Chapter 10.

controlled trials, it was performed on more than 50 per cent of women in some hospitals in the 1970s, and on an average of 41 per cent of women in the UK in 1974. The USA and Australia had similar rates during this period.

In the 1970s, complaints and criticism mounted, especially from consumer groups, about the increased use of induction to fit in with hospital routines. Doctors were accused of performing inductions not for the safety of mother and child but for increased efficiency and convenience. Doctors in turn argued that they were more alert and competent during the day when most inductions were performed than in the middle of the night.

The circumstances under which inductions were advised had widened considerably by the 1970s, and some women were booked in for induction at 38 weeks of pregnancy (2 weeks before the estimated 'due date'). What consumers were angry about was *'elective' induction*, i.e. routine induction without obvious medical need and often without any choice for the mother, as a study carried out by the sociologist, Ann Cartwright, illustrates: 'They all just came and did what they had to — no explanations whatsoever, and left me . . . I was scared stiff having things done and not knowing what it was, as though you were just a thing, not a person with a mind.' (quoted in Cartwright, 1979, p.95).

In 1978, Alison McFarlane was able to deduce from national statistics that many more births occurred from Tuesday to Friday than at weekends, and that at Christmas and Easter, irrespective of the day of the week, the number of births dropped sharply. But inductions were not only performed because doctors advised them; other studies also showed that some women preferred to plan when they were going to give birth:

> When you have other children it does help to make definite arrangements — everyone feels more secure. (quoted in Cartwright, 1979, p.107)

> You can plan for someone to look after the children and everything. Having had so many false starts — you get yourself all packed up and it stops. (ibid, p.107)

For a woman suffering from severe high blood pressure late in pregnancy or for an infant distressed in the womb from whatever cause, induction of labour makes obvious sense. But are *all* the inductions performed actually necessary, or even advisable on medical grounds? And are there risks attached to this intervention? Several studies have shown that induced labour is associated with an increase in the use of some *other* procedures — for example, more pain-killing drugs are given, more women ask for epidural analgesia and there are higher rates of forceps deliveries and Caesarean sections than with spontaneous labour.

□ Can you deduce *one* possible contributing cause for this 'cascade' of intervention?

■ Induction usually involves the woman being connected up to an intravenous 'drip', which confines her movements. Usually she is put to bed. Electronic monitoring devices are also very likely to be used which also makes the supine position much the most likely. As you saw earlier, lying down during labour can lead to complications which make further interventions, such as a forceps delivery, more likely.

Many women in the 1981 'Baby Survey' complained of restrictions in movement, e.g.:

> I had to be down all the time because of the drip and internal monitor. I found this very uncomfortable — I often had the urge to squat on all fours but couldn't. (Boyd and Sellers, 1982, p.101)

> The baby wasn't born until 8.15 p.m. so I was lying in bed, wired to the machine and on a drip for about ten hours. Apart from the labour pains, I felt very bedsore by the end of the day. (ibid, p.100)

The flow-chart in Figure 6.10 shows possible adverse consequences of induced labour.

□ If induced labour is more painful than spontaneous labour, more analgesia (pain-killing drugs) will be used. According to Figure 6.10, what might be the consequences of this for the baby?

■ This increases the likelihood that a forceps delivery will be needed, partly because analgesia 'damps down' contractions, but also because the mother may be dozy, and if epidural analgesia is used she may not be able to feel when to 'push'. Analgesics can adversely affect breathing and suckling in the newborn, and this, together with the use of forceps, make admission to a special care baby unit more likely. Separation of baby from mother further reduces her chance of establishing breast-feeding.

The association of these side effects with induction has persuaded many earlier advocates of the procedure to return to a much narrower set of criteria for indicating its use. For example, Alec Turnbull had done much to improve and popularise induction methods in Oxford but began to cut down on the practice when an increased risk of jaundice in newborn babies was implicated in its use. He wrote of the consequences of this decision: 'Since early 1974 the induction rate in my own unit in Oxford has fallen steadily, with no adverse affect on perinatal mortality — in fact the figures for the Oxford area in 1976 were as low as 9 per 1 000.' (quoted in Chard and Richards, 1977, pp.viii–ix).

The low PNMR in Oxford has been attributed to a predominantly well-nourished middle-class population,

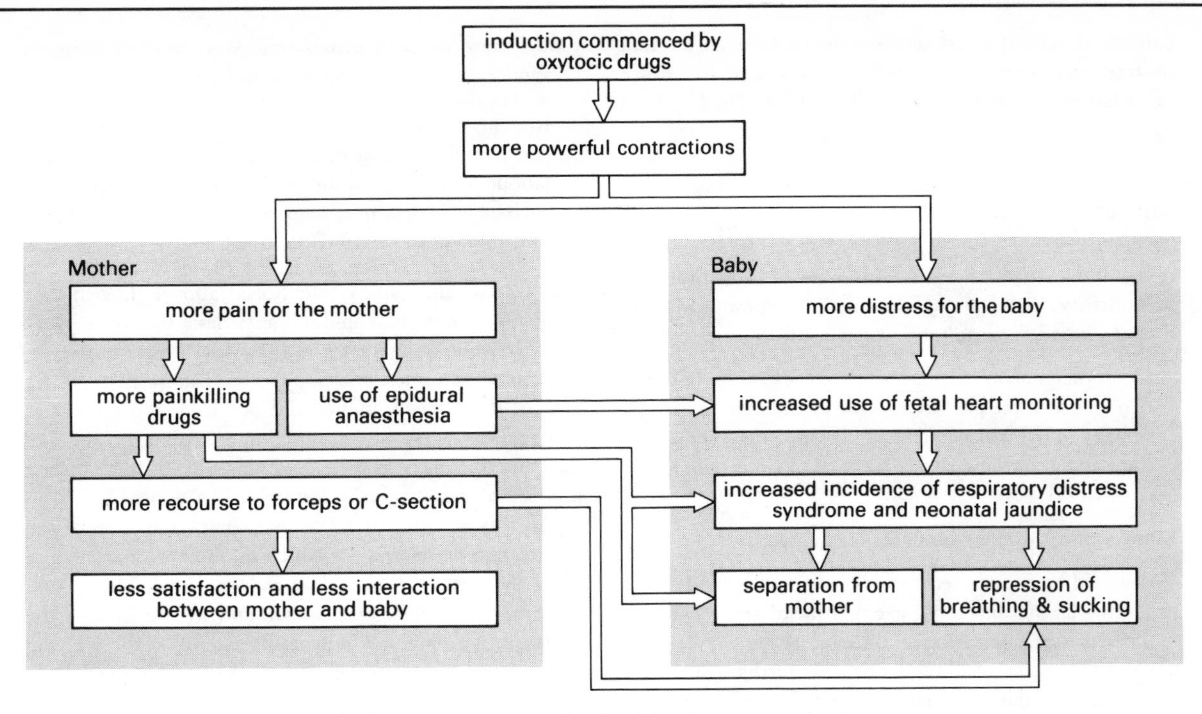

Figure 6.10 Possible consequences of induction. (C-section is shorthand for Caesarean section.)

but at St. Mary's Hospital in London, despite the high-risk working-class clientele, the PNMR was only 10 per 1 000 in 1982, with an induction rate of only 5–8 per cent of births for that period. This seems to discount earlier claims that high induction rates would reduce perinatal deaths.

In recent years the overall induction rate has levelled off at around one-third of all births (see Table 6.2), but critics have argued that it has continued to rise in a more subtle form. After a labour has started spontaneously, it has become increasingly popular to accelerate the progress of contractions by administering the same drugs as are used in inductions. This is often called the *'active management' of labour*. Juliet Wilmott, a midwife, is one of the many who are unhappy with this trend, as she wrote in a letter to the *British Medical Journal*: 'While wholesale induction has been publicly discredited ... it has been subtly replaced by acceleration. But the drugs used and the dangers for mother and baby are the same.' (Wilmott, 1981, p.115).

Supporters of the method claim that a shorter labour is safer for mother and baby. Whether or not this is true remains to be established. There is some evidence that a faster labour can be more painful for the mother and may put more pressure on a baby's head.

Thus far we have reviewed the case for and against routine rather than selective medical intervention in labour and delivery. Critics of these so-called 'high-tech' methods have themselves been labelled the 'back to nature' brigade. This raises the question of precisely what is meant by a 'natural' childbirth. As you saw in the foregoing discussion the supine position is 'normal' for our culture, but 'abnormal' in relation to most others; 'healthy' in that a birth attendant can monitor better what is happening to the baby, but 'unhealthy' in some of its physiological consequences; 'natural' in that we expect it and take it for granted, but 'unnatural' in relation to the forces of gravity. The problematic nature of these distinctions is revealed in the following statements.

> CONSULTANT Interesting, very interesting, most unusual.
> REGISTRAR You mean it was a normal delivery?
> CONSULTANT Yes — pushed the baby out herself!
> (Oakley, 1980, p.22)

Professor Max Elstein, obstetrician at St. Mary's Hospital, Manchester, expressed this view: 'We are not in the horse and buggy brigade. We are in the technology brigade and we must use it.' (*Sunday Times*, 7 March 1982, p.13), whereas Michael House, an obstetrician at the West London Hospital, Hammersmith, was more cautious: 'There is no proof that modern obstetrics is the best way. Equally, there is no hard evidence that having a baby naturally is either more or less safe.' (*Sunday Times*, 7 March, 1982, p.13). If this is the case, then perhaps the most pertinent question to ask at this stage is whether modern obstetrics takes sufficient account of the *humane* dimension of childbirth.

Satisfaction in childbirth

The delivery

A common medical view about what constitutes a 'satisfactory' outcome to childbirth is summarised by Richard Beard, a consultant obstetrician:

> A mother's main purpose is to have a healthy baby. To hell with the pleasures of having a baby. She needs a baby in the best possible condition. Safety comes first and everything else comes after. (*Guardian*, 6 April 1981, p.8)

Many women would wholeheartedly agree:

> I would have preferred to walk about and stand during labour, but recognize that foetal and contraction monitoring (and therefore lying still) is part of hospital technology for safer births — I would rather have this and a healthy baby than absolute freedom and no baby at all. (Boyd and Sellers, 1982, p.101)

Both these statements illustrate the view that 'pleasure' in child-birth is incompatible with 'safety', but is this always the case? For example, some women *prefer* the faster delivery that can result from the induction and acceleration of labour, as illustrated by these respondents in a large study by British sociologist Ann Cartwright in 1979: 'It's more pain, but because it's so much quicker, it's worth it.' (ibid, p.108); 'Towards the end, you get that fed up you just want to get it over with.' (ibid, p.107).

However, this raises the question of why these women wanted to 'get it over with' as quickly as possible. One of them referred to pain in labour, a subject that was investigated by Barbara Morgan and her colleagues at Queen Charlotte's Hospital in London. The researchers set out to investigate the fact that (as they put it), 'Obstetricians and anaesthetists have assumed so long as adequate analgesia is provided and the medical outcome is good, then maternal satisfaction will be automatic.' (Morgan *et al.*, 1982, p.808).

One thousand women were questioned at two days and again at one year after delivery about how much pain they had felt and what their memory of the birth was like in terms of satisfaction. It was found that the 536 women who had been given epidurals had the lowest pain scores, but compared with other groups experienced the lowest levels of satisfaction. The highest satisfaction was reported among the eighty women who had had no painkillers even though they had high pain scores. Morgan and colleagues conclude:

> It seems that the pain of labour is a more emotional and complex matter than it may first appear. Pain in labour is not comparable with other sorts of pain, such as post-operative pain, when there is no feeling of fulfilment or satisfaction. (ibid, p.809)

Ann Cartwright's study (mentioned above) showed that women who have had epidural anesthesia for one delivery tend to want it again for subsequent births. However, induction was much less popular, and more than 80 per cent of the women studied did not want the procedure repeated, for reasons epitomised in the comment: 'I'd like the baby to come naturally. I wouldn't like it to be rushed if it doesn't need to be.' (Cartwright, 1979, p.107).

All this adds up to a rich and complex picture of the wide range of criteria by which different women would judge the birth of their babies as 'satisfying'. There is no solution that will be best for all, and we are back to the question of a woman's right to have a say in the way the birth is managed. Criticism of the lack of choice and dignity available to women in modern obstetric practice has come from midwives such as Meg Taylor:

> I am concerned about the view of women that is implied. The integrity of our bodies is regarded as so unimportant that hourly rectal (examinations) or two hourly vaginal examinations are accepted as reasonable. The medicalisation of childbirth is unquestioned. (Taylor, 1981–2, p.19)

This raises another question — is midwifery still a 'satisfying' profession? The Association of Radical Midwives (ARMS) has campaigned strongly for more reliance on the traditional skills of midwifery, and less on technological aids — as this quotation from Mavis Kirkham, a midwife, illustrates: 'Midwives sometimes talk to an electronic monitor more frequently than to a woman in labour.' (*Nursing Mirror*, 9 June 1982, p.9).

Ann Cartwright's study discovered similar sentiments among some midwives interviewed:

> No job satisfaction at all. It's like a production line. I don't like working in the labour ward; everything is so quick and so rushed. (Cartwright, 1979, p.140)

> It's more a mechanical process now; less depends on the midwife's judgement. It's taken out of our hands now. (ibid, p.140)

> We tend to become more mechanical — we forget that mothers are human beings and have feelings and do belong to society. (ibid, p.140)

And what of the baby's father and his experience of the birth? Nowadays in the UK, hospitals usually allow him to be present during the delivery, although he may be asked to leave during routine examinations or 'emergency' procedures such as forceps delivery. Fathers are rarely allowed to witness a Caesarean birth. However, men who wish to be present may be prevented from being there by family difficulties (for example, caring for older children) or work responsibilities. If you have been able to see the TV programme associated with this chapter ('A suitable place to have a baby?') you will recall that one of the fathers we interviewed could not attend the birth of his first child because he had just succeeded in finding a job, and could not ask for leave so soon. There is no national scheme of *paternity leave* in the UK as there is in some other countries such as Sweden. Although many employers are sympathetic and give some time off, many are not and do not even grant unpaid leave. For example, an army wife in the 'Baby Survey' said:

> Although many wives know their husbands might be away at the time of delivery, mine was away until 5th March and baby was due on 4th March. It is sad that for close bereavement they are allowed home when they can do little, but birth, which occurs perhaps two or three times in a lifetime and is a very special time, is not considered important. (Boyd and Sellers, 1982, p.67)

And a father in a 1983 study of fathers and paternity leave by Colin Bell and co-workers, said emphatically: 'You only get paid leave for death!' (Bell, 1983 p.53). This study, 'Fathers, Childbirth and Work' found that 92 per cent of fathers would like paid paternity leave, and that twice as many working-class fathers lost pay as a consequence of being with their wives at birth, than middle-class fathers — a situation that produces hardship as well as dissatisfaction.

Finally, there has been a movement in recent years, headed by Frederick Leboyer (a French obstetrician), towards providing a more humane environment for the focus of all the arguments about safety — the baby herself. In Leboyer's view her emotional state is often forgotten amid the bustle of 'high-tech' births, with its bright lights, clatter of instruments and practices he considers terrifying and painful to the baby, such as the use of steel forceps and cutting the umbilical cord immediately the baby is born. Figure 6.11 shows Leboyer's famous photograph from the book *Birth Without Violence*, illustrating the insensitive handling that some babies receive.

Currently, a few hospitals in the UK provide 'Leboyer-style' deliveries with dimmed lights, minimal noise or intervention and a warm bath for the baby in which to adjust to life outside the womb. It is no longer routine practice to pick babies up by their ankles and slap them, but neither are they routinely delivered onto the mother's abdomen and encouraged to suckle within minutes of being born. As one of the women in our TV programme said: 'I wouldn't mind being allowed to hold the baby this time'.

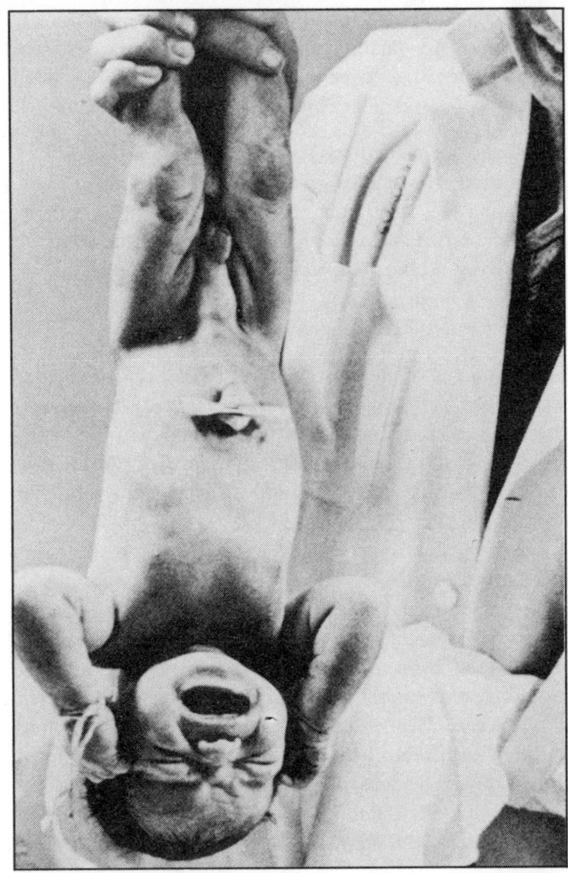

Figure 6.11 A doctor holding a baby upside down. Leboyer argues that birth practices such as this can traumatise the baby. (Leboyer, 1977, p.21; photo: International Magazine Service, Sweden.)

After the birth

The first two to seven days of a newborn baby's life in the UK are usually spent in a hospital with her mother, who may be close by all the time or only for certain periods of the day and night. Some hospitals allow the baby's father to visit whenever he likes, recognising that his working day may not fit in with official visiting hours; many restrict visits to specific periods, and limit the number of visitors. If there are other children in the family, they meet their new brother or sister as a small bundle in a plastic crib beside the hospital bed — their mother is in a nightdress as though she is ill, and the usual paraphernalia of temperature charts, stethoscope and thermometer, and nurses in uniform, are in evidence. A woman facing her fifth pregnancy describes how she tries to get over this barrier to intimacy between the new baby and older children.

> What I normally do to get over it (the fact that children are not allowed to touch the baby in hospital) — when I get home I line them up, put them on the settee and as soon as I get home I give them the baby. Make them feel it is their baby. I mean it *is* their baby, they've got to learn to live with it. (Homans, 1982, p.259–60)

The first week of life is a time of intense readjustment for all members of the family on several levels: major biological changes are accomplished by mother and baby, and the social world of the family must shift to incorporate the new member, causing everyone's role to change in subtle or profound ways.

The time in hospital has attracted all the arguments for and against routine surveillance that you have now met in regard to antenatal care (Chapter 5) and the birth itself. Attitudes have changed considerably during the last 25 years, so that babies are no longer kept in nurseries and just brought to their mother at stipulated feeding times, as used to be the case. Women are also encouraged to move around within hours of the birth, whereas once they were confined to bed for as much as two weeks. However, there is still considerable variation in policy from one hospital to another, as these respondents to the 'Baby Survey' testify:

> The baby was given to you from 5.30 a.m. onwards for feeds and then taken back to the nursery. Otherwise he was left at the end of the bed but we were not encouraged to get to know them. If they started to cry they were whisked away. It left you feeling very lonely and incompetent. (Boyd and Sellers, 1982, p.160)

> The baby was with me most of the time — which was lovely as when my first child was born I only saw him at feeding times. This was much nicer and I felt I knew my daughter so much better when I brought her home from hospital. (ibid, p.158)

Hospital routine suits some women and depresses or frustrates others, supplies support and reassurance or interferes with family relationships, depending on your viewpoint. Again, there is not much choice open to women who would have preferred to be at home.

The justification for this period of hospitalisation after birth is largely a medical one. The baby is given routine tests to establish that she is making the necessary biological adjustments to breathing air, maintaining body temperature, digesting food and excreting waste — all of these tasks performed for her in the womb. Aspects of her development are carefully tested for signs of abnormality; for example, the presence of certain characteristic reflex movements (Figure 6.12) show that her nervous system is functioning normally.

The mother, too, is carefully monitored for signs of abnormal blood loss, fatigue, anaemia, and so forth. Then, as suddenly as it began, the hospital stay is over and mother and baby return to the community to fend for themselves. A Health Visitor will call within seven days and there is a routine check-up after six weeks, but unless there are complications, the intense period of surveillance during pregnancy and birth comes to an abrupt halt. This sharp transition has been implicated as one factor in the development of a common and distressing condition in mothers — post-natal depression.

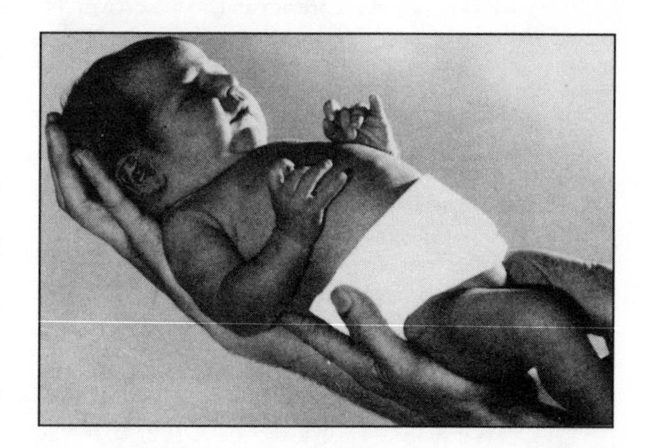

Figure 6.12 Reflex movements in newborn babies. When a newborn baby is held as in (a) and moved rapidly downwards as though falling, the baby's arms fly out with spread fingers, as in (b). This is known as the Moro reflex, and might enable the baby to grab onto something and break the fall.

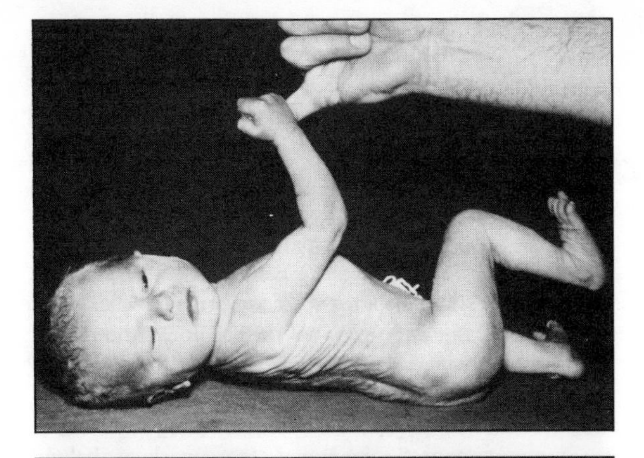

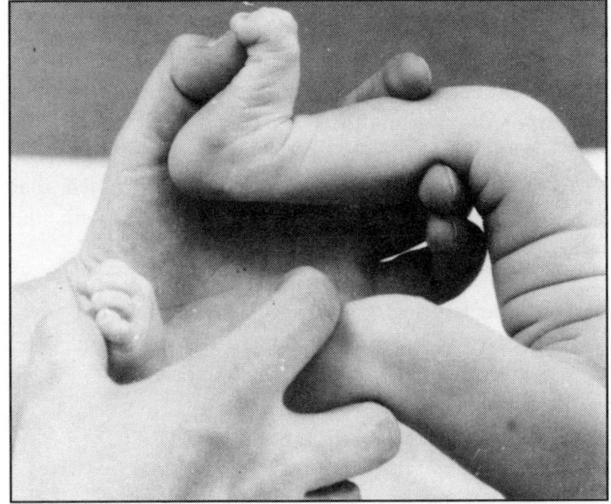

Figure 6.12 contd. (c) The strength of the hand grasp reflex: the baby grips so powerfully that he or she can be lifted off the mattress. (d) The so-called Babinski reflex; when the foot is pressed as shown, the baby's toes curl over and attempt to grasp. These 'primitive' reflexes disappear as the baby grows older. They may have some survival value, at least in our distant past. (Photos: Professor H.F.R. Prechtl; gripping reflex, photo: Dr K.S. Holt)

*Post-natal depression** — the 'baby blues' — can range from a day or two of tearfulness to months of severe psychological pain, even suicide. There has been little systematic research into the incidence of depression following childbirth, but provisional analyses estimate that half to three-quarters of women suffer some post-natal depression, and about 5 per cent are seriously affected by it.

There are a number of theories about the causes of the 'baby blues' but little solid evidence. Much emphasis has been placed on a biological explanation of post-natal depression in that it has been linked to hormonal changes in the mother's body after giving birth. One striking and well-researched change is that once the placenta is removed, levels of the 'sex' hormones, oestrogen and progestogen, which were high during pregnancy, drop sharply. However, it has not been demonstrated that these hormonal changes actually *cause* depression.

Another explanation has focused on the woman's personal history, particularly the incidence of previous episodes of mental distress, or on aspects of her personal social world such as marital status or financial circumstances. A wider social perspective has been taken by some feminist authors who see depression as an inevitable consequence of childbirth being 'taken over' by the medical profession, leaving women as irrelevant spectators at their baby's birth. There is some support for this interpretation in the higher than average incidence of post-natal depression in women whose babies were born by Caesarean section.

□ Can you suggest a way in which this theory could be investigated further, since 'medicalised' childbirth is standard practice throughout the UK?

■ You would have to investigate the incidence of post-natal depression in other cultures that still use traditional skills during childbirth.

Studies of the incidence of post-natal depression outside Europe and North America show it to be quite rare (see, for example, Stern and Kruckman, 1983), although caution must be exercised in drawing conclusions from this since sample sizes have often been small, and researchers may have been 'blinkered' by Western notions of what constitutes depression. However, even if such depression is rare in other cultures, this may not be solely due to the absence of 'high technology' in childbirth, but rather to the support offered to the new mother in the first weeks of her baby's life. To illustrate how very different this support can be from the common practice in the majority culture in the UK (that is, white 'Christian' housholds), we want you to read an article in the Course Reader by Barbara Pillsbury.† It is called 'Doing the month' and describes the elaborate rituals considered vital to the health of mother and baby in rural China. Read the article now (Part 1, Section 1.3), and then answer the question that follows.

□ What reason did Barbara Pillsbury put forward for the virtual absence of post-natal depression in Chinese traditional culture?

■ Pillsbury sees as crucial the great amount of attention and support that Chinese women had bestowed upon them by their families and society during the month after giving birth. For example, they are forbidden to undertake housework and must eat a specially nourishing diet, avoid exertion and keep away from draughts.

*Depression is discussed in Book VI, *Experiencing and Explaining Disease*, Chapter 8.

†Nick Black *et al.* (eds) (1984) *Health and Disease: A Reader*, The Open University Press.

This is in stark contrast to the experience of many women in the UK, who return home to relative isolation, the usual household tasks, possibly the care of older children, plus the heavy demands of a newborn baby. Feeling inadequate about being a mother and trying to pretend you can cope is a reason women often give for feeling depressed. For example, sociologist Hilary Graham found that two-thirds of a sample of 200 women she interviewed felt acutely inadequate when their babies cried persistently:

> The thing that really upsets me with this (crying) is you really don't know what it is and you can't do anything to console them. ... I thought if anything happens to her, it is my fault because I haven't done anything. (Graham, 1982, p.120)

This woman feels herself to be *solely* responsible for the baby. Even though the majority of women who have babies in the UK are married, the lack of any system of paid paternity leave prevents husbands who *would* help from doing so. And a culture that sees childcare and housework as a *woman's* responsibility prevents some men from perceiving the workload as a problem (a subject to which we return in Chapter 12). Other European countries offer more practical and economic support to families after a birth. For example, Holland has a system of maternity aides who help mothers adapt to normal life again by helping them with household tasks such as cooking and shopping. In Sweden, there is a paternity-leave scheme that allows fathers to stay at home and help their partners with their new babies.

The sense of being unable to cope once at home alone with the baby can be fostered by a hospital atmosphere that treats new mothers as 'amateurs':

> I didn't know how to feed him, I didn't know how to fold a nappy. I looked at the nappy and looked at his bottom and thought, 'Well, I don't see how it fits'. I'd no idea. No one had actually ever shown me. I had to go to my doctor and ask him. He didn't know either, actually! They used disposables in the hospital and when they took him away to get him dressed I said, 'Well let me come and watch', because I wanted to see how they did it and she said, 'Oh, no, you can't come, you've got to wait there'. It was all, you know, worked out, and so when I changed him for the first time I didn't know how to do it. (Welburn, 1980, p.80)

Some anthropologists have pointed to the ritual aspect of some cultures' practices following a birth, and hold these to be important elements in marking the transition of the woman and her baby back into the community. Rituals such as drinking the 'full month' wine in rural China acknowledge the importance of the event, so that the woman feels celebrated rather than neglected. It was once common in the UK, as elsewhere in Europe, for women to mark their return to the community by being 'churched'. After a period of seclusion, denoting her symbolic pollution, she walked to church to give thanks to God for delivering her from the 'great pain and peril of childbirth' (*Book of Common Prayer*). This act 'cleansed' her, and on her return she was welcomed and congratulated. Cleansing rituals are common to several of the religious groups that co-exist in the UK; whether it has an effect on post-natal depression to feel 'unclean' and then be absolved can only be guessed at. Nowadays, ritual christening or circumcision are the commonest ceremonies that mark a baby's incorporation into religious and social life.

In summary, then, the anthropological perspective on post-natal depression sees it as a consequence of cultural neglect of the new mother. An extensive review of the research in this tradition by Gwen Stern and Lawrence Kruckman, themselves anthropologists, concluded that post-natal depression was rare in cultures with the following basic features:

1 The structuring of a distinct post-natal period
2 Protective measures and rituals reflecting the presumed vulnerability of the new mother
3 Social seclusion
4 Mandated rest
5 Assistance in tasks from relatives and/or midwives
6 Social recognition through rituals, gifts, etc. of the new social status of the mother (Stern and Kruckman, 1983)

Finally, it is worth noting that these conditions would not be achieved simply by changes in the traditions and rituals of UK society. Several of them depend on the social and financial circumstances of the woman and those who are to take care of her. If relatives and friends are few, or at a distance; if there is not the cash to pay for help with childcare or household tasks; if other family members are out at work all day, or conversely, jobless and in relative poverty, depression may be a 'logical' response. Women are far more likely than men to be diagnosed as suffering from depression, and working-class women and single mothers are especially vulnerable. This suggests that the birth of a new baby may be just one of several disorientating events during a lifetime that can precipitate ill health, including depression, if the recipient is not given adequate personal or societal support. We shall return to this discussion in the final chapter of this book.

Objectives for Chapter 6

When you have studied this chapter, you should be able to:

6.1 Discuss the benefits and disadvantages of hospital and home births, drawing on medical opinion, epidemiological data and personal statements.

6.2 Discuss the complexity of the debate about medical intervention in childbirth, and the problematic nature of assessing the effectiveness of particular procedures.

6.3 Discuss the interaction of biological, social and personal factors in post-natal depression.

Questions for Chapter 6

1 (*Objective 6.1*) In a study of 155 home births occurring in the West Middlesex area in 1970–72, the researchers (obstetricians and paediatricians) concluded that 61 of the mothers (39 per cent) had one or more recognised 'risk' factors which should (in their opinion) have resulted in them being refused a home confinement. The number of medical problems which occurred during the birth or the first week of life in these mothers and the 94 'low' risk mothers is shown in Table 6.4.

Table 6.4 Home births: problems in the baby related to obstetric risk factors

	High risk	Low risk
number of mothers	61 (100%)	94 (100%)
number of birth problems	9 (15%)	9* (10%)
number of neonatal problems	4 (7%)	8 (9%)

* This includes 2 of the babies most seriously affected at birth.
(Data from Cox, Fox, Zinkin and Matthews, 1976, Table II)

Use these data to argue (a) that all babies should be born in hospital, and (b) that the presence of an obstetric risk factor is not an adequate basis on which to *refuse* a home confinement. (*questions continue overleaf*)

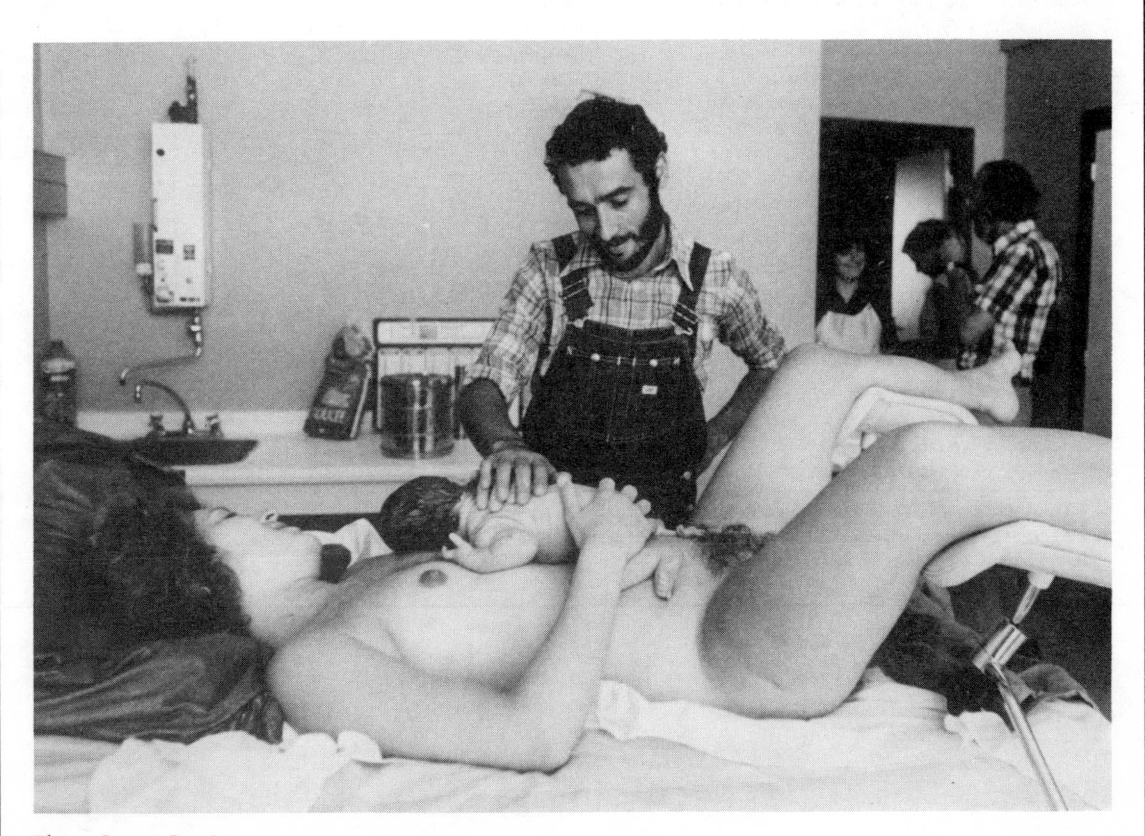

(Photo: Camera Press)

2 (*Objective* 6.2) Examine Table 6.5 carefully, and then answer the following questions.

(a) Which criteria for assessing the effectiveness of induction produced broad agreement between obstetricians and midwives that induction is beneficial?

(b) On which criteria did they broadly agree that induction might be disadvantageous?

(c) Comment on those criteria about which there was disagreement between obstetricians and midwives.

3 (*Objective* 6.3) What are the biological, social and personal factors that may have contributed to post-natal depression in this woman's account?

> As I say, me and my husband had this row over absolutely nothing. There was definite tension between us. Our sex life was absolutely nil because I was too damned tired for it. Also I had problems then that it hurt me because the wound didn't heal. In the end I took the baby for a walk and I ended up at my mother's house, and she lives eighteen miles from here. I walked there and my husband didn't know where I was. I realized when I got to Mum's that it must be me, I must be ill. (Welburn, 1980, p.175)

Table 6.5 Views of 379 obstetricians and 388 midwives on the effects of induction

Effect of induction on:	Views of obstetricians or midwives	Response/per cent*		
		decreased	increased	no effect
perinatal mortality rate	obstetricians	79	3	10
	midwives	66	3	24
satisfactory experience of labour for women	obstetricians	23	40	34
	midwives	47	21	22
job satisfaction for obstetricians	obstetricians	2	45	52
	midwives	2	49	36
job satisfaction for midwives	obstetricians	14	35	48
	midwives	32	18	45
Caesarean section rate	obstetricians	10	37	51
	midwives	12	33	52
development of jaundice in baby	obstetricians	0	52	45
	midwives	1	42	48
use of forceps to aid delivery†	obstetricians	21	15	63
	midwives	8	28	63
length of labour	obstetricians	69	8	20
	midwives	73	11	10
pain in labour†	obstetricians	3	35	58
	midwives	4	67	23
incidence of hypoxia in babies (low levels of oxygen in blood at birth)	obstetricians	23	13	60
	midwives	7	35	53

* Totals less than 100 per cent because 'no comment' and 'don't know' responses omitted.
† Assuming epidural anaesthesia is not given.
(Data from Cartwright, 1979, Tables 60, 78 and 79)

7

The changing image of children's health

This chapter is the first of four relating to childhood and adolescence. You will be asked to study an audiotape, 'Children's perceptions of health and illness' (cassette AC805), and there is an article associated with this chapter in the Course Reader, 'The causes of disease: women talking' by Mildred Blaxter (Part 1, Section 1.5).

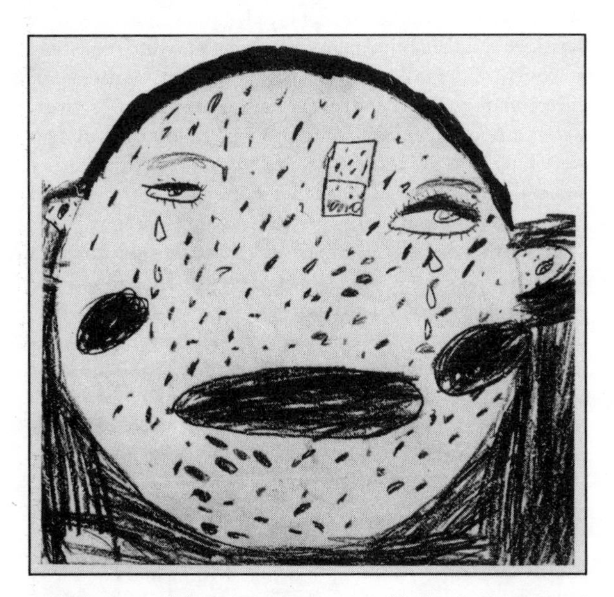

A child's view of the measles. (Reproduced by kind permission of the Health Education Council.)

In this chapter we move a little further along the lifespan and begin an examination of *children's health*. But before discussing the facts and figures about modern British children we shall pose a rather curious question. What do we mean by *'children'*, and in what ways (if any) are they different from *'adults'*? This may seem an odd place to start but, as you will see in a moment, the way in which we think of children is not 'given' — in the past, people's *views of childhood* were rather different. And one of the strands running through this book is a reappraisal of the things we take for granted about the way we live now. However, there is considerable leeway in what we mean by 'children', even in modern definitions.

□ What is the upper and lower age-limit within which you think of another person as a child, and what criteria did you use when deciding?

■ Most people would think of 'babies' becoming 'children' at about a year old, with the acquisition of certain skills — the ability to walk and say a few words. But there is rather more flexibility at the other end of the range; some people would consider childhood to end at puberty (around 11 or 12 years), choosing a *biological* determinant; others would consider someone a child until they left school at 16, or even later, choosing a *social* determinant; others would refuse to state an age, but look at each individual for signs of *personal* qualities such as 'responsibility' or 'good sense' that are supposed to be adult attributes.

So we cannot give childhood a fixed beginning and end, and we use the term to cover an enormous range of development, from the toddler to the adolescent.

□ List the biological, social and personal characteristics that you think are characteristic of children in the UK, as distinct from adults?

■ You may have thought of the following:

1 Biological features — children are less co-ordinated and skilful than adults and less able to make

accurate judgements about objects in their environment (e.g. the speed of a car, the difference between pills and sweets); they are more prone to infections and are more likely to be seriously ill or die from them; they are vulnerable to physical abuse from adults because of their smaller size and strength.

2 Social features — after the age of five they go to school; they do not have a paid job (except perhaps a paper round); they are not allowed to have sexual relationships with other children or with adults.

3 Personal features — they are believed to be more vulnerable psychologically than adults; trauma that might have been coped with in an adult may have a lasting effect on the emotional development of a child; children are usually described as innocent, carefree, spontaneously loving, full of wonder and mischief, but also little terrors!

In summary, children are human beings who have not yet completed their growth and development, and as a consequence are physically and emotionally vulnerable; they need the protection of adult members of society and the provision of an environment which fosters 'normal' development, for example schools and child health services. In Chapter 8 we shall be looking at the growth and development of children in some detail, and particularly at the way in which we decide on what is 'normal', but it is worth noting here that there are numerous biological differences between human beings who have not yet reached puberty and those who have completed the physical changes associated with it. Although there have been gradual changes over time in the age at which puberty is reached (as you will see in Chapter 10), there *are* distinct biological characteristics of childhood.

However, the social and personal features that we noted earlier as being characteristic of twentieth-century British children have seen very considerable changes. Consider this extract from a book by Philippe Ariès, a French social historian, writing about children who lived in the sixteenth and seventeenth centuries:

> The military paintings of the seventeenth century depicted young boys, whom we should describe as children, in the midst of rascally-looking old soldiers. As late as the end of the seventeenth century, it often happened that a young nobleman, destined for the service, would spend only two or three years at school. Thus Claude de Bonneval, born in 1675, entered the Jesuit college at the age of nine. He left at eleven ... to sign on as a marine in the King's Navy. At the age of thirteen he was a sub-lieutenant. (Ariès, 1973, p.187)

And what of the upbringing of the future Louis XIII, as recorded by the court physician:

> [At one year] in high spirits, he made everybody kiss his cock. [At three years] the Marquise de Verneuil often put her hand under his coat; he got his nanny to lay him on her bed where she played with him, putting her hand under his coat. (Ariès, 1973, p.98)

□ What do these extracts reveal about sixteenth- and seventeenth-century images of children compared with our own?

■ They differed from our own in at least two key respects — individuals whom we would consider too young for such experiences were given responsible employment and sexual attention.

Sexuality and work were not defined as belonging solely to some 'adult world' as they are today, nor were these areas of childhood activities confined to the ruling classes as you might have thought from Ariès' account. For example, working-class 'children' were wage-earners from an early age, working in factories and mines where their small fingers or stature was an advantage. Ariès argues that just as sexuality and work were seen as 'normal' in childhood, so many other aspects of life were shared between adults and children. Adults once played games that we now consider childish. Blind man's bluff was a favourite pastime at court, and riddles were a common adult amusement: even Jonathan Swift, the savage eighteenth century satirist, wrote a book of riddles. In schooling, children of all ages were taught in the same class, and in the sixteenth century some urban private schools were created which taught adults and children of all ages to read and write.

Thus there is reason to believe that the sharp distinction we now make between the world of childhood and the world of adulthood used not to exist. In consequence, children were not necessarily viewed as separate or special creatures with qualities radically distinct from those of adults. But does this mean that parents in past centuries loved their children less than we do today? It would be rather easy to think so given the prevalence of infanticide, and the appalling conditions in which working-class children laboured.

In modern society we tend to take it for granted that people love their children, and that within marriage it is rather 'unnatural' for a couple not to want a child. One of the ways in which many people show their love is by 'planning' the birth of each child, so that all may be given the best possible start in life; conversely, many others, such as Roman Catholics and Muslims, have large families because each child is precious and sent by God. When a child murderer is caught, crowds gather at the courthouse to spit on the accused and show their revulsion; men convicted of child abuse, incest or paedophilia are shunned or assaulted by fellow prisoners. This special regard for children cuts across ethnic, religious and class boundaries — *all* children are worthy of it regardless of colour or wealth, or physical and mental handicap. We also acknowledge that they can be 'little monsters' too, and demand a lot of hard work from parents, but by and large children are held to be marvellous and a precious resource.

However, it might have occurred to you to wonder if we can only afford to lavish so much affection on them because we have a reasonable expectation that they will survive. Consider the following quotations from the eighteenth century:

> One blushes to think of loving one's children. (Vandermonde, *Essai Sur La Maniere De Perfectionner L'Espece Humaine*, 1756, cited in Lorence, 1974, p.1)

The novelist Pierre Malraux, writing of his heroine's childhood:

> I pass over these years quickly, for I feel that detailed accounts of her early years will bore you. (*La Vie de Marianne*, 1713, cited in Lorence, 1974, p.2)

And here is the eighteenth-century historian Edward Gibbon who had five younger brothers and sisters, all of whom died in infancy:

> So feeble was my constitution, so precarious my life, that in the baptism of each of my brothers, my father's prudence successively repeated my Christian name Edward, that, in case of the departure of the eldest son, this patronymic appellation might still be perpetuated in the family. (cited in Lorence, 1970, p.5)

By one account, therefore, previous generations could simply not afford to become too attached to their children. Life was hard and many children died young. A child's lot was often brutal and short, as Figure 7.1 shows.

Only 150 years ago, almost half of all deaths occurred before the age of five.

□ Why has childhood mortality fallen so dramatically?

■ By far the most important reason has been the improvements in sanitation, housing and nutrition, though from the second quarter of this century specific medical measures have also played a part. Thus the virtual elimination of diphtheria and poliomyelitis in Britain and the complete elimination of smallpox, is almost certainly due to immunisation. For three major diseases, tuberculosis, whooping cough and measles, however, immunisation procedures were introduced

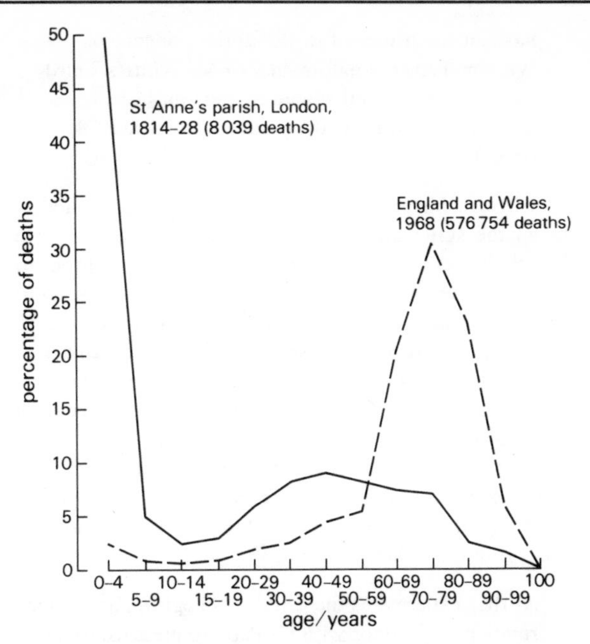

Figure 7.1 Percentage distribution of deaths by age-group in early nineteenth-century London and mid-twentieth-century England and Wales. (Data from Forbes, 1979, Figure 2, p.124)

too late to have much influence on the downward trend in mortality.*

However, the fact that children often died young is not in itself reason enough to suppose that parental love is a modern invention, any more than we can conclude that child labour is evidence of lack of caring.

> I should not like my little boy there, now 5, to begin before 9, and he shan't if I can help it, but if I am anyways obligated he must. He is but a little morsel, and if I were to get that little creature to work, I should have to get a scaffold for him to stand on, to reach, and with that it would be like murder-work, as you may say ...
>
> When children first begin work there is not one out of twenty but what knocks up, and has to stop and go out ... I've often said, 'Well, you had better go out for a bit' but when the child comes back he will perhaps be worse than ever the next time ... It's not much nourishment that a nailer can get ... Besides knocking up from ill-health, the young ones sometimes knock up from being lamed or burned ...
>
> It is quite right that the young ones should not work as long as they do, and should have some teaching. I am certain I should like my children to

*The decline of infectious diseases is discussed in detail in Book III, *The Health of Nations*, Chapter 8.

> have an easier time of it. (From the evidence of William Tether, a nail-maker, to Mr White's Third Report on the Metal Manufacturers of the Birmingham District, 1864; quoted in Pike, 1974, pp.129–30)

The British historian Linda Pollock has recently undertaken the systematic analysis of 144 American and 236 British diaries written between 1500 and 1900 in order to find out whether people really did think differently about children in the past and how far they were more cruel to them than we are today. Despite the obvious difficulties of taking 'diarists' as representative of the population as a whole, the diaries studied by Pollock do cover a very wide range of occupations, incomes and religious beliefs, and reveal that parents from the sixteenth to the nineteenth centuries all seemed to feel much the same as we do about children today, as, for example, Martha Bayard, writing at the end of the eighteenth century:

> As they expected us the Child was kept up, and came running to the door with his Papa to meet us; never did my heart experience more lively sentiments of maternal affection and joy than in the moment I clasped him to my bosom — I could not speak: the dear fellow observing my emotions burst out a-crying, and, with his little arms around my neck, begged me not to cry, now that I was with him. (cited in Pollock, 1983, p.104)

Similar evidence, as Pollock shows, can also be found in tribal societies. Even in those cultures that have an infant mortality rate as high as in eighteenth-century Britain, most parents are still stricken by the loss of a child, and still care for their surviving children with as much affection as we do. Of course, in every culture, not every parent manages to care for their children in the same way, but as a general rule, parental care and affection seem to be universal, both in past ages and across different cultures.

Thus, the inclusion of children in the worlds of work and sexuality cannot be taken as evidence that they were not loved. The concept of children as 'innocent', as fundamentally lacking adult sophistication, would have seemed as odd in the sixteenth and early seventeeth centuries as the idea of a 13 year-old naval lieutenant does to us today.

However, from the seventeenth century onwards, there began to appear, although very slowly at first, a new doctrine; a doctrine that children were both precious and easily corrupted. They had to be shielded from the adult world and carefully trained over many years until they were ready to gain entry to it. The primary responsibility for this vital task settled on women inside the family, and beyond them, on the State. Life slowly became divided into adults' activities and children's activities, and new institutions for children, schools, also began to divide children up into different 'years'. Such a separation of childhood from adulthood had two somewhat contradictory outcomes. On the one hand, there was a call for a much closer supervision or surveillance of children, so that 'bad' behaviour could be weeded-out. On the other hand, there was a new romantic doctrine which ascribed to the young child all kinds of special qualities that adults lacked — innocence, spontaneity, playfulness, unconditional love. The eighteenth-century Swiss philosopher Jean-Jacques Rousseau argued that society was a corrupting force and that we must strive to return to the values of little children, thus encouraging an entirely new image of childhood. This tradition was carried on by writers such as Wordsworth, Dickens, Edward Lear and Lewis Carroll, who fostered a sentimental '*cult of the child*':

> Three years she grew in sun and shower;
> Then Nature said, 'A lovelier flower
> On earth was never sown;
> This child I to myself will take;
> She shall be mine, and I will make
> A lady of mine own . . .
>
> She shall be sportive as the fawn
> That wild with glee across the lawn
> Or up the mountain springs;
> And hers shall be the breathing balm,
> And hers the silence and the calm
> Of mute insensate things.
> (From 'Lucy' Part (iv), verses 1 and 3, by William Wordsworth, 1770–1850)

From the seventeenth century onwards, the separation, commercialisation and surveillance of childhood began to gather pace; shops began to sell toys and games especially for children, and there was a growing interest on the part of the nation-state in children's general welfare. The nineteenth century saw the rise of a new type of mass army and with it a new type of warfare. And if armies were to fight well, the physical efficiency of the nation must be looked to. At the turn of the century, the national development of health-visiting in Britain owed much to the National Committee of Inquiry set up to investigate the débâcle of the Boer War, which was blamed partly on the poor physical health of recruits.

Children's education also became a matter of state policy, for nations compete by trade as well as by arms, and to compete successfully a nation must educate its children in the manner required by the new industrial technology; they must be literate, numerate and disciplined. Here, as an example of the new mood is an extract from a speech to the Ladies Sanitary Association in 1890 by Charles Kingsley (author of the Victorian children's classic, *The Water-Babies*), a prominent social reformer and the leading exponent of 'muscular Christianity':

> It is duty, one of the noblest of duties, to help the increase of the English race as much as possible, and to see that every child that is born into this great nation of England be developed to the highest pitch to which we can develop him in physical strength and beauty, as well as in intellect and virtue. (quoted in Haley, 1978, p.117)

Better health and education might serve other purposes besides those of individual growth and enjoyment, though these aims also motivated many reformers. Doctors joined in with this new view of children at a relatively late stage, and even when medical interest in children began to grow towards the end of the nineteenth century, they were still viewed as 'little adults'. Children were not given special attention, and, as with adult patients, the doctor focused on the disease rather than on the person who suffered it. One expert writing in 1909 stated: 'With few exceptions the pathological processes of youth and maturity are alike ...' and the name given to the Society for the Study of Disease in Children, founded in 1901, signified the subsidiary position of the child relative to interest in the disease. Looking back on the period prior to the Second World War, one paediatrician summed up the approach of this era in the following terms:

> ... [paediatric teaching had begun] with the assumption that the child is but a miniature version of the adult ... his diseases were the same as in adults but less severe ... his psychological make-up was the same as in adults but more innocent ... and that his treatment is identical except that it is scaled down to size. (P. Catzel, cited in Armstrong, 1983, p.61)

Paediatrics itself was for long a tiny specialism within medicine. Most children received medical care from doctors who also treated adult patients and who had themselves received little or no training in childhood diseases. All this was to change radically in the years following the Second World War. In addition to the special qualities of character ascribed them by the earlier 'Romantic' movement, the new paediatrics held that children had a radically different constitution, both physical and psychological, from that of adults. They could not be treated simply as adults. They had their own diseases and required their own special forms of care. Children, so it was argued, could only be understood if viewed as undergoing a complete process of biological, psychological and social development — something that Chapter 8 will deal with more fully. As such they needed their own special forms of medical specialist, the paediatrician, the child psychiatrist, the child psychologist, and the children's nurse. Moreover, they must be handled in special ways. Hospitals must be redesigned to cater for their special needs. Nowadays, visiting hours have been arranged to allow parents to visit frequently and mothers must be allowed to stay overnight where possible. Special games and toys must be given to children, special pictures placed on the walls.

In summary, therefore, the social theory of childhood argues that over the centuries there has been a dramatic shift in the European age-grading system. Children have been removed from the adult world and ascribed their own special qualities. Vast corps of adult specialists have been set up to observe, instruct and monitor their progress. Moreover, this process has by no means ended. It began first in education and in literature, but in this century has reached medicine and psychology. Doctors, too, now view children as special and have re-shaped their treatment of children accordingly. The modern British child is monitored and protected, schooled and nourished, so that mortality in childhood is now a rare event and we expect our children to develop 'in physical strength and beauty, as well as in intellect and virtue'. This evolution is graphically depicted in Figure 7.2 (overleaf), which shows children from the same primary school in East London lined up for the 'leaving day' photograph in 1900, 1925 and 1950.

□ What differences strike you?

■ Apart from the most obvious expansion of the school to include girls by 1950, there is a definite sense of children being 'healthier and happier' than they were earlier in the century. In 1900, the children look pastey-faced, rather unkempt, possibly grubby and decidedly miserable. By 1950, scrubbed and smiling faces confront the camera; children look taller and better developed; a few pairs of 'National Health' spectacles can be seen.

However, such an account smacks of the triumphant march of progress (called 'Whig history' by some historians), and it is worth remembering that despite the radical changes in the way we think about children and consequent improvement in their health and wellbeing we have been unable to eradicate class differences in children's health. At birth, children still enter a lottery in which the chances of dying, of being injured, or of suffering a wide range of diseases shows an unequal distribution that correlates closely with social class. We shall return to this aspect of children's health in Chapter 9, and in a moment we shall discuss the rise of new definitions of abnormal health during childhood. But so far in this chapter we have been guilty of a common adult failing — attending to adult images of childhood without asking what children themselves think about it. Part of the reason for this is that

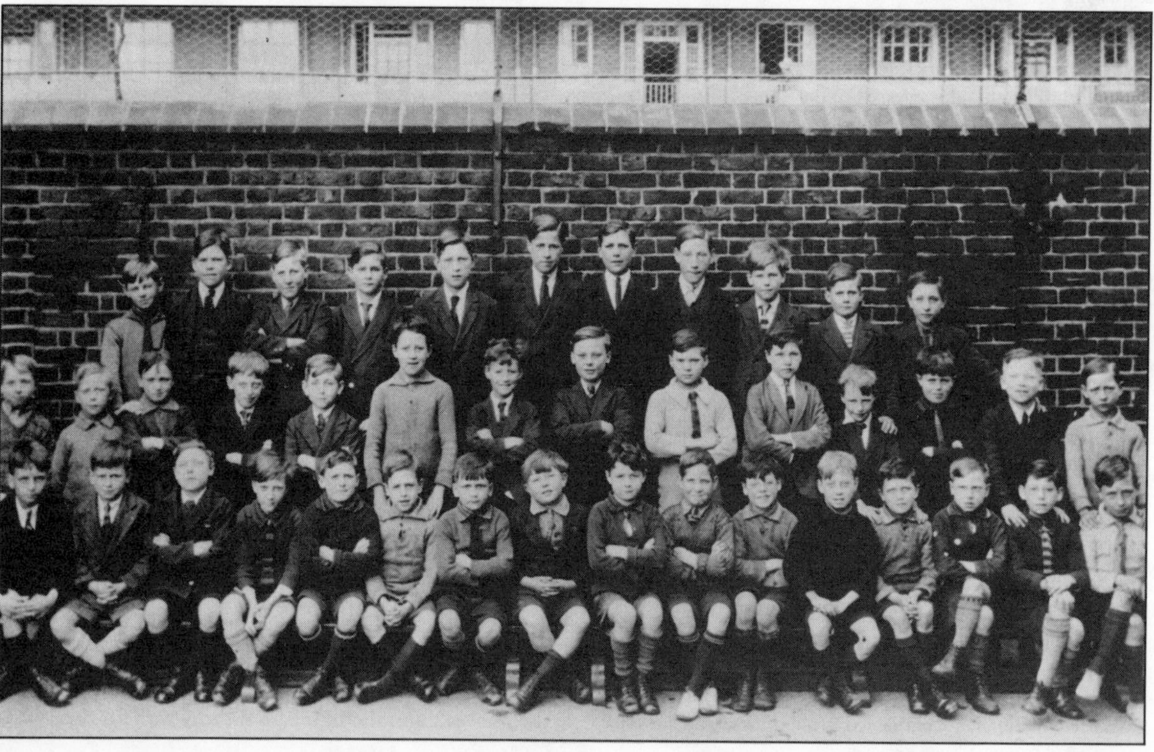

Figure 7.2 Leaving-day photographs of children at a school in Acton, East London, in 1900, 1925 and 1950. (Courtesy of Greater London Council Photograph Library)

children have very rarely been asked, so we cannot say whether their self-image has changed over the centuries. Even now, very little research has been done into children's knowledge and opinions. Nevertheless, we shall now make an attempt to bring them into the picture.

Children's perceptions of health and illness

How do children define health and illness in themselves and in others? How do these perceptions differ from what we know of adults' perceptions, and how do children acquire their definitions? We are going to use an audiotape of school children discussing questions of health and disease in order to explore some of these issues, but first we will provide a framework for analysing the material on the tape.

The fact that children's perceptions of illness can differ significantly from that of adults is illustrated in the two quotations below. The first is from a modern paediatrics textbook for medical students:

> Chickenpox is a common and highly infectious disease but it is usually mild in childhood. (Hull and Johnston, 1981, p.78)

> My last illness was chickenpox and it was dreadful. The first two days were the worst. I did not just have chickenpox but I was ill as well. I felt very lazy and I was asleep all day and I wouldn't eat. My brother had chickenpox at the same time as I did, but I had it worse than him and my brother wouldn't stop eating. Chickenpox was very itchy and my mum had to rub ointment on me three times a day.

> I think chickenpox is the worst illness I have ever had and I have had a lot. I still have a lot of scars. It was dreadful and I hope I never have it again. (quoted in Bartram, 1965)

The contrast between the two statements is obvious, but the child's words also serve to illustrate a number of themes that have been identified in research on perceptions of illness. She refers to a particular diagnosis (chickenpox), and particular physical sensations, visible signs and changes of mood and behaviour that together build up the picture of a sick child.

□ Go through her statement carefully, and pick out the phrases that reveal how this child knows that she is ill.

■ She starts with a diagnosis, which reveals that someone in authority (parent, doctor) has told her the *name* of her illness. But there is plenty of evidence of ill-health from her own experience: *physical sensations* — 'I was ill as well'; 'it was dreadful'; 'chickenpox was very itchy'; *visible signs* — presumably spots as evidenced by 'I still have a lot of scars'; *changes of mood or behaviour* — 'I felt very lazy'; 'I was asleep all day and I wouldn't eat'. She also notes a change in her mother's behaviour that is another confirmation of the illness — 'My mum had to rub ointment on me three times a day'.

This practice in analysing a child's statements about illness will be useful during the first part of the audiotape sequence 'Children's perceptions of health and illness' on cassette AC805, which you should now play. We recorded it at a Milton Keynes school in 1984, with two groups of 7 year-old boys and girls from white, mainly working-class, families. There were thirteen children in all. They were asked about their perceptions of their own health, and that of their parents' and grandparents' generations. We began by asking 'how do you know when you are ill?'. As you listen to the first part of the tape, keep in mind the way in which we analysed the child's statements about chicken-pox. Play the tape now.

□ What *visible* signs of illness do the children speak of using as confirmation that they are ill?

■ Two children mention looking in a mirror to see if they have spots or look pale.

□ One child mentions the behaviour of others towards him as confirmation of illness — what was it?

■ Taking his pulse to see if it was going too fast.

□ What example do the children give of where they 'draw the line' between illness and non-illness?

■ They do not consider that injuries are the same as being ill, even when they are serious enough to prevent them from going to school.

Table 7.1 Percentage of mothers and children attributing signs and symptoms as indicators of illness in the child

Condition*	Mothers	Children
fever, temperature	97.7	93.5
vomit, throw up	86.3	94.7
earache	85.1	65.9
sore throat	84.8	71.6
knocked out in fall	80.9	37.7
hurt all over	80.3	74.7
stiff neck or back	63.6	34.8
stomach ache	58.0	56.9
cough	56.8	40.8
toothache	47.9	18.6
irritable, cranky	45.1	26.3
headache	38.6	48.3
runny nose	35.0	32.6

* Conditions are ranked according to the percentages of mothers attributing illness to the child.
(Campbell, 1975, Table 1, p. 116)

This is in sharp contrast to adult definitions of illness, which usually *include* injuries (if you doubt this, listen to news reports on the TV and radio that habitually refer to people as being 'seriously ill in hospital' after a car crash, bomb explosion, shooting, etc.). This division between *children's and adults' definitions of illness* also emerged in research conducted by John D. Campbell at the National Institute of Mental Health in the USA. He asked mothers and their children *separately* to rate a number of conditions as possible indicators of illness in the child. The results are shown in Table 7.1.

□ For which conditions were the responses of children compared with the mothers most different?

■ The children were a bit less bothered about earache, stiff neck or back, cough, toothache and irritability than their mothers, but the really marked disparity is in their low rating of being knocked out in a fall.

It is also interesting to note that vomiting and headaches were the only signs of illness that were more strongly rated by children than by their mothers. On the tape we asked children 'what makes you ill?' and two of their answers revealed that being ill was closely allied to 'being sick', i.e. vomiting. When asked 'what causes illness?', they mentioned germs or bugs; not wearing warm enough clothes and getting cold; and eating too much or drinking sour milk.

These categories — infection, cold and 'wrong' food — are similar to some categories used by adults when making sense out of what caused them to become ill. You can check this by reading the article 'The causes of disease:

women talking' by Mildred Blaxter which is in the Course Reader (Part 1, Section 1.5). As you do so, note the similarities between the children's views about disease and those of women in their 40s and 50s interviewed by Blaxter.

The most important source of information about disease mentioned by the women in Blaxter's study was television and they were also influenced by their daughters, some of whom read more than their mothers.

□ In addition to parents, what other sources of information are there that shape children's opinions about what it means to be healthy or ill, how one should behave when ill, and how one should behave to keep healthy?

■ You might have thought of the following: teachers, contacts at school and friends at home; television, books, comics; their general experience of life and of being ill before; doctors and other health-care professionals they come into contact with.

These influences came out strongly on the tape when we asked the children 'what can you do to keep yourself healthy?'

□ What did they reply, and what clues were given about where these ideas had come from?

■ They agreed that they should eat vegetables, fruit and proteins, and avoid sweets and sugar; keep clean and brush their teeth; be careful not to have an accident while playing, and be especially careful when crossing roads. The knowledge about diet came partly from school work (these children were currently engaged on a project about teeth and eyes) and partly from parents who made rules restricting sweets, and made the child 'eat a sensible tea'. Parents also seemed to be the source of rules about washing, especially of hands before meals, and about keeping well wrapped up when outside. The children had a sharp awareness of the risk of accidents, particularly on the roads, and recalled a public education film about a traffic accident involving a child.

The children's emphasis on accidents is entirely realistic; accidental injury and poisoning cause more deaths between the ages of 7 and 15 years than any other cause, and for this reason are the subject of a case study in Chapter 9. In contrast to the women in Blaxter's study, the children accept that they *can* do something to preserve their health. They also identified two major causes of disease among adults which were not emphasised by the women Blaxter interviewed — smoking and drinking. The dangers of drinking and driving were also stressed by the children.

□ Which two diseases did they mention as being responsible for killing adults, and what did they think causes them?

■ The two commonest fatal diseases in adulthood were the ones that the children knew about — cancers and heart 'attack'. Their beliefs about what causes them were also partly accurate — they see cancers as being caused by smoking, and heart attack by getting very angry, having a sudden shock or a lot of stress, and one child hazarded a guess about diet and heart disease.

□ In what major way does this account differ from that of the women in Blaxter's study?

■ The most commonly mentioned disease was TB (reflecting its prevalence in Glasgow in these women's youth); they were unwilling to offer explanations about the causes of TB or cancers, and avoided using either term where possible. Heart disease was seen as caused by stress, or a 'weakness' in the heart brought on by an infection, most commonly measles.

Talking about heart attacks led to a more general discussion of death. The fact that children and babies can sometimes die was readily acknowledged, and mention was made of children being murdered and of a suicide. Adults sometimes express the view that children are 'innocent' about death and should be protected from knowledge about it — these 7 year olds seem to have escaped such protection. However, you may have noticed that after the discussion of what happens after death, the children rapidly turned the subject towards the likelihood of *old* people dying.

□ Why did the children think that death is more likely in old age?

■ They describe elderly people as though they are extremely fragile — 'they can die very easily by sleeping or something' — as though old age in itself is sufficient justification for death. One child suggests that old people are unhealthy because they didn't look after themselves properly when they were younger, and another because they are short of money. The majority view is that people seem to 'wear out' as they get older, and fall prey to more diseases.

The women in the Blaxter study were by contrast, less willing to talk about disease as an inevitable consequence of ageing — perhaps because they see themselves as 'getting on in years'.

When we asked the children, 'does the amount of money a family has make any difference to their health?' — their answers revealed an awareness of poverty and starvation in other countries through school projects, but that they had no real notion of an association between income and health in their own lives. However, one child speculated that older people might suffer more ill-health because they had less money. They also showed scant awareness of any sex differences in the health of children and adults, except for one remark about women being healthier because they drink wine, whereas men prefer beer and whisky!

□ How accurate were the children's perceptions of the age at which most people die?

■ The *average* life expectancy in the UK is about 75 years for women and 70 years for men. The children tended to push their estimates a bit higher than this — into the eighties, or even ninety. One child hopefully recalled a television programme on which she saw a woman of 103!

You may have been surprised by the general perceptiveness of such young children about their own health and that of the adults in their lives. In a broad sense, they know many of the same kinds of things about causes and prevention at 7 years of age as most adult members of the lay population. In this respect, then, even twentieth century children are 'little adults'; their knowledge and opinions are shared with and broadly equivalent to those of most grown-ups. However, we cannot conclude that the 'evidence' of this tape-recording is representative of children's perceptions about health and illness.

□ Why not?

■ There are several reasons:

1 We interviewed only 13 children, in two mixed groups. If the sample had been larger, or we had interviewed girls separately from boys, or each child individually instead of in a group, we may well have had different answers.

2 The children were predominantly working class and all were white — children from other socioeconomic backgrounds or ethnic groups may have different views.

3 The children were all 7 years old: not only might older or younger children have different perceptions about health, but 7 year olds of the past or future may also feel differently — these children have been affected by what has happened in the 7 years prior to 1984.

However, since there have been few systematic investigations of children's views about health and disease, you must draw your own conclusions about the representativeness of the children on the tape. But we *can* touch down on firmer ground by concluding with a discussion of the facts and figures about children's health in modern Britain. This will at least give you a basis from which to consider the children's image of their own health, and lay a necessary foundation for the chapters that follow. However, as you will see, the *medical* image of the healthy child is also subject to change.

The changing statistics of childhood illness

The image people in the industrialised world hold of their children's health has changed dramatically since the nineteenth century and continues to evolve. Today in Britain most people who have children do so in the expectation that they will be born healthy and without deformity, or even without blemish. Survival is assumed and families of one or two children planned. Before the baby is born, girls or boys names are chosen and baby clothes bought. Sometimes the school that the child will attend has been chosen, or a place booked in a nursery. Colds, minor accidents and passing 'childhood' illnesses are usually expected, but death and handicap are not. In comparison with past centuries and with most Third World countries today, this optimism is soundly based. If you look back at Figure 7.1 you will see that less than 3 per cent of deaths now occur below the age of 5, and the percentage falls still lower between 5 and 20. Another important shift in patterns of childhood mortality over time can be seen from Figure 7.3, which shows the distribution of deaths under 5 years of age.

□ What is the main difference between the early nineteenth-century data and 1968?

■ Of the 17 669 deaths occurring in England and Wales in 1968 to children under 5, almost 90 per cent of them took place during the first 12 months; thereafter child mortality was extremely low. By contrast, the 1 430 child deaths in a single London parish were spread across the first 5 years, though declining with increasing age.

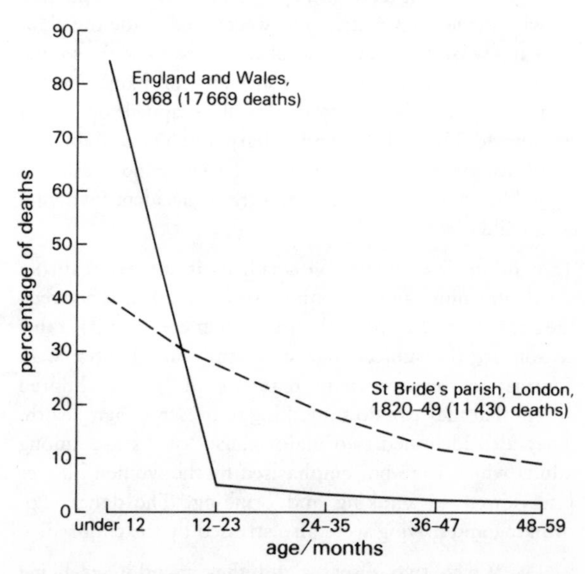

Figure 7.3 Percentage distribution of deaths under 5 in St. Bride's Parish, London, 1820–49, and England and Wales, 1968. (Data from Forbes, 1979, Figure 3, p.125)

Table 7.2 Main causes of death in childhood, England and Wales, 1980

Cause	Total number	Total percentage	Under 1 year number	Under 1 year percentage	1–14 years number	1–14 years percentage
all causes*	10 870	100	7 899	100	2 971	100
congenital abnormalities (i.e. defects present at birth)	2 519	33	2 113	26.8	406	13.7
diseases of respiratory system (mainly infections)	1 131	10	802	10.2	318	10.7
injury and poisoning	1 094	10	191	2.4	903	30.4
sudden infant death syndrome ('cot deaths')	1 048	10	1 021	12.9	27	0.9
cancers	565	5	45	0.6	530	17.8
diseases of the central nervous system	387	4	152	1.9	235	7.9
non-respiratory infectious and parasitic diseases	254	2	126	1.6	128	4.3

* All causes includes a number of causes not shown on table. Percentages therefore do not add up to 100.
(Data from Registrar General, 1982, pp. 32–64)

What can account for this shift and why is the first year of life still relatively (although not absolutely) perilous?

□ Look at the data in Table 7.2 and see if you can deduce the answer.

■ The major causes of death under 1 year old, accounting for about 40 per cent of infant deaths in the UK today, are *congenital abnormalities* and *sudden infant death syndrome* ('*cot deaths*'). Neither of these groups of fatality is easy to prevent since the underlying cause is mostly unknown or untreatable. The major infectious diseases which claimed the majority of lives in earlier times are now rarely fatal, mainly because they are much less common, but also because of improvements in treatment.

Sudden infant death syndrome remains a mystery, and one that we shall not attempt to analyse here. Very little is known about why apparently healthy babies simply stop breathing, and although there are correlations between such a death and some social variables, there is as yet no way to predict or prevent them. Much the same is true for most congenital malformations; some, like Down's syndrome, are chromosome defects; others, like spina bifida, *may* be linked to some social factor such as diet. Table 7.3 shows small but tantalising variations in prevalence in different parts of the country. (Anencephaly is a fatal condition in which the brain fails to develop.)

Table 7.3 Prevalence at birth of some congenital malformations

Type of defect	Prevalence per thousand births: Birmingham 1950–54	Liverpool 1960–64	South Wales 1964–66
anencephaly	2.0	3.1	3.1
spina bifida (without anencephaly)	2.2	3.4	3.9
cardiac defects	4.2	5.0	4.4
clubbed feet	5.7	2.7	3.4
dislocated hip	0.9	0.7	0.9
cleft lip/palate	2.0	1.5	2.1
Down's syndrome	1.6	1.4	1.0
total defects	23.1	23.9	35.7

(Richards, 1980, Table 7.4, p. 132)

Some conditions that were once always fatal or profoundly handicapping have yielded to advances in medical technology, which now enables many more children to survive in good health. Not so long ago, many premature babies died or grew up with significant handicaps. For example, a study in Edinburgh showed that nearly half the babies born prematurely between the years 1953 and 1960, and weighing below 1 500 g, had moderate or severe handicaps still in evidence by the age of 11–13 years. By contrast, similar babies born in 1966–70 and examined two or three years later, revealed that only 22 per cent were similarly handicapped. On the other hand, new technology has also meant that some children who would once have died at birth now survive with some degree of handicap — spina bifida is the most obvious example. (The ethical considerations that this raises will be discussed at the end of this book, in Chapter 19.) A 1974 estimate by the Department of Education and Science suggested that in England and Wales more than 150 000 pupils either required or received special education on account of a handicap. This represents 18 per 1 000 of the school population. Two-thirds of these children were classified as educationally subnormal and of the rest, the next largest group were those classified as maladjusted, followed by those with physical impairments. We shall return to the subject of 'mental' retardation or abnormality in a moment.

After the age of 12 months, the commonest causes of death are injuries (some deliberately inflicted, but mainly accidental) and poisoning, with the rare childhood cancers coming second. At no point in a British child's life are infectious diseases — once so fatal — now the most prominent cause of death, although they still claim several hundred lives a year. The decline in childhood mortality in all industrialised countries has meant that most parents confidently expect their children to reach adulthood. It is perhaps not surprising that parental and medical concern has switched from the lethal conditions to the chronic or recurrent problems — from mortality to morbidity. So, how healthy are British children?

Some light is shed on this question by the first *British Perinatal Mortality Survey*, which collected information on almost every child born in one week in March 1958. This group, numbering some 17 000 in all, have been investigated at different ages throughout their lives. When seen at the age of seven, many had already accumulated a history of common conditions, as shown in Table 7.4.

Most of these conditions consist of 'acute' episodes — that is to say, they do not last long and a complete recovery is made, even if the condition recurs periodically.

□ Which are the chronic (long-term) conditions in Table 7.4?

■ Tooth decay, speech defects, visual defects including squints, and hearing difficulties are all chronic conditions, though the table does not show the proportion of minor defects in each category.

Table 7.4 Percentage of children in the first British Perinatal Mortality Survey who had suffered from common conditions by the age of 7 years

Condition	Percentage
dental caries (tooth decay)	88
earache	32
bronchitis	18
periodic vomiting	17
speech defects	16
periodic abdominal pain	15
visual defects other than squints	14
recurrent ear or throat infections	13
bedwetting after the age of 5	11
hearing difficulty	10
recurrent mouth ulcers	10
squints	6

(Data from Pringle *et al.*, 1966)

You may have wondered about the inclusion of bedwetting in the list, along with illnesses and physical defects. Certainly it is a source of worry, embarrassment and inconvenience in families where a child regularly wets the bed, but is it a sign of 'ill-health'? The image we have of the 'sick child' in modern times has clearly undergone a radical change, to include behaviour along with eyesight, speech and hearing. Charles Kingsley's address to the Ladies' Sanitary Association is being put into practice in earnest. But the increased surveillance of children's health required to detect the growing list of treatable physical conditions may have another, less desirable, consequence. Consider Table 7.5.

Table 7.5 Chronic physical disorders among children aged 10–12 years in the Isle of Wight, 1962–3

Condition	Age-specific incidence rate per 1 000 children
asthma	232
eczema	104
epilepsy	64
cerebral palsy	46
other brain disorders	37
orthopaedic (bone) disorders	34
heart disease	24
deafness	18
neuromuscular disorders	12
diabetes	12
other disorders	37

(Rutter *et al.*, 1970, Table 18.1)

□ Are there any surprises for you in the data in Table 7.5?

■ According to this study, almost a quarter of 10–12 year olds (at least on the Isle of Wight) suffer from asthma, just over 10 per cent have eczema, and around 6 per cent are epileptic. These may have struck you as surprisingly high rates, particularly that for asthma.

The severity of these conditions varies markedly from child to child. Asthma can be relatively mild or, in extreme cases, prove seriously disabling. Likewise, only one child in a thousand is born profoundly deaf, but several more have some serious degree of impairment. Cerebral palsy may mean only a mild degree of incoordination, but it can also mean profound physical handicap. However Table 7.5 could be interpreted as meaning that British children are not particularly healthy after all — they may not 'die like flies' any longer, but a large proportion seem to suffer from chronic physical conditions.

□ Can you think of an alternative interpretation?

■ The diagnosis, for example, of asthma, may have been expanded in recent times to encompass children who would not formerly have been considered asthmatic.

This possibility raises an interesting set of questions: for example, what effect does a diagnosis of, say, asthma have on a child? Some undoubtedly benefit enormously from treatment, but others will have such a mild condition that none is considered necessary. What difference might it make to these children's lives to be in receipt of a medical diagnosis? We might also ask whether the parents sought help for their child or whether the diagnosis followed routine surveillance of the child's health at school, detecting a 'problem' that had not previously bothered either the child or the parents? There are no clear answers to these questions, but they point up an area of disagreement about the health care offered to children in the industrialised world. On the one hand, the growing ranks of professionals who specialise in children's health tend to argue for more surveillance so that more of these chronic conditions can be detected and treated; on the other, there are some doubts about the wisdom of such a policy. This dilemma is amply demonstrated by the rise in the diagnosis of hearing difficulties caused by '*glue ear*'.

In this condition, fluid collects in the middle ear, a cavity that is normally filled with air to enable sound to be conducted from outside the body to the inner ear, where the organ of hearing — the cochlea — is located. It is not known what causes the fluid to accumulate and in most children the condition is self-limiting, that is, the fluid clears without any treatment. However, in some children the fluid becomes progressively thicker until it attains a glue-like consistency. The presence of such material in the middle ear interferes with the transmission of sound, causing some degree of deafness. This condition has long been recognised. However, since the 1950s in the USA and the 1960s in the UK, the frequency with which it has been diagnosed by doctors has increased. This has resulted in an unprecedented rise in the number of surgical operations conducted to remove fluid from the middle ear. In the Oxford Health Region the rate of surgery more than doubled between 1975 and 1983.

There are several reasons for this '*surgical epidemic*'; some of them are to do with the changing concerns of those responsible for the development of children — parents, teachers and health professionals. With the demise of profound or complete deafness resulting from infectious diseases and other conditions, attention could be redirected to children suffering some slight loss of hearing. The latter went largely undetected by doctors as long as there were children with chronic ear infections needing treatment, and for the same reason went unnoticed by parents and teachers. In this sense, glue ear can be seen to represent the particular stage that the image of child health and the priorities of health services have reached in the 1970s and 1980s.

There may also have been a similar increase in the frequency with which children are diagnosed as suffering from 'mental' conditions — that is, a disorder that has no known underlying biological defect. The Department of Education and Science's 1974 estimate of pupils requiring special education as a result of handicap classified the majority as educationally subnormal or maladjusted. A study by F.J.W. Miller and colleagues (1974) of over a thousand children in Newcastle from their birth to their fifteenth birthday revealed that 40 per cent of the children had caused their parents to worry at some time, whether their offspring were emotionally disturbed.

Among younger children, bedwetting and lack of bowel control, or being abnormally timorous or fearful are common causes of parental anxiety. Among older children and adolescents, the commonest psychiatric diagnosis is '*conduct disorder*'. In a survey of 2 000 ten year olds in the Isle of Wight (by B.M. Rutter and colleagues, 1970), the prevalence of psychiatric disorders was found to be 7 per cent, with the rate in boys being twice that of girls. Of that 7 per cent, two-thirds were conduct disorders. What precisely does this mean?

According to the *Oxford Textbook of Psychiatry*, conduct disorders are characterised by

> ... severe and persistent anti-social behaviour ... the essential feature is persistent abnormal conduct which is more serious than ordinary childish mischief. It is usually first evident in the home as stealing, lying and disobedience, together with verbal or physical aggression. Later, the disturbance is often evident outside the home as well, especially at school, as truancy, delinquency, vandalism, and poor school work, as well as reckless behaviour or alcohol and drug abuse. (Gelder *et al.*, 1983, p.652–53)

□ Can you see any problems in this definition?

■ It is not always clear how far the problems may lie more with the parents or school than with the child. Is truancy from school *always* a sign of psychiatric disorders, or might it sometimes be reasonable avoidance of an intolerable regime?

Such problems about the proper uses of psychiatry affect adult patients as well as children.* To raise the problem is not to argue that there is no such thing as a 'conduct

*This subject is discussed more fully in *Experiencing and Explaining Disease*, Chapter 13, The Open University (1985) U205 *Health and Disease*, Book VI.

disorder'. Some children do indeed engage in persistent and extreme anti-social behaviour with which it is very hard for parents, schools or psychiatrists to cope. Moreover, the outlook for such children in adult life is not always promising. However, this is not so for other childhood psychiatric conditions. The best long-term follow-up studies tend to show that 90–95 per cent of the psychiatric conditions diagnosed among children do not persist into adulthood. In Chapter 10 we shall be considering one such condition, anorexia nervosa, in depth.

In summary, then, there has been a gradual change in the focus of concern about children's health. As the infectious diseases declined as a cause of death, attention switched to children who were considered less than perfect in mind and body. New categories of ill-health such as glue ear or conduct disorder have been described, and increasing numbers of children have been found to be suffering from them. We cannot yet be certain that the new image of the 'healthy child' has not become a rapidly dwindling club that few will join. It has now become standard procedure to monitor every child's health closely so that abnormalities can be detected at the earliest moment — but how is 'normal' growth and development to be defined? We shall tackle this difficult question in the next chapter.

Objectives for Chapter 7

When you have studied this chapter, you should be able to:

7.1 Discuss the changing image of children's health, drawing on differences between contemporary social and medical attitudes to children and those of past ages.

7.2 Give a brief account of the range and severity of common medically-diagnosed conditions in childhood in the UK in recent years.

Questions for Chapter 7

1 (*Objective 7.1*)

> Men, be human beings: this is your first duty ... Love childhood, indulge its games, its pleasures, and its loveable nature. Who has not looked back with regret on an age when laughter is always on the lips and when the spirit is always at peace? Why take from these little innocents the pleasure of a time so short which ever escapes them ...? Why fill with bitterness and sorrow these first swift years which will never return for them any more than they can for you? (Jean-Jacques Rousseau, *Émile*, first translated 1762, cited in Coveney, 1967, p.46)

(a) Rousseau is often claimed to be the key founder of a new image of childhood. How far does this quotation reflect a shift in attitudes towards children, compared with those of earlier centuries?

(b) In what ways have medical views of childhood and medical services for them changed since Rousseau wrote this and why has this occurred?

2 (*Objective* 7.2) 'Childhood is, above all, a time of high morbidity.' Comment on this statement.

8

Growth and development in childhood

This chapter discusses the difficulties of assessing what is 'normal' in childhood development, and at the same time sketches in the broad details of the stages through which adequately-nourished, healthy children pass. The definition of 'normality' was discussed in Chapter 2 of this book, and also in Book I, *Studying Health and Disease*, Chapter 3. References are also made in the text to topics discussed in Book IV, *The Biology of Health and Disease*, particularly Chapter 6, where the *plasticity* of neurological development was described. You may need to refresh your memory of this term.

This chapter is about normal growth and development in childhood, but what is meant by 'normal' in this context? Most parents worry at some stage in their children's lives that their offspring are not keeping pace with the generally expected milestones on the path to adulthood. Perhaps a particular child seems 'late' in learning to crawl, another cannot write her name when others of her age-group do so easily, another is a 'slow reader'. Common sense leads most parents to note that the same child may seem relatively 'advanced' in other respects: perhaps she cut her first tooth earlier than expected or was quick to walk — at any rate things seem to balance out. Against this background of extreme variation, how can we conclude whether or not a child is developing 'normally'?

No part of the human life cycle reveals more clearly the subtle interplay between genes and environment, between biological and social constraints and possibilities, than the two decades of transition between the helpless dependency of the newborn baby and the physically, emotionally, legally and perhaps financially independent adult. It is a period of enormous and obvious changes in size and shape, from a baby weighing perhaps 3.5 kgs and measuring 75 cm in length to an adult of around 70 kgs in weight and 1.75 m in height. It is a period of vast transformations in skills: a child must learn to walk, to grasp and to manipulate objects in her environment; to sense and interpret the myriad sights, sounds, and tastes the world presents to her; to communicate with others, especially by speech, but in a host of other subtle ways, and indeed to interpret the communication of others to her.

Children are often referred to in casual speech as though they are a homogeneous group (for example, 'children watch too much television nowadays' or 'children are better at maths now than they were in my generation'). The rapid changes occurring between birth and puberty render such sweeping generalisations meaningless. A child beginning to walk at twelve months of age is very different from a three-year-old who can construct simple sentences, control her bladder and buckle her shoes. Do they both watch too much television or manage algebra with ease, or were the 'children' referred to actually eight, or ten, or twelve? It is important to be clear about the stage of growth or development attained by the children we discuss.

□ What do you think is the difference between *growth* and *development*?

■ *Growth* denotes increase in size as well as change in proportion. It can be monitored with some degree of reliability in terms of physical measurements, e.g. height and weight.

Development encompasses increase in complexity of structure, but particularly of function — like learning to walk and talk — and is much more difficult to measure.

Normally these processes are harmonious, though not necessarily in step, but sometimes growth and development become uncoupled and incompatibilities and inconsistencies result. Although it is possible to *describe* the chronology of events, the physical, emotional and cognitive aspects of growing up (and we will do so in this chapter), to *explain* them in a way that makes clear biological and social sense is not so easy. We have chosen to focus on two aspects of growth and development to illustrate the difficulty of unravelling social and biological influences upon them: first, growth in height, and second, the development of skills and abilities. But before beginning the detailed discussion, it is worth delineating three general areas of difficulty in trying to define what is 'normal' in children's growth and development, and how to explain the variations between one child and another. Before reading on, you might like to reflect on what these areas of difficulty might be. Make your own list and compare it with the account which follows.

First and foremost, there is not one strict path along which all children must develop. As you will see in some of the graphs that follow, the 'normal range', within which growth and development occur, may be pretty wide. We all know children who are short or tall 'for their age', who suddenly seem to shoot up almost overnight or who 'mark time' in size while their schoolmates grow around them. The point is that there are many possible pathways to a given final height — or any other aspect of being an adult. Looking at the state of an individual at any stage of their development is like a freeze-frame on a video; whatever there is in view at the moment, the ultimate outcome is a long way down the tape, and judging 'normal' growth and development from the snapshot is a tricky business.

Second, the processes of growth and development are not smooth and linear. Take an apparently simple measure like weight gain: a baby doubles her birthweight by five months of age, doubles it again by two years, but takes until eight years old to double it yet again. Weight gain is not continuous and regular throughout life: different parts of the body grow and develop at different rates, as Figure 8.1 shows.

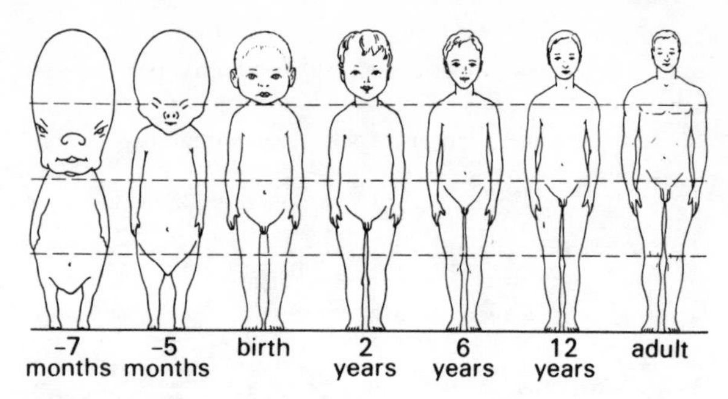

Figure 8.1 Changes in the proportion of different parts of the body, from the fetus 7 months before birth to the adult male. Notice, for example, that the head forms half the body length in the early fetus, but less than a quarter of body length in the adult.

For example, the brain of a six month old baby is 50 per cent of its adult weight, whereas the baby herself is only about 10 per cent of adult weight; the brain is 75 per cent of adult weight at two-and-half years, 90 per cent at six years, and 95 per cent at age 10. Since different parts of the baby are growing and developing at different rates, one cannot assume that because a child is within the 'normal' height range for her age that she will be normal in all other respects.

The third main issue concerns the *relationship of genes and environment* during development, and their contribution to the variations we observe. Every child — with the exception of identical twins — has a unique set of genes at birth; every child — including identical twins — develops in a unique economic, social, and physical environment. The old debates about the relative contributions of *'nature'* or *'nurture'* used to assume that the genetic programme of the child simply unrolled during development to a greater or lesser extent depending on the environment. The metaphor was that of a pint jug. The pint was the full adult complement of height or intelligence or whatever, as determined by the genes. Depending on the environment, the jug would be more or less filled during development, but there was a clear limit — 'You can't get a quart into a pint pot'. A healthy environment would simply fill each child's jug to the limit given by the genes.

□ What is wrong with this argument?

■ What constitutes a healthy environment for a child with one set of genes is not necessarily the same for another. (For example, an environment containing the amino acid phenylalanine in the diet is unhealthy for a child with the gene defect resulting in phenylketonuria, but healthy for children without that particular genetic 'abnormality').*

*Phenylketonuria is discussed in Book IV, *The Biology of Health and Disease* Chapter 12.

The result is that one cannot separate out a fraction of a child's height or weight — or indeed any part of its behaviour — as consisting of such and such a percentage due to genes, and such and such a percentage due to the environment. A better metaphor than that of filling a pint jug is to view development as a bit like baking a cake: you start with flour, eggs, butter, sugar, milk and spices; you beat them and heat them together for a certain time. The resulting taste depends on all the ingredients and how they have been mixed and baked, but you can't say that such and such a percentage of the taste of the cake was due to the flour, such and such to the milk, and so forth. Cake baking and child development both involve *qualitative* change. Trying to disentangle the contribution of genes and environment when trying to decide whether a given child's growth and development is *normal* is a hazardous occupation. This is simply illustrated by considering an apparently straightforward case, that of growth in height.

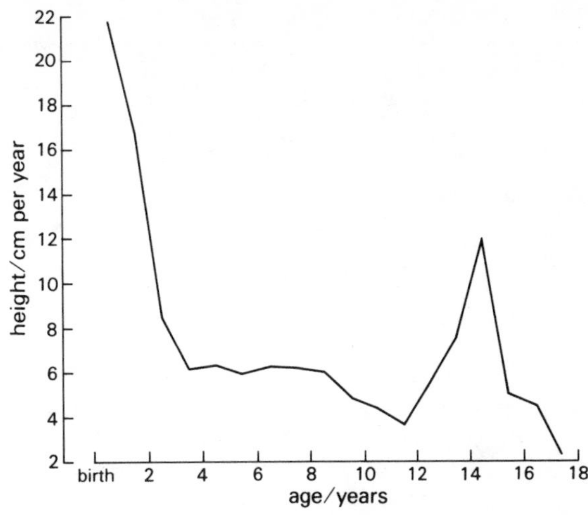

Figure 8.3 The velocity of growth in height in each year from birth to 18, showing that most height is gained in the first 2 years and that a second 'growth spurt' takes place during puberty. (Ebrahim, 1981, Figure 6.1, p.73)

Growth in height

Figure 8.2 plots height against age for a boy between birth and 18 years old. The graph is not a straight line, but is steepest between 0–2 and again between 13 and 15. The second graph (Figure 8.3) is calculated in a different way, and shows the amount that height increases over a series of fixed time intervals. This is called *height velocity*. This way of expressing the data shows more clearly the periods of rapid growth, one from birth into the toddler period and the other associated with puberty.

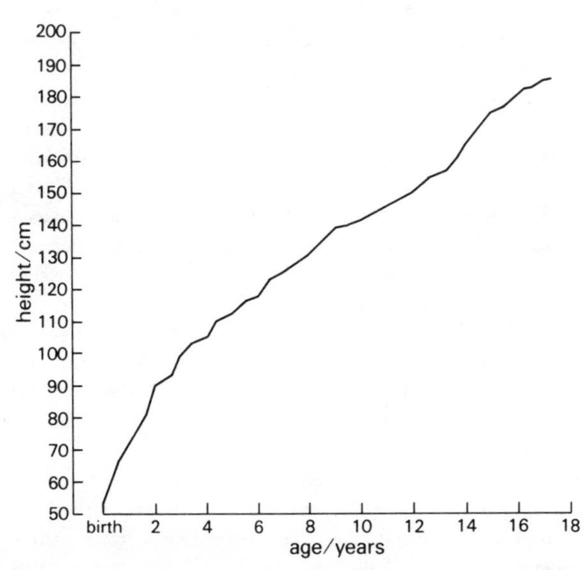

Figure 8.2 Average growth in height from birth to 18 years in human males. The gradient is steepest during periods when growth is fastest. (Ebrahim, 1981, Figure 6.1, p.73)

What do you think is the normal height of a five year old child? This question cannot be answered simply, if at all. We all know short and tall adults as well as fat and thin ones. Are they normal? How can we tell if a child is the normal height for her age? As a starting point, let us look at growth studies where a large group of children has been measured regularly, and a set of 'norms' has been produced for boys and girls.

□ What factors do you think are likely to limit growth in children?

■ You might have thought of infection or debilitating diseases, genetic or chromosomal abnormalities and diet. In addition, you may know that growth is under hormonal control.* In the absence of certain pituitary and thyroid hormones, dwarfism occurs; excess of pituitary growth hormone can result in gigantism.

Now look at the height curves given in Figures 8.4 and 8.5 (overleaf). Do not be put off by these complicated charts. They are interpreted as follows. For every 100 children of a specific age, the number written at the end of each curve represents the number of children out of 100 of that age whose height is below that measurement. Separate charts are required for boys and girls. For example, if we took 100

*This is discussed in Book IV, *The Biology of Health and Disease*, Chapter 6.

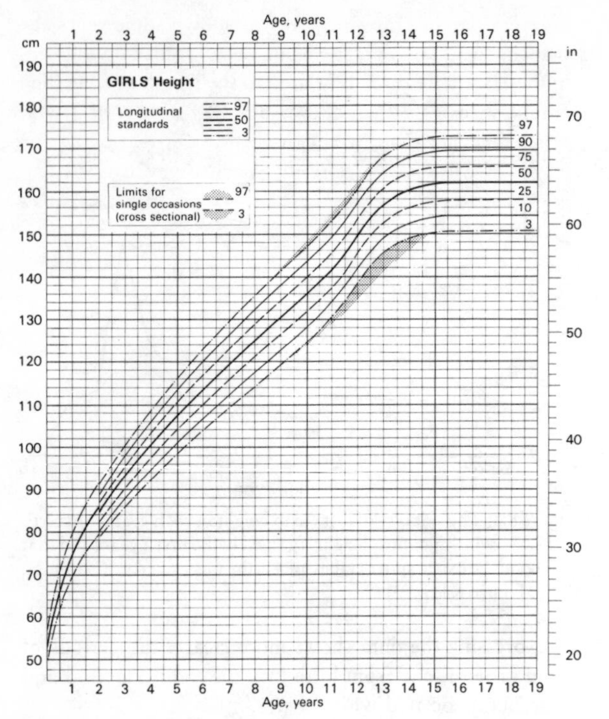

Figure 8.4 Standard height chart for girls aged 0–19 years. The range of growth that is considered medically normal is between the 3rd and 97th centile, but most children outside this range are simply short or tall for their age. (Tanner and Whitehouse, 1976, p.107)

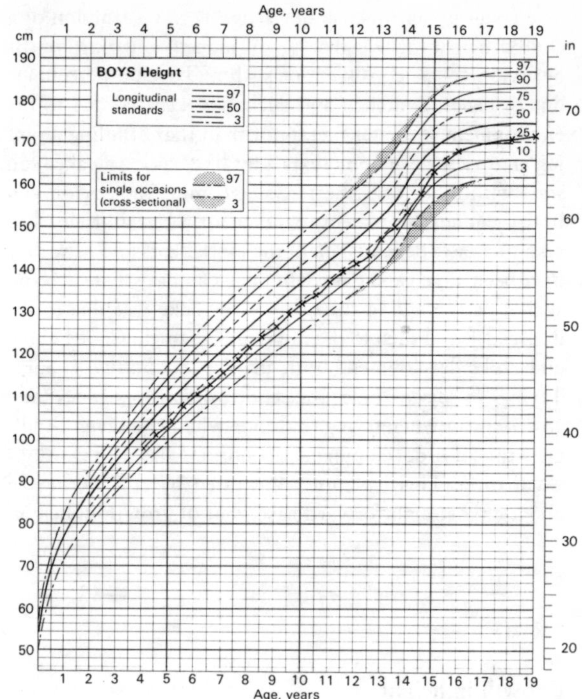

Figure 8.5 Standard height chart for boys aged 0–19 years. (Tanner and Whitehouse, 1976, p.107)

ten-year-old girls and lined them up in order of height, 90 of them would be smaller than 144 cms and 10 would be taller. Only 3 would be smaller than 124 cms. You can check this on the graph by finding the age of the child, in this case 10 years, running your eye along the vertical line at age 10 until you reach 124 cms. You will see that the intersection is on the curve marked '3'. Now run your eye further upwards vertically until you reach 144 cms; you will find that this intersection is on the curve marked 90. These curves are called *centiles*. Thus the 75th centile (for example) shows the height that 25 out of 100 boys or girls would *exceed* at a given age, and 75 out of 100 would be shorter than. Children between the 3rd and 97th centile are said to be of 'normal' height. Thus 3 out of 100 children would be classified, medically, as smaller than normal and 3 out of 100 as taller than normal.

□ What is the range of normal height (3rd and 97th centile) for a boy of 2 and a girl of 5?

■ For 2-year-old boys, the 3rd centile intersects at 80 cms, and the 97th at 92 cms; the range of 'normal' height specified by these parameters for 5-year-old girls is between 98 cms and 116 cms.

Children whose heights are below the third centile are usually referred for a medical opinion, although most are medically quite normal, just small. For example, a community study in Newcastle carried out by K.A. Lacey and J.M. Parkin in 1974 showed that only 16 out of 98 children below the third centile for height had obvious medical problems.

These charts are also useful for showing whether a child's height has undergone abnormal acceleration or deceleration. Each child tends to grow along a particular centile, at least after eighteen months of age or so. Thus a child whose height falls on the 7th centile at 3 and 4 years of age is likely to have a height near that centile when she is 10 years old. After the first 18 months of age, the crossing or more than one centile is usually held to indicate that investigation of medical, hormonal, nutritional, or social problems is needed. Similar charts are available for weight, head circumference and other physical measurements, and are interpreted in just the same way as we have illustrated for height.

We have, so far, treated 'normality' from a biological and medical viewpoint, but a child who is within the biologically normal range may nevertheless have serious social problems. Tall girls and small boys, particularly around the growth spurt during puberty when height and sexual development show such great individual variations, often suffer because of socially-determined attitudes to them — an issue of even more importance to adolescents, and one which is discussed in Chapter 10. You can probably think of children you know who have problems because their height or weight is not what is expected of them by their parents or friends. But why is there such variation between individuals?

Factors affecting height

□ What factors might be involved in determining the final height reached by an 18 year old?

■ Your list should have included sex, genetic differences, social-class factors, nutrition and disease as possible variables.

We can consider each of these in turn.

Sex

The range of heights for men and for boys tends to be higher than that for women and girls. That is not to say, of course, that all boys aged 7 years are taller than all girls aged 7. It simply means that the average (mean) height is greater for boys, and so is the range. For example, look back at Figures 8.4 and 8.5 and compare centiles for 8 year old boys and girls. Why should this difference occur? In many species, not only humans, males are different in size from females; often the males are bigger, sometimes the females. These differences reflect underlying genetic differences between the sexes, but, as you will see for humans, neither the absolute average height nor the differences between boys and girls are fixed, but vary over time. Differences in height between adult men and women in industrial countries like Britain were greater in the nineteenth century than now — in this, as in other measures of 'physical' growth and strength, such as sporting performance, females are steadily catching up with males.

Genetic differences

Apart from differences between males and females, height tends to 'run in families'. A person's height *tends* to be distributed around the 'mid-parent' height — that is, the height of the father, plus the height of the mother, divided by two. But one can also ask whether average heights differ between populations, such as *ethnic groups*.* Most people would agree that the pygmies are small people, the Chinese and Japanese are also small, while the Scandinavians are tall.

But how 'fixed' are such differences? A good population in which to study this question is the USA, where records have been kept over many decades and the population includes successive generations of immigrants from many different parts of the world. It was shown some years ago that changes in the average height of children of immigrants to the USA were directly related to the length of time their parents had lived there. For example, children of Jewish origin born in Europe were consistently shorter than the US mean, whereas those born 10 years after their parents' arrival were consistently above the mean. The same is true for children of Sicilian parentage.

Now look at Figure 8.6 which shows the heights of three groups of Japanese boys; two groups born in Japan and the other in the USA, in 1900, 1952 and 1957.

□ What can you say about the height of Japanese boys born in the USA compared with those born in Japan during the 1950s?

■ American-born Japanese are taller.

□ Now compare Japanese boys born in 1900 and 1952 in Japan.

■ The Japanese boys born in 1952 are taller than their counterparts half a century earlier.

□ How might this help to explain the differences in height between Japanese and American children?

■ It would indicate that the differences are unlikely to be due solely to a simple genetic difference between the two populations.

So we need to look for other explanations. Obviously the period 1900–1950 was one of great social change and economic growth in Japan, but also, in the 1950s at any rate, California was still a much richer society than Japan. But are these social differences enough to account for the differences in height? A comparison of two ethnically identical groups in Rwanda, Africa, showed very clearly

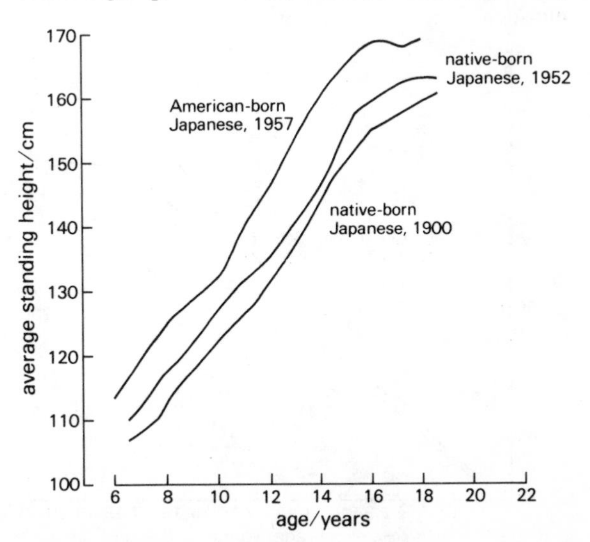

Figure 8.6 Average standing height of Japanese boys, comparing native-born Japanese in 1900 and 1952, with American-born Japanese in 1957. (Gruelich, 1958, p.515)

*A discussion of the biological and social definitions of 'race' and ethnicity is contained in Book I, *Studying Health and Disease*, Chapter 11.

that children in better social and economic conditions were taller. Similarly there is evidence from Nigeria, that children of elite Nigerians may be of greater average height than those of Europeans, although the 'average' height of Nigerian children is well below that.

□ What do these studies imply?

■ The implication is that better nutrition and social conditions have a profound effect on growth, and that what are sometimes assumed to be 'genetic' differences leading to shorter children may in fact be related to poverty and poor nutrition.

Social class

As far back historically as there are reliable measures, clear social-class differences in height have been found, mean heights tending to decline with social class. In a classic study in 1936, the nutritionist John Boyd Orr showed that in 1883 boys from the professional classes had been on average a striking 8.4 inches taller than those from the working class (see Figure 8.7.) He also showed that, whereas heights for all classes had risen by the 1930s, the class difference was still apparent. Studies of pregnant women in the 1930s, and more recently in the National Child Development Study (1958), showed that class differences in height persist. (By contrast, in Sweden, a society with a much more extensive welfare state than in the UK, class differences in height have now disappeared.)

What could explain these persistent class differences in height in Britain? The very fact that they have changed over time in England and have disappeared in Sweden, makes it reasonably likely that it is not *genetic* factors which are involved. The two obvious alternatives are disease and nutrition.

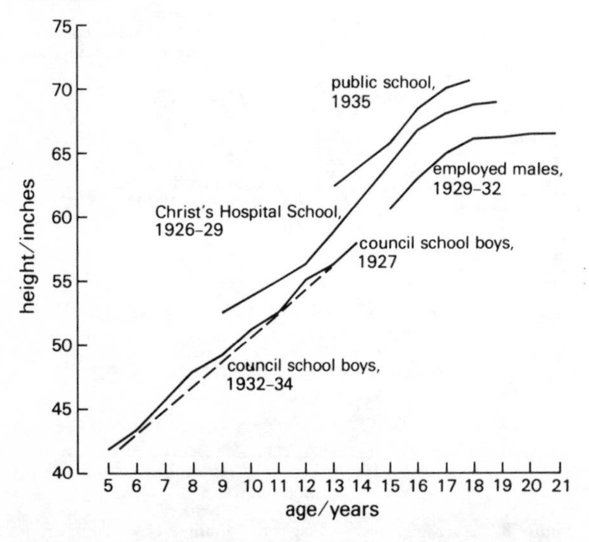

Figure 8.7 Average standing height of boys and young men from different social backgrounds in the 1920s and 1930s. (Orr, 1936)

Disease and nutrition

Apart from specific disease factors, like chromosomal or hormonally caused disorders, chronic or recurrent childhood diseases can impede normal growth. For example, in developing countries children with recurrent illnesses (in particular diarrhoea and infections) are below average height (though they are likely also to be suffering from lack of food). When we look at British children, we have suggested that those below the 3rd centile for height for age may show other medical problems, but in the Newcastle community study mentioned earlier, of 98 children below the 3rd centile, only 16 had definable problems of illness or hormonal deficiences. The other 82 children were 'normal', but short. This points to the importance of *nutrition*.

Families in social class V are poorer than those in social class I. In Third World countries today (or in the UK during the Industrial Revolution), the difference between rich and poor means the difference between life and death, between health and disease, and the effect of poor nutrition resulting from poverty on children's growth is clear. Malnourished children do not grow properly.

Severe forms of malnutrition, such as we see on Oxfam posters showing the effects of famine, occur and are dramatic. If food shortage is *acute* then the child becomes thin and wasted. But if food shortage occurs over a long period and is less severe, the child appears to be normal until he or she is seen alongside a well-nourished child of the same age (Figures 8.8a and 8.8b). The stunting effect of chronic food shortage on height is startling.

There seems to be little doubt from studies of dietary intake and growth that poverty leads to poorer food intake, both in quality and quantity.* The evidence from Third World countries, in particular, shows that growth throughout childhood improves as nutrition improves. However, it should already have occurred to you that this account, which seems to see nutrition as an isolated factor, is too simple.

□ Why might this explanation be inadequate?

■ If nutrition is being improved, it is likely that other things in the society, from health care to housing, water supply to family income are also improving. We cannot rule out that these factors are involved in a complex interaction.

However, an indication of the importance of nutrition itself comes from the observation that, especially in poor families, first-born children tend to be taller than those born later, a difference which cannot be accounted for by genetics, but could be explained if the larger the family, the less food there was to go round (see Figure 8.9).

*Poverty, nutrition and the distribution of disease are discussed in more detail in Book III, *The Health of Nations*, Chapter 7.

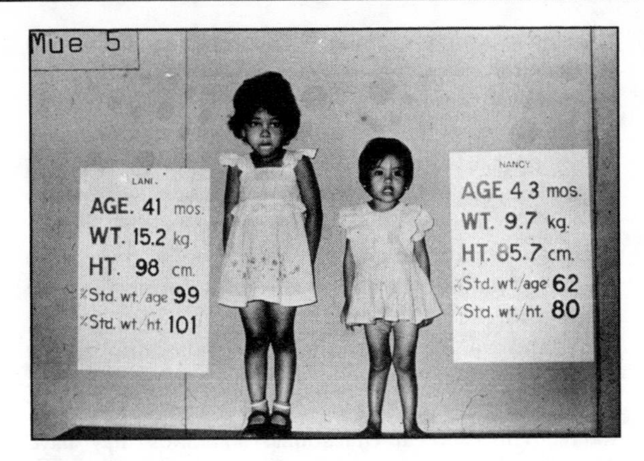

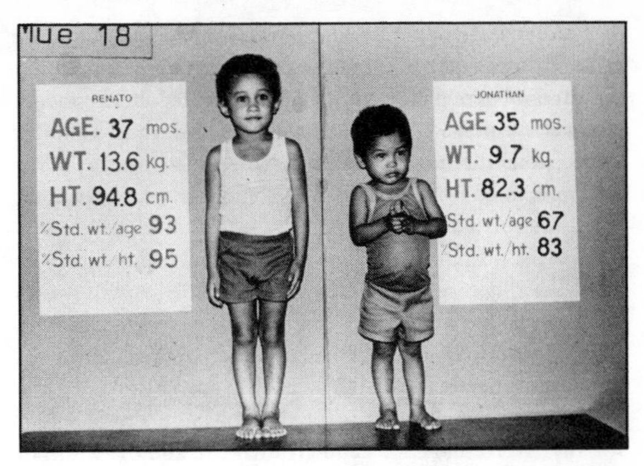

Figure 8.8 Growth of malnourished and well-nourished urban children of similar ages in the Phillipines. (**a**) Lani, on the left, is 99 per cent of the standard weight of a child of her age, and 101 per cent of the standard weight of a child of her height. Nancy, on the right, is only 62 per cent of standard weight for age and 80 per cent of standard weight for height.

(**b**) Renato, on the left, is 93 per cent of standard weight for age and 95 per cent of standard weight for height. Jonathan, on the right, is 67 per cent of standard weight for age and 83 per cent of standard weight for height. (Photographs courtesy of Teaching Aids at Low Cost (TALC) P.O. Box 49, St. Albans. Details of TALC materials sent free on request.)

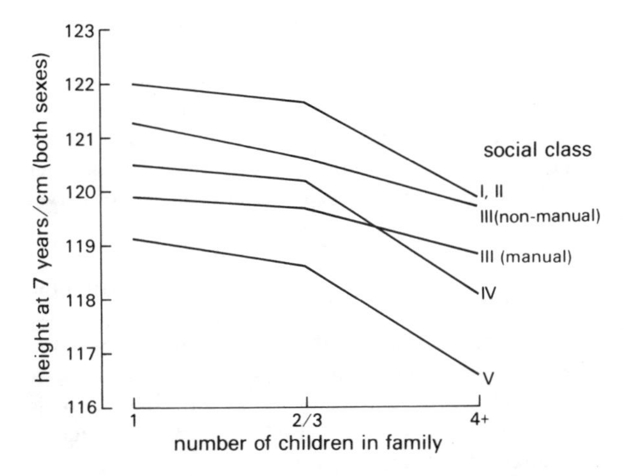

Figure 8.9 Height of British children (sexes combined) at 7 years according to the number of children in the family and socio-economic class. (Data from National Child Development Study, 1965, graph redrawn from Tanner, 1978, Figure 49, p.152)

But there are yet more subtle factors than biology and social structure at play, as everyone who has had much to do with children might suspect. Even adequately fed children may 'fail to thrive' in an environment in which they are not given love and attention. Their *personal history* affects their growth and development. One of the most striking examples of this comes from a study in a German orphanage by E.M. Widdowson in 1948 (published in 1951) (see Figure 8.10). The children were divided into two groups, A and B. Group B children were given dietary supplements that increased their energy intake by 20 per cent and their growth was compared with that of the children in Group A over a 6 month period. Contrary to expectations, Group B children showed *inferior* growth. When the reasons for this were studied, it was found that at the same time as the nutritional supplement study was begun, the Group B children were put into the charge of a strict nurse, Frl. Schwarz, who had favourites. The eight favourites gained the most weight

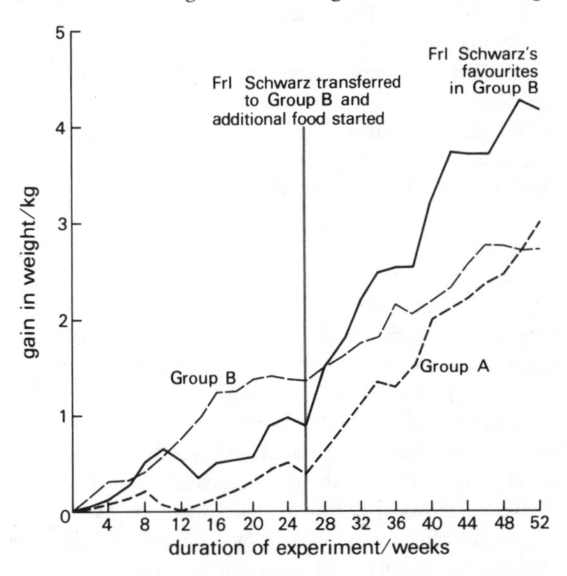

Figure 8.10 Average gain in weight of children from a German orphanage in 1948. Group A children received the normal orphanage diet whereas Group B children received additional food and vitamins. Weight gain for eight children in Group B who were 'favourites' of the nurse in charge is plotted separately. Frl. Schwartz had been in charge of Group A children *before* the experiment began. (Widdowson, 1951, p.1317).

— more than Group A children — but the remainder of the children in Group B gained less weight than the happier children in Group A, even though Group A children were less well nourished. Some other studies have shown similar effects, but the interpretation is still controversial; some researchers have concluded that the differences in weight gain was related to poor appetites in the children, though this leaves unstated the reasons for the poor appetite.

What this case study of factors affecting growth shows is that even for an easily determined measure, like height, the reasons why any particular child, or population of children, reaches the heights it does are complex. Thus trying to determine what is for example, a 'normal' height for any given child is exceedingly difficult, and the width of the accepted range of normality (children between the 3rd and the 97th centile) reflects this. When we come to study more complex features of development, such as skills and abilities, we must consider ourselves fortunate if we are able to describe the phenomena relatively unambiguously; to disentangle the multiple interactions that influence such development is beyond the scope of present-day biological and social sciences.

Development of skills and abilities

Growing up involves learning to act upon and modify the world around one. The child must learn to understand the vast range of *sensory information* with which she is bombarded — sounds, sights, touches, tastes and smells. She must also learn to distinguish desirable from undesirable outcomes of her actions, to communicate with others, and she must develop her own sense of personal identity, of selfhood. A multitude of competing theories attempt to describe these processes; some — the various psychoanalytic theories — emphasise conscious and unconscious processes of emotional growth; others concentrate on *cognitive development*, how the child develops concepts, 'maps in the mind' of the external world, so as to be able to influence it. In this chapter we can do no more than describe some of the features of this development, and, in doing so, try to ask how closely one can relate changes in behaviour, in capacity to act on the world, with changes in the growing child's biology.

A child grows up through a long period of dependence in a world which is so shaped by language, culture and economic forces, that to disentangle these factors involves techniques which make the study of human development a very special exercise. Indeed this long period of dependence in the human during development is a unique evolutionary development. This dependency in childhood allows enormous amounts of time for learning the very complex skills of social interaction which are the unique features of the human condition, and which may have contributed to its evolutionary success.

However, some social anthropologists have argued that this period of dependency has been extended in modern times by the introduction of compulsory education. Nowadays, one of the ways in which we distinguish adults from children is by their level of attainment of certain educational goals — most 8 year olds cannot read and write as well as most 18 year olds. The goals we now set take many years to achieve. In the past, this separation between adults and children in a mainly illiterate population did not exist and children reached the average adult standard of literacy for the time at a much earlier age than they do today. This shift in educational standards may have contributed to the 'invention of childhood' which we discussed in the previous chapter.

In biological terms, however, children are not merely 'small adults'. One problem in understanding the nature of development in childhood is that the child has to do two quite different types of thing simultaneously. It is *both* becoming an adult *and* surviving at being a child. Now the activities needed for these two states are quite distinct.

To take obvious examples, at birth a child has a rooting reflex — that is, she will spontaneously suckle at an appropriate object like a nipple or even a finger (Figure 8.11). Later in her development, she will not suckle but chew. But suckling involves quite different sets of nerves and muscular movements from chewing. A suckling baby is not practising suckling in order to learn how to chew, but in order to exist as a baby. Similarly, a child learns to crawl before she walks, but crawling is not just 'practice' walking. On the other hand, as a child begins to speak she is clearly rehearsing and practising communication skills which will increase with age. So the question of which skills are for the here-and-now and which are aimed at future development, is never straightforward.

However, with these provisos about the difficulty of the task, we shall record some of the stages through which developing children pass. A newborn baby lies horizontally unless held. During her first year of life she learns to sit upright and during the next years acquires different paces and physical skills, such as running, stopping, climbing, jumping, swimming and so on. A newborn baby can only open and close her hand automatically, but by the end of the first year of life she can pick up tiny objects neatly, transfer them from one hand to the other, mould her hands around them, poke her index finger into the parts that interest her, and explore the object with her hands. During the next few years she acquires the ability to hold objects more precisely and to use her hands skilfully. For example, a four or five month old baby will try to pick up an object by swiping at it with both hands, often transmitting her excitement to her whole body. Contrast this with the

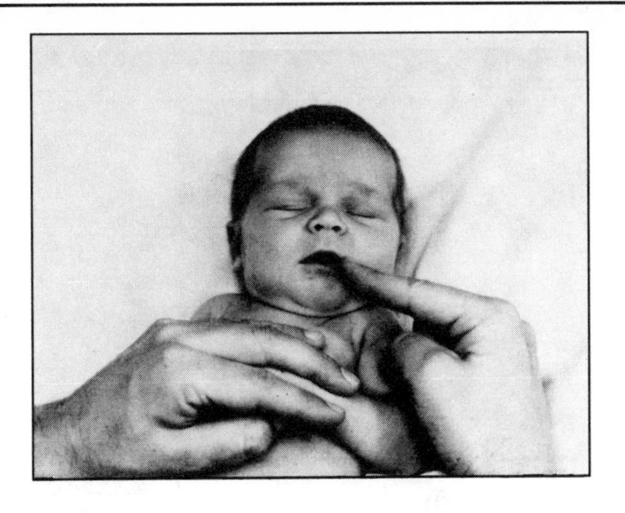

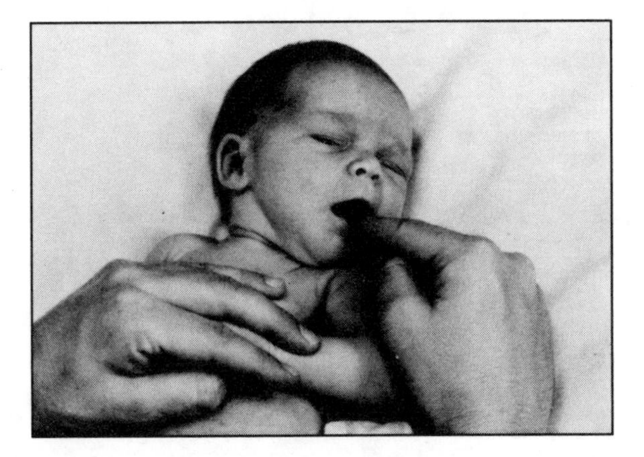

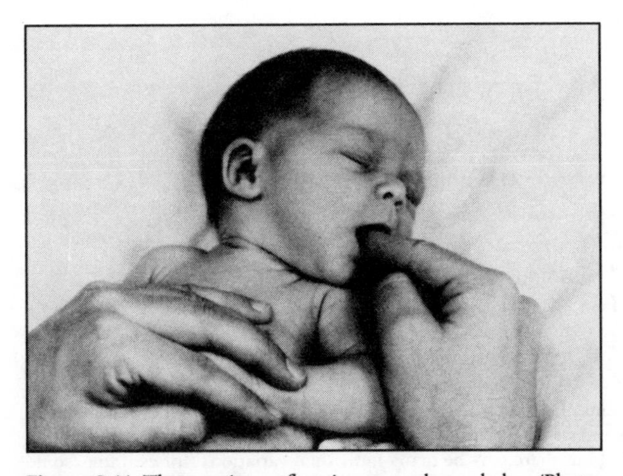

Figure 8.11 The rooting reflex in a newborn baby (Photo: Professor H.F.R. Prechtl)

efficient way a 5 or 6 year old uses a pencil to draw a very small circle.

How far can a child's acquisition of these skills be related to the development of the body organ most concerned with their coordination — the brain? Nerve cells in different parts of the brain mature and make connections with one another and with the sensory inputs and motor outputs, at different times after birth. In particular, there is increasing 'control' over body processes by the 'highest' region of the brain, the cerebral cortex, so that the *primitive reflexes* (like the grasp reflex) which the month old baby shows, disappear, to be replaced by more conscious, coordinated holding of objects. Even a child of a few days old can turn her head towards faces and sounds. By 3 months she can focus her eyes on an object and move her hands towards it, and can be soothed by a familiar voice. During this time, the regions of the brain responsible for coordination of hand and eye and for the accurate recognition of sounds are beginning to develop.

Activity in the nervous system which enables us to act on the outside world is known as *motor activity*. Information about the world around us is gathered in and interpreted by *sensory activity*. Meaningful behaviour involves complex interactions between the two. The skills developed by young children involve relatively straightforward sequences of *sensori-motor activities*, although they vary with the individual child and her circumstances: speech is advanced in some, walking retarded in others, and so forth. There are, as we said at the beginning of this chapter, many developmental paths to a final maturity. However, the *sequence* in which a normal child acquires these skills is fairly predictable ('you must learn to walk before you can run') and it is possible to think of this development proceeding in stages. But for the reasons we indicated at the beginning of this chapter, you should not see these stages as proceeding in a mechanical, clockwork way. Look at Figure 8.12 (overleaf). The sketches give you a few 'stills' from what is obviously a 'movie' of a developmental sequence. If you have children of your own or have watched other people's children, you will realise that the ages mentioned are only approximations.

Development of complex motor skills is obviously dependent on the maturation of body systems, the growth of connections from nerve cells in the brain to control muscle movement, and the growth of these muscle systems themselves. Differences in physical skills naturally emerge between children, but if a child falls *very* far behind in the acquisition of these skills it may indicate a subtle deficiency — a retardation due perhaps to failure in brain development but affected too by cultural variables, such as play and interaction with grown-ups in the child's world.

Play is a crucial feature of childhood development. All children play, as do the young of other mammals.

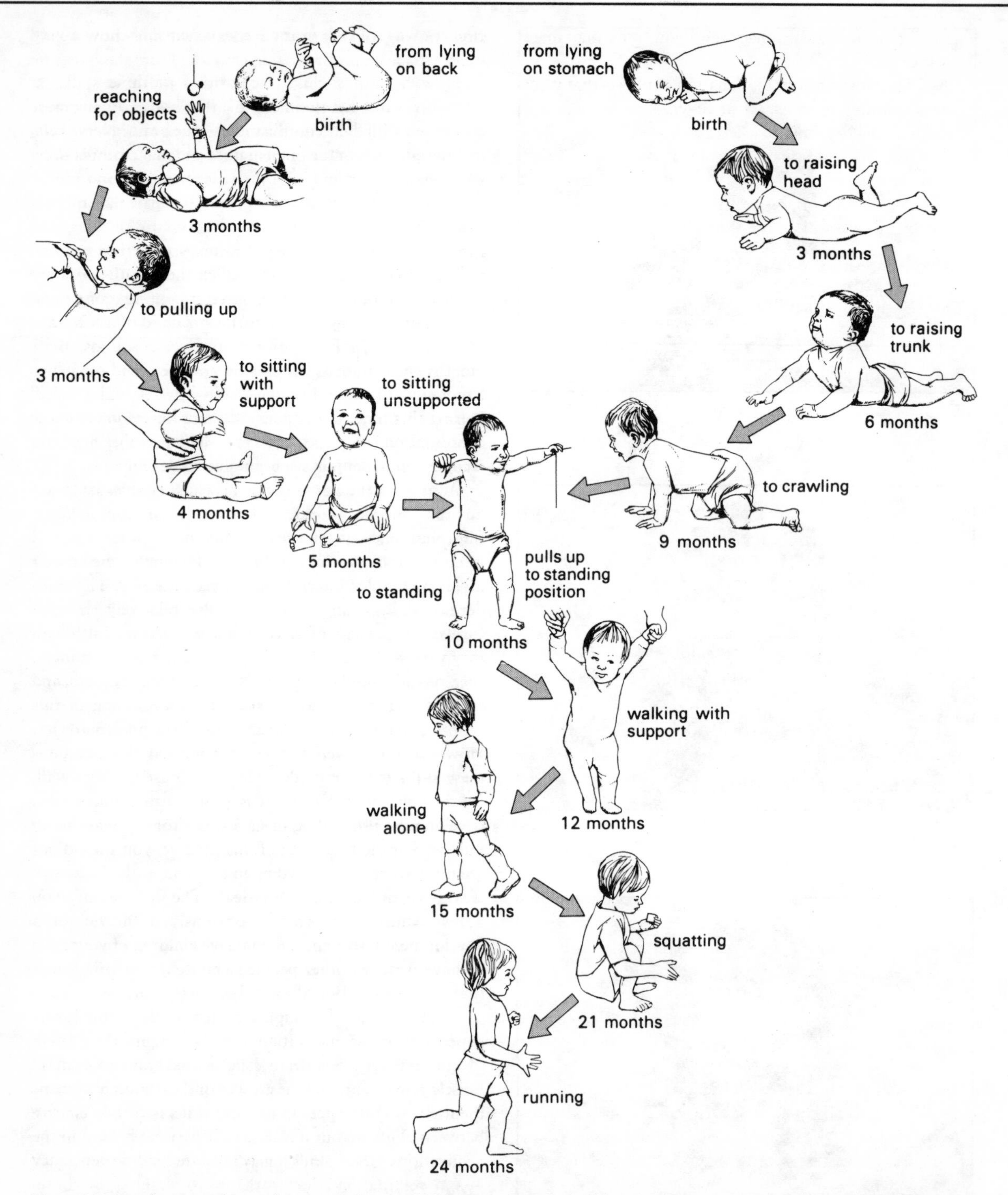

Figure 8.12 Development of strength and co-ordination in the movements of a child from birth to 2 years (known as 'motor development'). Notice that (i) the process is one of continuous development, not steps and stages; (ii) the sequence is the same for all children (for example, head control always comes before sitting, sitting before crawling, etc.) but there may be many individual variations (for example, some babies do not crawl but progress straight to walking); and (iii) the age at which a particular motor skill is achieved varies within certain limits. (Illustration designed by Dr Pam Zinkin, Institute of Child Health)

□ What biological function do you think play might serve?

■ The most obvious explanation of play is that it acts as a continuous *rehearsal* or practice by the infant of skills that will be needed in adult life. A kitten playing with a ball of wool can be regarded as practising hunting for mice. A human child's playing is practice in communicating with other humans (the social environment) and in manipulating the physical environment.

But of course, our question begs another: the assumption that all behaviour we can observe must promote the biological well-being of the organism. Although this is a fundamental premise of certain evolutionary theories, it is not unanimously accepted as true.

Failure to play and communicate with others in childhood is often taken as a sign of some biological and/or psychological damage (in a rare, acute form, this withdrawal of the child from communication is called autism). Differences soon begin to emerge in play between male and female children. For instance, in those cultures that have been studied, boys indulge more in what is called *'rough-and-tumble' play* than girls. Among any given class and ethnic group, by the age of 3 years boys are already better at kicking balls than girls. Is this because boys have an inherently better ability to kick? Or is it simply because we are more likely to encourage a boy to kick a ball than we are a girl? Girls around this age are better at catching, and boys at throwing.

□ Why? Suggest two contrasting explanations for these gender differences.

■ The two contrasting explanations might be that:

(a) The differences depend on underlying biological differences between the sexes: for instance, boys have relatively more of the hormone testosterone than girls, and testosterone may be involved in 'aggressive' behaviour like rough-and-tumble play. On this analysis, it is 'natural' for the differences to emerge.

(b) The differences are culturally imposed; parents and other adults expect and encourage boys to play in one type of way, girls in another. Boys are *supposed* to like football, whereas girls should prefer playing with skipping ropes.

These issues are far from resolved, and indeed it is probably true that they cannot be, for they are inextricably intertwined. There is no good evidence that biological *sex differences* determine the observed social differences in behaviour between *genders* in humans. It is interesting, however, that sex differences in play behaviour (such as rough-and-tumble play) also occur in non-human primates, like monkeys. But rough-and-tumble play is a label the observer gives to particular types of behaviour, whether observed in monkeys or children, and certainly how a child behaves is profoundly modified by the culture she grows up in.

As an example of some of the difficulties in sorting these issues out, consider the following examples of *cultural differences* in the development of skills. In a study in West London carried out by C.A. Cox, P.M. Zinkin and M.F.J. Grimsley in 1977, it was found that on a simple test (picking up a small block from a table) 6 month-old babies of mothers from the Indian sub-continent performed less well than the children of white ('Caucasian') origin. On the other hand, babies of African origin have been shown to have better head and back control at birth, to sit, walk and be more visually alert earlier than white children. So are there racial differences in development? In fact, such differences are probably to do with the way that mothers treat their children. The Asian mothers were more likely to be at work during the day, and less likely to sit and play with their children. When they were encouraged to do so, the differences in manipulation skills disappeared within 1 to 3 months. Similarly, a study by K.F. Holt, published in 1960, showed that American babies tended to crawl, and be about 2 months ahead of British babies in aspects of motor development while lying prone (face-down). British babies, by contrast, were more advanced in hand use. The difference could be accounted for by the fact that at the time these comparisons were made in the 1950s, it was the fashion for British babies to be placed lying in the cot on their backs, whereas American babies were placed on their fronts. Thus the latter were more likely to practise raising their heads, whereas British babies could practice hand movements more easily.

Another study in Kenya showed that babies in rural areas sat up before town babies. It appeared that from an early age rural babies were very actively encouraged to sit; they were almost always in contact with their mothers, being carried in a sitting position, and holes were dug in the sand for them to sit up in. The town babies were treated in the same way as British babies, and their average age of sitting was in between that of the rural Kenyan and British babies. This suggests that both ethnic and cultural (handling) influences affect this simple aspect of motor development.

Other studies have shown social-class differences in the development of motor skills from as early as 6 months. (One of the reasons for this early difference may be that mothers with a professional background are more likely, deliberately or not, to play with their children appropriately for 'passing' developmental tests.)

Beyond the first two years of age, relationships between biological changes, such as those of brain development and the development of skills, are less easy to map. However, it is possible to say that the nervous pathways, particularly of the 'highest' regions of the cortex, go on developing and becoming richer and more complex partly, if not entirely, as a *result* of experience. (One of the most interesting of findings from experimental animals is that if they are reared in a 'rich' environment, with plenty of 'toys', social interactions, training and handling by the experimenter, their brains get bigger and more connections between nerve cells are made. If this is true for children as well — and it seems reasonable — the implication would be that the more they were cuddled, played with and taught, the bigger and better their brains would get!)

As the child develops over the next few years of life, she begins to achieve a measure of capacity to understand, control and recognise the limits of her control over the world. It is possible to think of these later changes also taking place in stages. To begin with the child starts to use picture images as symbols to replace real things — the objects which earlier filled her universe — and *language*, as a system of verbal symbols which 'stand for' objects, begins.

□ What do you think is the main difference between picture images and language?

■ While images may be 'internal symbols', meaningful only to the child, language is the most common means of achieving communication with others. Language, unlike images, is non-representative — a crude sketch of a bird looks something like the 'real thing', but the sound made when we speak the word *bird* bears no direct relationship to the creature, it is purely conceptual.

There is much debate in the literature of psychology and biology about the origins of language; the extent to which the capacity to speak is 'wired in' to the individual, and the extent to which it is learned by trial and error (the two positions are held in their most extreme form by Harvard linguistic philosopher Naom Chomsky and behaviourist B.F. Skinner, respectively) but we can do no more than mention this issue in passing here. What is true is that all children, in whatever culture, seem to begin speaking (using language) at about the same age, even though the languages are of course widely different.

In any event, language is the basis for the uniquely human capacities of abstract thought and analysis. As the child develops towards puberty, she becomes more adept at using language to interpret and discover rules about the world. For example, she begins to use concepts such as *more* and *less*, *longer* and *shorter*, *heavier* and *lighter*, and perform simple operations which relate weight, height, and so forth, in a logical manner. As time goes on, these semi-abstract concepts can be manipulated in more sophisticated ways; experiments, in the genuine scientific sense of the word, can be made.

The fact that children acquire these complex skills in widely differing environments is a tribute to one of the most conspicuous features of the biology of the child — a capacity known as *plasticity*.* This refers to the relative ease with which a child's biology can respond to, adapt or recover from injury or other forms of damage from, for example, drugs or deprivation. Childhood malnutrition can result in huge losses in body weight and retardation in growth, and yet restoration of the child to an adequate diet *can* result in an apparently perfect 'catch-up'. (There are many routes to the ultimate adult destination.) But this plasticity is not infinite. For example, exposure to agents such as thalidomide or X-rays during key stages of pregnancy can produce lasting damage. Similarly, there are periods of particular vulnerability during the development of the child once she has left the sheltered environment of the womb. Because the brain grows so dramatically over the first year or so of life, the effects of acute starvation occurring in this period — or of other more specific poisons like environmental lead — are more dramatic than they would be later, and sometimes irreversible.

In the next chapter we shall focus on two sharply contrasted situations in which a child's physical or emotional development may be at risk: first, the complex circumstances that make a child more likely to suffer an accidental injury or poisoning. Second, we shall look at the controversial question of whether a child's emotional development is adversely affected in the long term by certain common features of modern family life, e.g. parents who divorce, or a mother who goes out to work. As you study Chapter 9, bear in mind the complexities of assessing 'normal' development that we have discussed here. In summary, they are that growth is uneven; it may take one of many paths — though not *any* path — to a given end-point; there are problems in unravelling the relationship of genes to environment during development, and children have to survive as children while growing into adults. These problems are confounded by the difficulties of studying such a complex process as human development in a rigorous scientific manner.

*This is discussed in Book IV, *The Biology of Health and Disease*, Chapter 6.

Objectives for Chapter 8

When you have studied this chapter, you should be able to:

8.1 Describe the major conceptual problems identified in the text in relation to interpreting the phenomena of growth and development in childhood.

8.2 Discuss the influence of sex, ethnicity, class, disease and nutrition in the attainment of adult height and use these variables to discuss the difficulty of assessing 'normal' growth.

Questions for Chapter 8

1 (*Objective 8.1*) Imagine that a study of English children's mathematical ability shows that for children matched for socioeconomic class in the 7 to 9 year age-group there are no differences in average test scores between boys and girls. In a group of 15 year olds tested at the same time, however, boys perform significantly better than girls. What can you conclude about sex differences in mathematical ability from these data?

2 (*Objective 8.2*) A school doctor recording the heights of children notes a 7 year old girl with a height of 110 cm. What height might the doctor expect her to be at the age of 9? (Use the height chart in Figure 8.4.) When the girl was measured at the age of 9, she was 114 cm high. Should the doctor be concerned, and what explanation for this apparent failure to grow might be offered?

9

Trauma in childhood: counting the cost

This chapter examines two aspects of children's health: childhood accidents, and the effects of maternal employment and parental divorce on the wellbeing of children. The distribution of adverse effects on health is not evenly spread across the population, and various sorts of explanation for this are discussed. You may find it helpful to look back at Book III, *The Health of Nations*, Chapters 9–11, which analysed the distribution of ill-health among adults in the UK from a number of different perspectives.

As you read in the previous chapter, the human child remains dependent on adult care and protection for much longer than the young of any other species. It takes time to develop the immensely subtle and complex circuits of nerves and muscles which enable the development of skilled, co-ordinated movements, accurate judgements and communication in language. Below the age of about 7 years, a child left to fend for herself in even the mildest of environments would be unable to feed herself adequately, find shelter or avoid hazards. In most parts of the world children remain dependent on adults for some aspect of their survival until they are at least 10–12 years old.

Traumas that occur during this long period of vulnerability cause great concern to parents, child-health specialists, policy makers and politicians, because they may have lasting repercussions on a person's life. Self-evidently a child who suffers an injury (be it physical, mental or both) must live with the consequences for a very long time. It may interfere with their education, job prospects, relationships, leisure activities and so forth. If the trauma is severe enough to cause death, then the years of life lost are many, even though in percentage terms deaths among children are few.

In this chapter we shall present two case studies of possibly traumatic events that are relatively common among British children: first, *accidental injury and poisoning*, and second, *aspects of family life* that are commonly held to be damaging to childrens' development, namely maternal employment and parental divorce.

□ In what major way are these two categories of 'trauma' different?

■ There is no dispute about the physical harm caused to a child that has been injured or poisoned, whereas there has been much debate about the long-term effects on children whose mother has a job outside the home, or whose parents divorce.

□ In what way might explanations for accidental injuries to children be concerned with the circumstances of family life?

■ The emotional and material circumstances experienced by a family may affect the likelihood of a child sustaining an accident.

Accidents

Accidents are the commonest cause of death among children of either sex between the age of 1 and 15 years. Among males they remain at the top of the league of fatalities until the middle 30s (as you will see in Chapter 10). Every year about 1 000 children die in an accident in the UK and thousands more are injured, some permanently. Data on non-fatal injuries are difficult to come by, but some idea can be gained from the estimate that 128 000 children aged between 1 and 14 years were admitted to hospital in 1977 following an accident.* However, the risk of suffering an accident is unevenly distributed across all children: we shall examine the details of this distribution and gradually tease out alternative explanations for the patterns that emerge.

The distribution of childhood accidents

An important dimension of the *unequal distribution of childhood accidents* is the child's age; younger children are more likely to suffer a fatal accident than older ones, as Figure 9.1 shows.

- □ What sort of explanation could you offer for this?
- ■ The explanation is a *biological* one, in that the younger the child, the less likely it is that he or she will be able to judge the speed of a car, know that lakes and ponds are dangerous, understand what 'poisonous' means, etc. Younger children may also be less robust than older ones and so more likely to die from their injuries.

Table 9.1 sheds more light on this by breaking down deaths from injury into different categories and age groups.

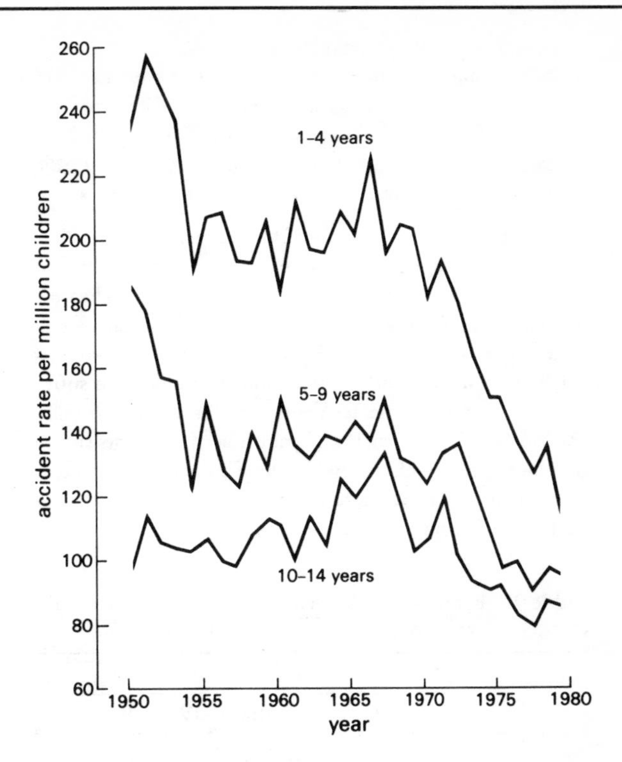

Figure 9.1 Accidental deaths in childhood: rates per million children aged 1–4, 5–9 and 10–14 years. England and Wales 1950–79. (Office of Health Economics, 1981)

The commonest cause of death in the two youngest age-groups is a motor vehicle collision with a child pedestrian. Rates for 5 to 9 year olds are higher than for older *and* younger children.

Table 9.1 Causes of death among children aged 1–14 years from accidents and violence in England and Wales, 1968–74

	Total	Age-group/percentages 1–4	5–9	10–14
all accidents	93.8	91.9	96.1	94.2
all violence	6.2	8.1	3.9	5.8
Major types of accident				
motor vehicle collision with child pedestrian	33.6	26.2	46.8	27.6
other motor vehicle and transport accidents	16.7	8.3	15.4	31.6
fires	8.3	14.4	5.7	2.3
accidental poisoning	2.5	4.1	0.9	2.1
falls	5.7	6.5	4.2	6.6

(Data from MacFarlane and Fox, 1978, Table 4)

*Data from the Hospital In-patient Enquiry (quoted in Office of Health Economics, 1981).

□ How would you explain this?

■ Younger children are less likely to be near a road without adult supervision, whereas older children are better able to judge the speed of traffic (but note that 10 to 14 year olds fare worst in other types of traffic accident, particularly involving child cyclists).

The next greatest hazards to children aged 1 to 4 are fires and drowning, again because small children cannot comprehend the dangers of, say, matches, paraffin heaters or deep water as accurately as older children. Small children are also more likely to swallow poisonous substances inadvertently, but are much less likely to suffer in other sorts of traffic accidents, such as where the child was riding a bicycle. So, the distribution of accidents shows that biological development has some influence on accident rates. Table 9.2 shows two other dimensions of inequality that emerge from the patterns of accidents.

Table 9.2 Fatal accidents in childhood by sex and social class, 1–14 years olds (rates per 100 000 population)

	Social class of father						
	I	II	IIIN	IIIM	IV	V	all
Boys	25.8	39	44.5	56.3	66.2	122	58.6
Girls	18.8	19	21.4	24.4	35.1	63.1	29.4

(Data from OPCS, 1978, in the Black Report, DHSS, 1980, Table 6.7, p. 175)

□ What does this table reveal?

■ Boys are (on average) twice as likely as girls to have an accident; this difference is seen in all social classes except I, where the difference is much smaller. This fits in with research showing that boys indulge in more 'rough and tumble' play (Chapter 8). However, much steeper gradients are seen across the social classes: in effect, the risk of dying from an accident is almost 5 times greater for boys in social class V than for boys in social class I and over three times greater for girls.

Though Table 9.2 does not show it, *social-class differences* in accidental deaths from particular causes are especially marked. In 1959–63 there was, for instance, a five-fold difference in the mortality rate from motor vehicle accidents for children aged 1 to 14 years in social classes I and V. Similarly, deaths from falls, fires and drowning for boys aged 1 to 14 in social class V in 1970–72 were ten times greater than for boys in social class I (Townsend, 1979).

□ What sort of explanation is suggested by these class differences?

■ A *social* explanation, that is, one that looks at differences in the material circumstances of children from different socioeconomic backgrounds or at differences in child-rearing patterns.

There are also regional variations: in 1978–9 the rate of fatal accidents for the whole of England and Wales was 102.6 per million children aged 1–14, but varied between 122.9 deaths per million in the North West of England to 76 per million in Wessex. These rates, too, correspond to 'richer' and 'poorer' parts of the country.

There is one further piece of evidence which might help us in disentangling the many factors that interact to produce the patterns of childhood accidents described. Data from a cohort study of the health of a large number of children born in 1970 and followed up in 1975 — the Child Health and Education Study (CHES) — has made possible an analysis of the incidence of non-fatal childhood accidents in different family types. The results are illustrated in Table 9.3.

Children living in different types of families show small but significant differences in accident rates: the risk is greatest in *step-families*, and least where the child lives with both natural parents. However, children in step-families or one-parent families are *twice* as likely to be admitted to hospital after an accident than are children from two-parent families.

□ Can you suggest some possible explanations for this?

■ There are three main ones: first, it may be that children in 'broken homes' lead less settled lives, or are less well supervised by a single or step-parent and consequently suffer more serious accidents — this is a 'personal history' type of explanation. Second, hospitals might have a different admissions policy for children from different types of families. You may recall that we suggested in Chapter 4 that families who do not fit into the 'nuclear' family type might be viewed as inevitably having problems and doctors might be more concerned to admit such children for observation. For example, doctors may be more likely to suspect that the child has suffered '*non-accidental injury*' (i.e. deliberately inflicted) if the family has a single or step parent. Third, a

Table 9.3 Accidents and hospital admissions after accidents by family type, Great Britain, 1975

Family type	Percentage of pre-school children with one or more accidents	Hospital admissions after accident
two-parent family*	42.7	5.8
step-family	52.6	10.8
one-parent family	47.3	10.3

* *Two-parent family* refers to a family with both natural parents.
(Data from Wadsworth *et al.*, 1983, p. 101)

single parent may be less able to provide nursing care at home, though this does not explain the raised admissions for children from step-families.

So far, the data we have presented have suggested a number of different types of explanation for the unequal distribution of childhood accidents, ranging from the biological to the social and personal. These explanations demand closer examination, since, although it may be helpful in theory to separate them out in this way, in practice they are all interrelated. This may become clearer if you consider who or what is 'to blame' when a child has an accident. Is it the child's biological development or sex, a lack of parental supervision, or a hazardous environment — or a complex mixture of these and other factors?

Explaining childhood accidents

Biological explanations of childhood accidents focus on the individual child — their age, sex and ability to explore and play as a means of practising co-ordinated movements and perfecting skills. From this viewpoint it is inevitable and 'natural' that children will suffer accidents. Younger children are more at risk than older ones for the reasons we discussed earlier, and boys are more at risk than girls because they indulge in more 'rough and tumble' play. But, as we pointed out in Chapter 8, there is evidence to suggest that at least part of this sex difference in behaviour flows from *cultural expectations about gender roles*; rough play and risk-taking is more likely to be tolerated, or actively encouraged, among boys than among girls.

□ Look back at Table 9.2. How far would it confirm a hypothesis that boys are more likely to suffer accidents than girls as a result of inherent biological differences between the sexes?

■ For this hypothesis to be confirmed, the difference between accident rates for boys and girls should be the same across all social classes. But the difference is very much less for children in social class I. Thus there must be other factors at work as well as the child's biology.

When a child suffers an accident, the parents commonly feel guilty, and most people would agree that it *is* part of parental responsibility to protect small children from hazards and to teach older ones about, for example, road safety and the danger of playing with matches. Thus there is a general acceptance that parents are at fault when a child is injured, and if the child is young, then blame is particularly attached to the mother. As you will see later in this chapter, this is a common viewpoint in instances where the mother goes out to work. Research also indicates that accidents are more common among the children of younger mothers, particularly those in their teens, who are held to be less skilled in parenting and perhaps less attentive to the needs of the child.

□ If parents are 'to blame' for children's accidents, how could the social-class differences in accident rates be explained?

■ You would have to propose that people in lower social classes make 'worse' parents: for example, that they place less emphasis on child discipline and self-control, are less likely to supervise children in the home and at play, and less likely to teach them about hazards. You would also have to propose that women from lower social classes are more likely to marry young and to go out to work.

There is little research data on the quality of parenthood, but, in fact, mothers in the highest social classes are as likely to be in employment as mothers in social class V. So the simple absence of a mother because of employment cannot explain the social-class differences in accident rates.

The sorts of behaviour that parents from different social classes are prepared to sanction in their children may partly explain why boys from social class I experience accidents only slightly more often than girls of this class. Working-class parents may tolerate their children (especially boys) taking more risks. Whether you see one set of parents as overprotective or the other as irresponsible will depend on *your* view point!

Another aspect of family life that may have a bearing on accident rates is that nebulous phenomenon known as 'stress'. For example, in a study by J.R. Sibert in 1975, the family circumstances of 100 children under 5 who had been admitted to hospital after accidentally ingesting poisons were compared to a control group of 100 families where there had been no accident. It was found that 30 of the affected families had more than one of five 'major stress factors': serious family illness, pregnancy, a recent move, one parent away from home, and anxiety or depression in one or both parents. The fact that accident rates are slightly higher among children living in step- or one-parent families may indicate that such families experience more stress than their 'nuclear' equivalent. However, the relationship between family stress and childhood accidents is not straightforward.

□ How might illness in a family make an accidental poisoning among the children more likely?

■ There may be several factors involved. It might mean that there are more drugs in the house which a child could accidentally swallow. Alternatively, or even additionally, the demands of caring for a seriously ill person in terms of both time and mental energy might make parents less attentive to what children are doing, or the parent might be the one who is ill, with obvious consequences.

Explanations that focus simply on the attentiveness of

parents or the child's biology omit one very important factor, which is also a major source of stress and of physical hazards.

□ What might this factor be?

■ The material circumstances of the child's life must have a bearing on accident rates: the *social-class gradients* (as in Table 9.2) are too great to exclude a social explanation.

Accidents involving burns and scalds, for example, are more common among children living in overcrowded conditions — an aspect of housing disadvantage shared by families in lower social classes and those with one parent. In a major study of poverty in the UK, the social policy analyst Peter Townsend (1979) found that 41 per cent of one-parent families and 29 per cent of households headed by a partly-skilled or unskilled worker lived in overcrowded conditions compared to 5 per cent of households headed by a professional or managerial worker.

There are many specific dangers to children in poor housing, from faulty electrical wiring and unsafe window catches, to badly lit stairs and non-safety glass in doors. All these hazards cost money to put right, which is beyond the reach of families on low incomes. Simple safety equipment such as a saucepan-guard for the cooker or a stair-gate may be too costly, and cheap but relatively hazardous forms of heating such as paraffin stoves may be all a family can afford.

Poor circumstances outside the home may also be important. Peter Townsend found that 44 per cent of children aged 1 to 4 years living in families with a partly or unskilled parent had no safe place to play near their home, compared to 25 per cent of children aged 1 to 4 with professional or managerial parents. He also found that 43 per cent of children aged 1 to 10 in one-parent families had no safe place to play. More generally, as the DHSS Report on Inequality in Health (known as the Black Report after its chairman, Sir Douglas Black) pointed out:

> ... apart from the specific dangers of road traffic it is likely that the working-class child lives in a more dangerous physical environment than middle-class children. Derelict slum housing about to be cleared, deserted canals, mineshafts and factories, railway lines, rubbish tips; all these present dangers to the child in the urban industrial area. (DHSS, 1980, p.329/ Townsend and Davidson, 1982, p.189)

Such an environment might also be expected to contribute to the regional differences in accident rates. In this context it is illuminating to note that Townsend found that 55 per cent of all children aged 1–14 in the Northern Region, Yorkshire, and Humberside had no safe place to play near their home compared to 29 per cent in South-east England and Greater London.

□ In what ways do explanations in terms of a child's material circumstances overlap with explanations that view parental attentiveness as a key factor?

■ Relative poverty clearly has consequences for safety within and outside the home, but living in poor physical conditions may also be expected to sap the mental and physical energies of parents, especially mothers at home all day, and so contribute to 'inattentiveness'.

The hazards to children and the pressure on parents that poverty can create are more easily grasped if the circumstances of an actual child's life are described. Consider this case study from a report of the Child Health and Education Study (*The Social Life of Britain's Five-Year Olds*).

> This family, comprising two parents and four children under five, lived in grossly over-crowded conditions in a tenement flat, which appeared to consist of a large kitchen (i.e. 6 feet or more wide) and one other room. The study child shared a bed with two of her younger siblings in one room while the other three members of the family slept in the kitchen. There was no bathroom or hot water supply, and the only lavatory was outside and shared by other households. The family did not have such basic items of equipment as a refrigerator, washing machine or spin drier, nor did they have access to either a telephone or car. There was, however, a black-and-white television set. (Osborn, Butler and Morris, 1984, p.13)

Parents do clearly carry some responsibility for their children's health, but in conditions such as these the task must be particularly difficult. The patterns of childhood accidents in society are similar to those associated with many other causes of ill-health or death, among adults as well as children. There is no single explanation for these patterns, but rather an interaction of biological, personal, cultural and material factors. For policy-making purposes it is often crucial to recognise these links. For example, child-proof medicine containers are a social initiative that exploits a biologically-based lack of strength and co-ordination in the hands of a young child; health education films alert parents and children to hazards such as the dangers of traffic. But policies directed at the individual or the family have less chance of success at preventing childhood accidents if the environment remains intrinsically hazardous and outside the control of the individuals involved.

Child health and the family

In the case study of accidents we considered the social distribution of one particular threat to childhood health in the UK today and looked at different ways of explaining these patterns. Responsibility for the prevention of accidents is often seen to lie first and foremost within the family, but the responsibility that parents, and particularly mothers, bear for the health of children is not confined to the avoidance of physical and chemical hazards. Childhood health and ideas about the family are intricately linked. As knowledge about the psychological factors in the development of children has grown, so too have ideas about which family forms and relationships meet their needs. In the early part of this century, highly influential theories about psychiatric problems were developed, such as those of Sigmund Freud (1856–1939), which sought the origins of adult disorders in childhood experiences, and in particular in relationships with parents. From this and other factors, there evolved the belief, still prevalent today, that only the full-time love and care of a mother, supported by a father who provided for the family's economic needs, could ensure the optimal psychological, social and intellectual development of children.

□ Recalling your reading of Chapter 4, which two recent trends in family life would present the greatest threats to this model?

■ The employment of mothers of young children outside the home, and parental separation and divorce.

Both of these trends involve the absence from the home of at least one of the parents, and it is this *absence* that has formed the major focus of research into the impact of maternal employment and divorce on children's health. However, a closer look at the research in these two areas suggests that this focus has been too narrow.

Maternal employment and child health

Research in this area has typically made little use of indicators of *physical* health. Rather it has chosen measures of *intellectual* development, such as vocabulary tests or school performance, and behavioural indicators such as measures of 'antisocial' or 'neurotic' behaviour. Indeed, so many different measures have been used that one researcher was driven to conclude that: 'One can say almost anything one desires about the children of employed mothers and support the statement by some recent study.' (Stolz, 1960, p.773). Given this variety, conflicting results are not surprising. However, research has tended to neglect a range of other factors beside the simple fact that a mother has a job, that may be equally relevant to the question of how maternal employment might affect children.

□ What might some of these other factors be?

■ The type of work a woman does; the reasons why she works; the level of pay she receives; the quality of substitute care; the characteristics of the individual child; the material circumstances of the family; the extent to which two parents share childcare, etc.

If one takes account of these types of factors, a much richer picture of the interaction between maternal employment and child development begins to emerge. Consider for example the results of the Child Health and Development Study (CHES) (Osborn *et al.*, 1984). Data were collected on a range of indicators including a measure of antisocial behaviour and a vocabulary test. The researchers used sophisticated techniques to identify the separate effects of different factors on childrens' behaviour and vocabulary. They found that:

1 The influence of maternal employment on both childrens' behaviour and vocabulary was less important than the type of family they lived in and even less important than their socio-economic circumstances.

2 Children of mothers in full-time manual employment had the highest antisocial behaviour scores. Children whose mothers were in full-time non-manual employment had significantly lower scores. Children whose mothers had been full-time housewives for the whole previous five years had the lowest antisocial behaviour scores.

3 Children with mothers in full-time manual work had the poorest vocabularies, and those whose mothers had been full-time housewives for the five year period had the best. Children whose mothers had given up employment in the previous five years and those with mothers in full- and part-time non-manual employment had a score mid-way between the two extremes.

□ What tentative conclusion can you draw from these findings regarding the relative importance of different factors on child development?

■ Maternal employment *may* have an adverse effect on child development, but consider the following points:

(i) Whatever the influence of maternal employment, socio-economic circumstances appear to exert a much greater influence.

(ii) Full-time employment *per se* is not as important as the type of work which is done. Manual work, presumably more physically demanding and less intrinsically and possibly financially rewarding, appears to have a greater adverse effect.

(iii) The scores for children whose mothers had given up employment in the previous five years suggest that it is not simply the *absence* of the mother that is potentially damaging.

These points demand further consideration. For example, it is important to note that the idea that mothers most often work for 'pin money' has now been discredited; indeed the Central Policy Review Staff in the Cabinet Office estimated in 1980 that there would be three or four times more families living on incomes below supplementary benefit level if it were not for mothers' earnings (Central Policy

Review Staff, 1980, para 6.14). This clearly must be set against any adverse effects of mothers' absence on children.

The CHES study also found that those mothers who had given up employment during the first five years of their childrens' lives had the highest risk of experiencing depression compared with other groups of women. This finding is supported by other research suggesting that employment outside the home may protect certain groups of women from depression.* By 'protecting' the health of some women and raising family income, maternal employment may have a positive contribution to make to the well-being of children in certain families.

The research does not indicate that maternal employment *per se* is inevitably bad for children. Arduous work must reduce the time and energy mothers can give to children, and low pay may make good quality alternative care difficult to obtain. But this situation can be made more damaging by the assumption that childcare is the *mothers'* prime responsibility. This is discussed further in Chapter 12. Finally, it should be pointed out that while maternal employment is the subject of much research and debate, the possible adverse effects on children and families of *fathers'* employment has received little attention, yet, as we suggest in Chapter 12, the effects can be considerable.

Divorce and child health

Maternal employment raises the issue of absent mothers; divorce, however, primarily results in absent fathers. As you saw in Chapter 4, in recent years there has been a dramatic increase in the number of marriages ending in divorce, and a considerable number of children are involved. The divorces occurring in 1981, for example, involved some 159 000 children and of these a quarter were under five. The increasing numbers reflect in part legislative reforms which have made divorce available to everyone, where once it required a special Act of Parliament and was feasible only for the very wealthy. In many respects such reforms represent a major social advance, for people need no longer be trapped until the end of their days inside an unhappy marriage. But divorce also involves considerable disruption in the lives of everyone in the family.

It is clearly important to ask what, if any, long-term impact the experience of divorce is having on the children involved. But, although this is an important question to ask, it is difficult to answer. Two particular issues can be singled out. First, as with maternal employment, there are many different factors that will influence how a child reacts, and the focus on parental relationships, in particular on parental absence, has tended to obscure the importance of some of these other factors. Second, we must be careful to separate immediate effects from those that operate in the long term. The latter are very hard to study, however, since they cover the whole of a person's life, and studying a whole life is a long and difficult task. We are therefore at present far from having a complete understanding of this controversial matter.

□ What factors might be expected to influence the way a child adapts to parental separation or divorce?

■ The most obvious would be the child's previous relationship with the parents; the nature and extent of marital conflict; the child's age and whether or not there are other brothers and sisters; who the child ends up with and how far contact is maintained with the other parent; the financial situation of the family both before and after the divorce; how the parents react to the divorce; the nature of any new relationship each parent may embark upon, etc.

Loss of contact with the parent who does not have custody is a common feature of divorce, even though many children desire continued contact. British studies, for example, suggest that only around a half of 'absent' parents are regularly visiting their children at the time of divorce proceedings — a proportion that appears to *decline* over time. But there is evidence that other factors may be of equal if not greater importance to understanding children's adaptation, than the 'simple' absence of a parent. For example, in the short term, many children seem to adapt better to the loss of a parent through death than divorce.

□ Which of the factors mentioned above as influencing a child's adaptation to a divorce would be very different from the child's viewpoint if the missing parent had died?

■ When a parent dies, the child is faced with accepting the finality of the loss but usually does not feel 'rejected' by the dead parent. This is in sharp contrast to the experience of many children following a divorce — the separation may not be final but intermittent and unreliable, and if contact is broken altogether the child knows that the parent stays away by *choice*. Conflicts between the *custodial* and *non-custodial parent* are another common source of anxiety to children.

The financial circumstances of bereaved and divorced families also differ significantly. You might expect that the death of a spouse would lead to more financial problems than their absence from home through marital breakdown. In fact the reverse is true. Where life-insurance cover exists, it will pay off major debts in bereaved households, and such families are more likely than their divorced or separated counterparts to own their own homes. The majority of one-parent families are headed by a divorced or separated woman, yet in 1979 only 6 per cent of all lone parents relied on maintenance payments from an absent partner as their

*See Book VI, *Experiencing and Explaining Disease*, Chapter 8.

Table 9.4 Proportion of one-parent families receiving supplementary benefit in 1981

Marital status of lone parent	Number	Per cent receiving supplementary benefit
widows	102 000	9.8
divorced	342 000	38.5
separated	162 000	83.9

(Data from DHSS, 1983, Table 34.32)

major source of income. In fact, as Table 9.4 illustrates, over 80 per cent of separated parents and 38 per cent of divorced parents are dependent on *supplementary benefit*.* The high proportion among separated parents reflects the considerable economic uncertainty experienced at the time of marital breakdown, an uncertainty which does appear to improve with time.

In contrast to divorced and separated parents, however, less than 10 per cent of widowed parents depend on the means tested supplementary benefit — in most cases they are eligible for a widowed mothers allowance which is more generous and incidentally carries less of a stigma.

In addition to the obvious direct effects of poverty on health, it is often very difficult for children to understand and accept a sudden significant change in family finances. There are other factors also that may make the experience of divorce more disruptive than that of bereavement. Following divorce, for example, it is much more likely that the family will have to move house than after a parent's death.

None of this is intended to imply that the experience of bereavement is any less distressing than divorce, but rather that for children they do appear to be different experiences. In both situations, the absence of the 'lost' parent can be adapted to more easily if the child is given adequate support and reassurance. However, the marital conflict that almost inevitably precedes separation and divorce, and the financial difficulties that often follow, make it harder for parents to give adequate attention to childrens' needs at such a time. And in some families, children are used in complex manipulations by distressed adults trying to punish each other for marital failure. Even without such extreme behaviour, children suffer emotionally during periods of conflict between their parents, and are usually very distressed if separation results.

*The level of income provided for within the supplementary benefit scheme for a single person (including housing costs) represented around 29 per cent of average earnings in the United Kingdom, by the end of 1984 (see Book III, *The Health of Nations*, Chapter 10). This proportion is usually greater in households with children.

Martin Richards and H. Dyson have reviewed the research on the emotional responses of children of different ages to their parents' marital breakdown. Table 9.5 shows how reactions vary depending on the age of the child at the time of the separation or divorce.

Table 9.5 Summary of effects of divorce and separation on children of various ages.

Preschool children 2.5–6 years
Preschool children were frightened, confused and blamed themselves. There was a great need for physical contact with adults. Children expressed fears of being sent away or being replaced. Only 5- and 6-year olds were able to express feelings and to understand some of the divorce-related changes.

Young school children
Children expressed feelings of sadness, of being abandoned and rejected, although they did not blame themselves. They had difficulty in expressing anger towards their fathers. They felt angry at the mothers (custodial parents) for sending their father away but were afraid of incurring their mothers' wrath. They held an intense desire for reconciliation of their parents, believing that the family was necessary for their own wellbeing.

9–11 years
Older school children had a more realistic understanding of separation and were better able to express their feelings of intense anger. They did not feel responsible but were ashamed and morally outraged by their parents' behaviour. Their loyalties were divided between their parents and they frequently felt lonely and rejected.

Adolescents (12–18)
Children in this group were most openly upset by separation. They expressed strong feelings of anger, sadness, shame and embarrassment. Separation forced them to see their parents as individuals and to reassess their relationship with each other. They also re-examined their own beliefs about marital and other relationships. Many were able to disengage themselves from parental conflicts within a year.

(Richards and Dyson, 1982, Table 3, p.29.)

□ What are the most common feelings and what are the major differences between children of different ages?

■ Common feelings are those of anger, sadness, guilt, shame, aggression and rejection. Younger children appear to be less able to understand or to come to terms with the separation, being less open about their feelings.

Older children express their feelings more openly and also seem to 'accept' the situation more easily.

One child's perception of the separation of his parents is vividly illustrated in the extract below, taken from an 11-year old boy's school essay. (The names have been altered to preserve anonymity.)

> *The Worst Day of My Life*
> It was a Saturday morning. I went into my Mum and Dad's bedroom to say Goodmorning. My dad wasn't in bed. He wasn't downstairs either. 'Mum, where's Dad?' 'He's gone to Spain on a meeting.' 'When will he be coming back?' 'I don't know ... Oh wait a minute, I want to tell you something. We're going around Beryl's to sleep for the night.' We got our stuff packed and went round to Beryl's. We had dinner and went to bed. I woke up in the night and heard my Mum crying.
>
> It was Sunday morning and my Mum came into the front room. I was reading a comic called 'Beano.' 'Paul, I've got something to tell you ... I know you're going to take this hard but I better tell you. Dad's left.' I felt tears coming into my eyes. It's been about two years since my dad left. The lady who he is living with is called Mabel Brown. She has two sons called Pete and Garry. Garry is in the fourth year and he is a big fat ugly pig. So is his Mum. Pete is the nice one. If I had two wishes, I would wish Garry and Mabel was dead and my dad would come back. (quoted in Richards and Dyson, 1982, p.4.)

It is clear that for many children the immediate impact of divorce is highly unsettling. What of the longer-term effects? The child who wrote the essay above was writing two years after the events he describes and is clearly still upset by them. One American study found that around a third of their sample of 270 children were intensely unhappy and dissatisfied with their lives five years after their parents' separation and could be classified as depressed. This is, however, still a relatively short-term effect. What are the consequences of such unhappiness across an entire lifetime?

As yet there have been no studies that have followed a group of children of divorced parents over the years and checked their progress throughout their entire life compared with children whose parents stayed together. (This type of study is known as prospective or longitudinal.)* There have, however, been two American studies which interviewed a cross-section of American adults and tried to see if those whose parents had divorced or separated before they were 16 coped better or worse with life. One of these was conducted in 1957, the other in 1976 and both were reviewed by Kulka and Weingarten in 1979. When factors such as age, social class, education, religion or marital history were controlled for, as in the two American national surveys, it was found that adults from intact parental homes and from homes disrupted by divorce were remarkably similar as regards their psychological adjustment. They reported similar levels of happiness, worry and morale about the future.

The differences between the two groups were minor, though still of some interest. For example, young adults (those in the 21–34 age group) whose parents had divorced did seem significantly less happy than their older counterparts. They also reported significantly more ill-health. Curiously, married men whose parents had divorced reported higher levels of current marital harmony than similar men from intact parental homes.

□ In what way might parental divorce actually help psychological adjustment in later life?

■ It is feasible that children whose parents divorce may grow up rather better informed about the problems that can affect intimate relationships and the need for sensitive handling.

Caution is required in applying the results of research in one country to another. But these survey results would support the conclusion that, although divorce may prove highly problematic for children in the shorter term, in the longer term their psychological wellbeing seems to be relatively unaffected, as long as the effects of relative poverty are taken into account. In the next chapter we turn to the problems faced by children as they enter adolescence and attempt to identify themselves with the world of adults.

*This is defined in Book I, *Studying Health and Disease*, Chapter 4.

Objectives for Chapter 9

When you have studied this chapter, you should be able to:

9.1 Discuss the biological, social and personal factors that may influence the distribution of childhood accidents in the population, and illustrate interactions between these factors.

9.2 Discuss the effects of maternal employment and parental divorce on the physical and emotional development of children, and demonstrate a knowledge of those factors other than the absence of a parent that must be taken into account.

Questions for Chapter 9

1 (*Objective 9.1*) Does Figure 9.1 support the view that biological factors relating to the development of the child are the most important determinant of accident rates?

2 (*Objective 9.2*)

> Much research on single-parent families overtly or indirectly implies that remarriage would be of advantage to children. A new partner would at least in theory be able to share the practical and emotional strains of parenthood as well as increasing the family income ... More widely, of course, remarriage is seen to be socially desirable and as a way of restoring the status of a 'proper' family. (Richards and Dyson, 1982, p.43)

A number of research studies have thrown such assumptions into doubt, by reporting that accident rates, indicators of emotional disturbance such as sleeping difficulties or temper tantrums, and delinquency, were greater among children in step-families than among children living in single-parent families. In what ways might a 'substitute' parent be more problematic to a child than an 'absent' parent?

10
Adolescence to adulthood

This chapter builds on the discussion of the control of reproduction by the so-called sex hormones, discussed in Book IV, *The Biology of Health and Disease*, Chapter 10. A more general overview of hormonal control mechanisms was given in Chapter 6 of that book. The final part of this chapter refers to theories about *gender roles*, that is, the culturally-determined, learned aspects of female and male behaviour as opposed to the biologically determined differences between the sexes; this subject was previously discussed in Book II, *Medical Knowledge: Doubt and Certainty*, Chapter 8, in relation to the diagnosis and 'causes' of hysteria in women. At the end of the chapter you will be asked to listen to the audiotape sequence 'You just live for your bike' on cassette AC805, Band 2.

The transition from childhood to adulthood is marked by a series of bodily changes; by a shift from characteristically childhood diseases to a distinctively new pattern; and by a series of changes in social behaviour, some of which have important consequences for health. It is also the subject of major public and professional debate, some key aspects of which will be explored in this chapter.

It is revealing to begin by looking at some of the terms we use to describe this period of life. Young children tend to be described in superlatives; they are 'marvellous', 'wonderful', 'little angels', and also 'monsters' and 'terrors', for their character is not portrayed as wholly good. But they are commonly believed to possess a special quality, distinct from the problems and prejudices of adult life. Unlike adults, children are loved regardless of their class, race or physical appearance. However, as they get older and begin to approach adulthood, they acquire new and far more ambiguous qualities in adult eyes; they become *adolescents*. Adolescents are also commonly seen as separate from adults, as forming a distinctive group with their own special properties, but they are rarely described as wonderful or marvellous. Instead, they constitute a 'social problem'.

Social problems are the sort of things that people write letters to the newspapers about and politicians promise to alleviate. A glance in any library confirms this attitude towards adolescence as a 'problem'. Indeed, all the terms that we use for the age-group have an awkward feel. There is no neutral way of describing it: 'youth' has an air of causing trouble and needing clubs, 'juveniles' are obviously delinquent, 'adolescents' most likely to have problems and 'teenagers' to have spots.

Why should adolescents be viewed in this way? What might render the *transition to adulthood* so apparently problematic? As you will see in a moment, adolescence does present its own special health and social problems that cause a good deal of adult worry. Not only is the death of an adolescent shocking, since they might expect to have many years of life in front of them, but adolescents are a society's future, they are the rising generation. In a period of life when good health is expected, sickness or injury are obvious causes of concern.

According to some authors, the problems of adolescence are major and extensive: every adolescent undergoes serious difficulties in the transition to adulthood, some serious enough to result in major harm to both mental and physical health. But, according to others, the problems of this period have been blown up out of all proportion to their real importance: adolescence is mostly a trouble-free and healthy period of life. A few individuals may certainly experience more serious problems, but one cannot generalise from their condition to that of the rest.

We shall examine this controversy between those who take adolescence to be generally problematic and those who dispute this, having first looked at those aspects of adolescence that are less disputed: the biological changes of puberty, and the general experiences of this age-group. And, finally, we shall consider some of these issues in more concrete detail via two case studies: anorexia nervosa and motor-cycle accidents.

Puberty: biological changes in adolescence

Adolescence is a period of significant external and internal biological changes, which ultimately enable the individual to produce fertile eggs or sperm and so reproduce. This transition to reproductive maturity is termed *puberty*, and takes several years to complete. However, these physical changes are commonly held to be a sign of 'growing up' in a wider sense — adolescence cannot begin without them. Individuals differ enormously in the rate at which they become biologically mature. Chronological age *alone* cannot always be used to indicate the transition from child to adolescent.

□ What are the main *physical* changes by which you judge someone to be leaving childhood and entering adolescence?

■ The most obvious changes are enlargement of the genitals in both sexes; growth of body hair; breast development and the beginning of menstruation in girls; and deepening of the voice in boys.* Around puberty, girls and boys seem to 'shoot up', rapidly gaining in height and weight.

These changes result from increasing levels of the so-called sex hormones, released from the ovaries in females and the testes in males. A significant consequence of these bodily changes during puberty is the increase in *sexual dimorphism*: that is, the differentiation of two distinct body forms, female and male, from the rather undifferentiated body shapes of childhood. Boys, on average, grow taller than girls and develop a greater proportion of muscle tissue relative to total body weight. As a result they tend to be physically stronger than girls of the same age, if strength is measured by the ability to lift heavy weights. After puberty, boys develop lower pitched and louder voices than girls, and a lot more body hair.

*These are the secondary sexual characteristics discussed in Book IV, *The Biology of Health and Disease*, Chapter 10.

These physical changes associated with a person's *sex* are woven into cultural expectations about how a person of that sex should behave — in other words, their *gender role*. Males are expected to be more 'physical' than females, more aggressive and active; females by contrast are supposed to be more passive, submissive, gentle and nurturing. It is difficult to disentangle the biological from the cultural contributions to these rather 'stereotyped' pictures of male and female.†

In this chapter we are concerned first with the *actual* bodily changes that take place during puberty and the experience of those changes for individual adolescents, and secondly with theories about the contribution social expectations make to ill-health during this period of life. There are, broadly, three significant types of bodily change that constitute puberty. These are: (i) general changes in body shape, including changes in distribution of body fat and muscle; (ii) the adolescent 'growth spurt'; and (iii) further development of the reproductive system.

We will describe each of these briefly, but, first, we need to consider how they relate to age. Obviously, in a very broad sense, they are age-related in that these changes are generally accomplished between the ages of 10 and 20. There is, however, considerable variation between individuals. Figure 10.1 (overleaf) shows three girls and three boys who are all of the same *chronological* age but who have clearly reached different stages of development. Chronological age, then, is not necessarily a good indicator of changes in puberty. Nonetheless, it is the yardstick by which we tend to measure our children's development and you will see 'age in years' used in some of the diagrams which follow, referring to the *average* age for the population at which that event occurs.

The variation between individuals can be a source of considerable anxiety. Parents, or the young person going through puberty, may feel concerned that the changes of puberty are not occurring at a 'normal rate'. They may even seek medical advice. The selection of letters that follows from the 'problem page' of a comic aimed at girls aged around 8–14 illustrates the kind of distress that can arise from expectations about the 'normal' age for these changes to occur.

†If you are interested in pursuing this question, you could consult another Open University Course — U221, *The Changing Experience of Women*, Units 2 and 3, *Nature and Culture*, The Open University Press, 1983, which examine this issue in depth.

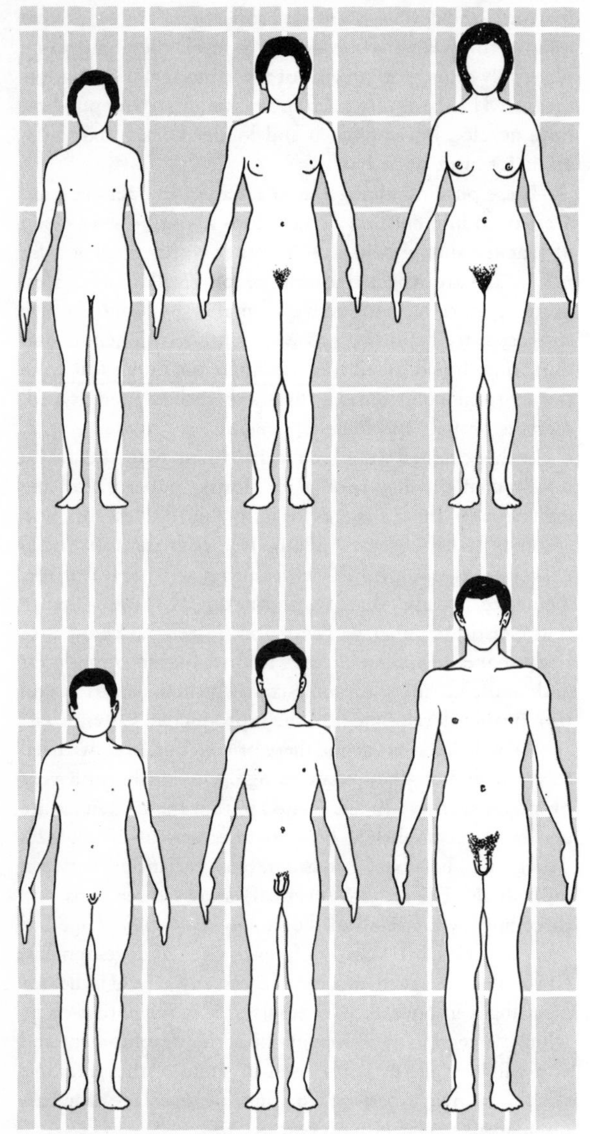

Figure 10.1 The variations in range of development of three girls aged 12.75 years and three boys aged 14.75 years. The girl and boy on the left have not yet reached puberty, those in the middle are part way through it and the girl and boy on the right have finished their development. This range of variation is completely normal. (Based on Tanner, 1975, p.73)

My mum treats me like a two year old! I need to know about things like periods, bras and getting rid of hair under my arms. Every time I ask her she either changes the subject or refuses to talk. I'm 12. (*Girl*, 10 December 1983)

Everybody makes fun and teases me. Although I'm only 9, I look at least 14. Also, I've got a very bad problem with BO. I know I ought to use a deodorant, but Mum says it's much too early for things like that. (*Girl*, 13 November 1982)

I'm very worried. I think I need to wear a bra. I'm only 11 but my bust measures 34 inches ... None of my friends are bigger than about a 28–30 bust. Please help. (*Girl*, 16 April 1983)

□ The problems of assessing 'normal' growth and development were discussed in Chapter 8 of this book. Can you recall the two main reasons why 'normality' is so difficult to define?

■ The first is the extreme variation between individuals who are in good health; thus, comparing a young person's biological development with others of the same age is unlikely to resolve whether they are developing normally. Secondly, development tends to proceed via a sequence of changes through which all individuals pass, but at varying rates of change; thus there are many routes to the same common end, and the fact that a particular person reaches a certain 'stage' of development earlier or later than average is not in itself evidence of abnormality.

In discussing the three main types of physical change that constitute puberty (which we listed above), we will focus on the variation between individuals and how they might be compared.

Changes in bodily shape

A variety of general bodily changes occur during puberty. Perhaps one of the most noticeable is the change in body-fat distribution and in muscle mass. In girls, fat is laid down during puberty around the hips and breasts; boys by contrast, tend to develop a greater muscle mass for their body size by building up a larger number of muscle cells, and also tend to lose much of their childhood fat. Certain changes in fat and muscle can be used as an index with which to compare adolescent development. It is possible, for example, to measure the amount of fat in proportion to muscle in the limbs, and since the proportion changes with age and sex this might be used as one measure of development. Figure 10.2 shows the increasing divergence with age between the sexes in the width of the muscles in the upper arm and calf.

Other differences between the sexes, such as average heart size, or lung capacity, also emerge during puberty. This emerging sexual dimorphism is mainly influenced by differences in the levels of circulating hormones in the two sexes but it is important to bear in mind that it is also influenced by practice. Muscle composition and heart volume, for instance, can both be changed by appropriate physical training. Thus sex differences in these parameters during adolescence are partly due to the fact that rather

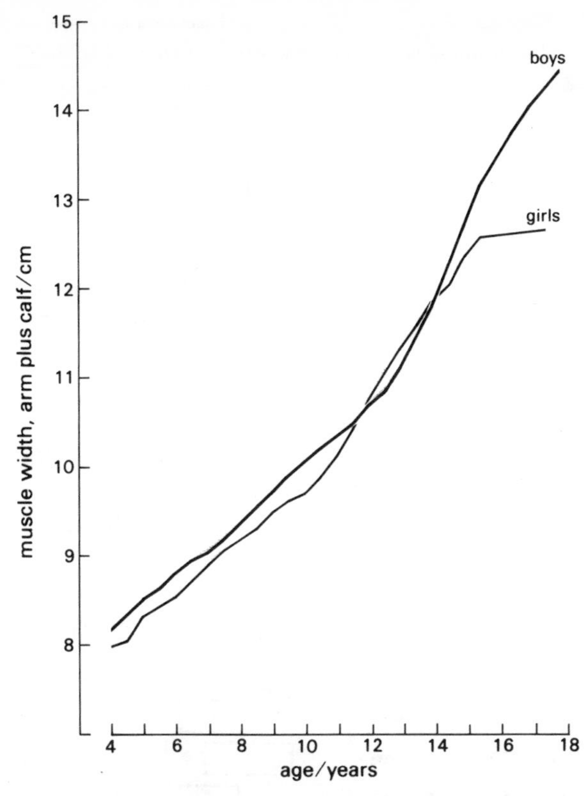

Figure 10.2 Muscle growth in adolescence: the sum of widths of upper arm and calf muscles in boys and girls. (Tanner, 1978, p.73)

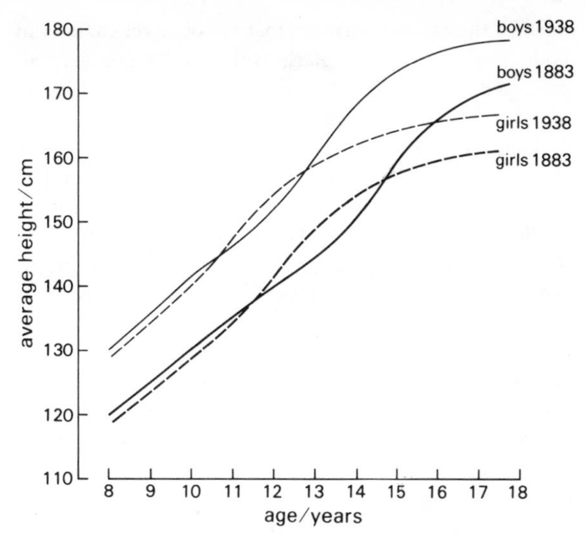

Figure 10.3 The secular trend in height, Swedish boys and girls, 1883 and 1938. (Haviland and Scarborough, 1981, Figure 2.2)

more adolescent boys than girls engage in hard physical sports. Finally, note that one dramatic consequence of these muscular changes is that the strength and stamina of the individual after puberty are greatly increased — an increase which occurs in both sexes.

The adolescent growth spurt

Adolescence is also a time when the body grows rapidly in height. Figure 10.3 shows the change in height of children between the ages of six and eighteen. This figure shows four sets of data on the growth in height of Swedish children; the solid lines indicate growth curves for boys and the dotted lines represent growth curves for girls, both taken in the year 1938 as well as the year 1883.

□ Look at the curves shown in Figure 10.3. The most obvious point is that children were taller in 1938 than in 1883 (a phenomenon discussed in Chapter 8). What other information do they contain?

■ The adolescent 'growth spurt' occurs approximately between the ages of 11 and 16. Prior to that, the *rate* of growth is fairly steady (that is, the curve climbs upwards at an even gradient), but as the child enters puberty, the growth is accelerated (that is, the curve takes a steeper gradient.) It then levels off again after puberty. The graph also reveals clear sex differences. Before puberty, there is little difference in height between the sexes; for girls, however, the growth spurt occurs much earlier than for boys, but then levels off at about 15–16 years. Boys tend to go on increasing their height until they are at least 18.

Another point you may have noticed is that the *onset* of the growth spurt for both sexes occurred at an *earlier* age in 1938 than in 1883. This slow change in the average value of a particular measurement is called a *secular trend*, meaning a slow but persistent change over a period of time. So adolescents not only reach a greater final height nowadays than formerly, but also begin the rapid phase of growth earlier.

□ Recalling the discussion of factors affecting height in young children (Chapter 8), what do you think is most likely to underlie the trend towards taller adolescents over the last century?

■ Improvements in diet are thought to be the major contributor to the secular trend in the earlier age of onset and extent of the adolescent growth spurt. Such trends cannot be explained by changes in other factors that influence height, such as the genetic constitution of the population, diseases that stunt growth or the effects of emotional state on appetite.

Changes in the reproductive system and its control

The most significant change occurring during puberty is the dramatic increase in sex-hormone secretion from the *gonads* (the ovaries and testes) which is associated with most of the external changes that we observe; changes in body shape, deepening of the voice and so on, are all produced by changes in the level of *sex hormones* in the bloodstream.

Figure 10.4 shows the timescale of some visible changes that occur during puberty in the average boy and girl. For boys, one of the more noticeable changes is the enlargement of the penis and growth of body hair, while for girls, one of the first changes is slight enlargement of the breast around the nipple to form what is termed a breast bud. Other changes, such as deepening of the voice in boys, or the advent of menstruation (termed *menarche*) occur rather late in puberty. The bars in Figure 10.4 show the timescale over which the different events might occur in the average individual. Thus, the average age at which menstruation begins in the UK is 13½ years but the normal range is between 10 and 16. Growth of the breasts, penis and pubic hair occurs gradually over several years. As with all aspects of biological development during puberty, there is considerable variation between individuals; for example, pubic hair may begin to grow at any age between 8 and 14 in girls, and 10 and 15 in boys.

Like the start of the growth spurt, the average age at which menarche occurs has shown a secular trend. Figure 10.5 shows the average age of menarche for girls from several European countries since the mid-nineteenth century. Whereas girls in Europe around 1910 did not begin to menstruate until they were, on average, 15 years old, the age of menarche has now dropped to about 13½. Age of menarche can vary too by geographic region: Figure 10.6 shows the variation in age of menarche for girls in urban and rural areas in different parts of the world. One of the most striking features of these data is that menarche tends to occur *earlier* in girls growing up in urban areas. Better nutrition is thought to be the main contributor to these secular and geographical trends. Such changes from one generation to the next may underly some of the tension that certain parents feel about their children maturing 'too fast'.

In this brief review of the biological changes of puberty we have concentrated on the major physical consequences — the most obvious external signs of 'growing up' and the attainment of reproductive potency. However, it is worth mentioning in passing that the hormonal changes we have discussed have other effects which may be minor in biological terms, but can feel major to the individual. The letters quoted earlier from the 'problem page' referred to body hair and body odour, and we could have printed dozens more cries for help about spots, sweating, blushing, as well as fears that the body shape being developed would

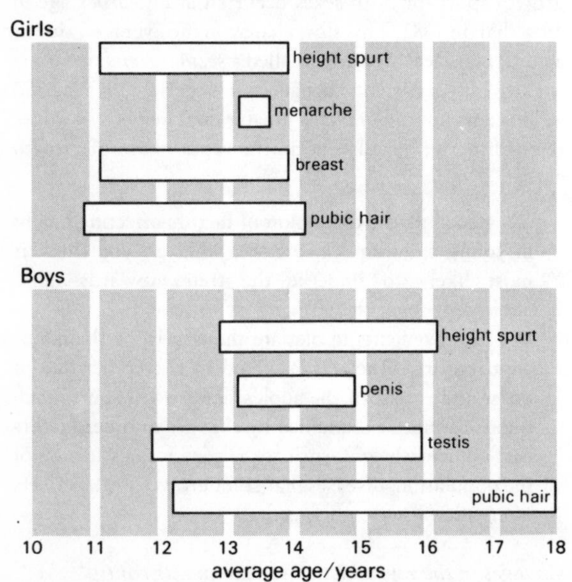

Figure 10.4 Range of the ages during which the physical changes of puberty occur, on average, in girls and boys. (Data from Marshall and Tanner, 1969 and 1970)

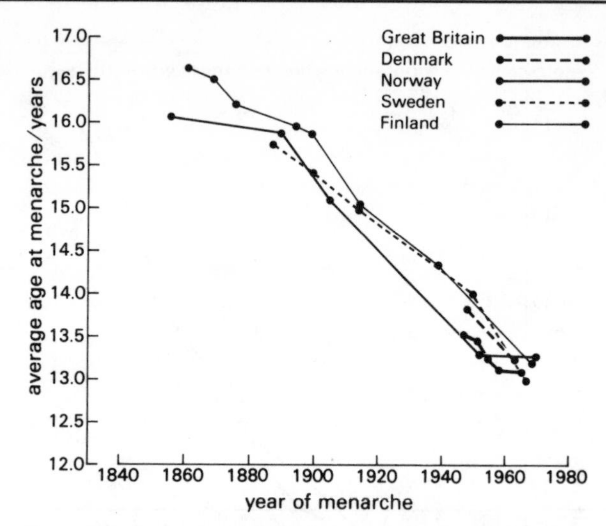

Figure 10.5 Secular trend towards an earlier age at menarche in girls from Western Europe. (Tanner, 1978, p.152)

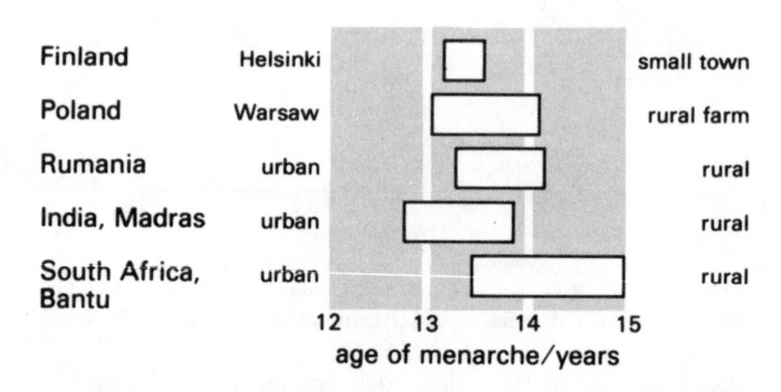

Figure 10.6 Range of the ages during which menarche occurs in urban and rural areas throughout the world. (Tanner, 1978, p.145)

be unattractive. Such anxieties are by no means confined to adolescence — spontaneous body changes go on throughout life even without the influence of diet and exercise — but the body may be experienced as a source of embarrassment for the first time during puberty, when changes take place so rapidly and so much is beyond the individual's control. For some adults, this embarrassment never entirely goes away.

However, despite the anxieties that most adolescents experience at some time when going through these physical changes, adolescence is also one of the healthier periods of life. Our next task is to examine the pattern of ill-health in this age-group and to consider its unique features.

Health in adolescence

As Table 10.1 illustrates, adolescence is a period of life in which mortality is extremely low.

Table 10.1 Annual death rates per 1 000 people within each age-group in 1978 in England and Wales

Age/years	Males	Females
0–1	15	12
1–4	0.6	0.5
5–9	0.3	0.2
10–14	0.3	0.2
15–19	0.9	0.4
20–24	1.0	0.4
25–34	1.0	0.6
35–44	2.0	1.4
45–54	6.8	4.2
55–64	19	9.8
65–74	49	25
75–84	112	70
85+	234	191

(Data from OPCS Mortality Statistics, in Goldacre and Vessey, 1983, Table 1, p. 2.3)

□ What else does this table suggest about the health of those in transition from childhood to adulthood?

■ For both sexes, the death rate slowly starts to creep up towards the late teens. By their twenties, males have three times the death rate that they had between ages 5 and 9, though that rate is still very low compared to males in their fifties and sixties. The other striking feature is the difference between male and female death rates. At every age, female mortality is lower than that of males. However, whereas this difference is smallest during the childhood years, it reaches its greatest extent during the years from 15 to 24. At no other point in the lifespan is male mortality more than twice that of females.

What can account for the striking difference in the relative mortality of males and females during this period? Table 10.2 provides some answers and also compares the changes in the causes of death as adolescents move into young adulthood.

□ Look at Table 10.2.

1 What is the major cause of the difference between male and female mortality in 15–24 year olds?

2 What are the principal changes in the causes of death between the ages of 15–24 and 25–34?

■ 1 Although male mortality rates are higher at 15–24 for all the listed causes of death, the overall difference is principally due to the much higher death rate among males from accidents, a rate over three times that for females.

2 In both sexes, accidents remain a major cause of death in 25–34 year olds, killing twice as many men as any other cause. However, for both males and females, mortality from accidents is significantly less in the older age group, particularly among men, where it is down by a third. By contrast, death rates for all the other causes have increased and, among women, cancers have overtaken accidents to become the leading female cause of death.*

Table 10.2 Death rates per million in people aged 15–24 and 25–34 years, England and Wales, 1978

	Males		Females	
Causes	15–24	25–34	15–24	25–34
cancers	92	178	64	184
circulatory diseases	36	132	28	82
respiratory diseases	35	49	25	35
accidents	662	445	191	156
all other causes	122	131	85	131

(Goldacre and Vessey, 1983, Table 3, p. 2.4)

*Cancers are discussed in detail in Book VI, *Experiencing and Explaining Disease*, Chapters 3–5.

Of course, for all the prominence of accidental death among adolescents and young adults, the overall death rate is still very low. Nevertheless, the following facts should still be borne in mind. First, whereas Chapter 9 showed that accidents accounted for 30 per cent of all mortality among children aged 1–14 years, in the age group 15–24 the percentages are far higher, accounting for 70 per cent of all deaths for males and 48.6 per cent for females; a most striking increase. Second, remember that although the overall mortality from accidents is low, the people who are killed in them are mostly young and would normally have had many years of life in front of them. A study in Canada which examined deaths in all age groups, showed that motor vehicle accidents accounted for only 8 per cent of all deaths, but 18.2 per cent of all years of life lost (Romeder and McWhinnie, 1977, Tables 2 and 4).* By contrast, coronary heart disease, which largely affects a much older age group, was responsible for 26.2 per cent of all deaths, but only 15.1 per cent of lost years. And third, in addition to those who are killed in accidents, there are many more who are maimed for life. American research suggests that for every young person killed in an accident, twenty more are severely injured — some permanently.

In summary, as judged by mortality rates and the prominence of accidental deaths, adolescents and young adults do have distinctive health problems from other groups of the population, young men particularly so. What about other varieties of problem? There are a large number of ways in which adolescent behaviour is often judged unusual, threatening or deviant.

□ What are the best publicised forms of *youthful deviance*?

■ Any list would include some of the following and possibly several others: vandalism, football hooliganism, petty theft, teenage pregnancy and drinking, mugging, rowdyism, punks, mods and rockers, loud parties, student revolts, glue-sniffing.

Some of these activities clearly have direct consequences for health and some may also be the result of ill-health, such as a disordered mental state, or so many have argued. Whatever their interpretation, and we shall discuss this later, the statistics on juvenile lawbreaking are most striking. Research has shown that the majority of adolescent boys admit (privately) to offences against the law, and one-fifth of all boys are actually convicted of such an offence — the peak age of police contact being 15–16 years. Despite this widespread delinquency, most offences are trivial and only half the offenders are re-convicted.

The relationship of mental disorder to *juvenile delinquency* is controversial, and most pyschiatrists now hold that the two phenomena are rarely connected. What about less controversial mental disorders? The major *mental disorders* affecting adults (schizophrenia, manic-depressive psychoses and severe depression†) are rarely seen among adolescents. Suicides account for a greater proportion of deaths in people aged 15–34 than in older age groups, but this is mainly due to the rarity of other causes of death during adolescence and young adulthood.

However, one disorder that has no known biological cause and which is treated predominantly by psychiatrists, occurs predominantly in adolescents and young adults — the eating disorder known as anorexia nervosa. We shall discuss explanations for this condition later in the chapter. There are no definite estimates of the prevalence of anorexia nervosa, but research suggests that though it is rare in boys, in Britain around 1 per cent of adolescent girls may suffer from it, and many more experience a brief episode in a less extreme form. Almost all sufferers seem to come from the higher social classes. The average age of onset in the UK is between 16 and 17 years. Prognosis is uncertain: one of the best studies which followed up 102 patients who had attended a London hospital for treatment, found that eight years later, 2 of them had died of starvation and 16 were still seriously underweight (Hsu, 1980). However, more than 80 per cent had made a partial or complete recovery.

In summary, therefore, adolescents and young adults are a pretty healthy lot compared with other age groups, but their patterns of ill-health show certain distinctive features which sharply divide the sexes. Accident rates are relatively high for both sexes compared with older ages, but are very much higher for teenage boys and young men than for their female counterparts. Minor criminal offences are also particularly prevalent among young males. Conversely, the eating disorder anorexia nervosa predominantly affects teenage girls and young women. How can these differences be explained? Could there be a *genetic predisposition* to criminal or risk-taking behaviour in young men, and a similar in-built tendency towards eating disorders in young women? Or must we seek a solution in the pressures of conforming to the social roles ascribed to young people in the modern world — that is, to their *gender* rather than their *sex*? And, above all, are adolescents really a problem anyway, or have they been cast in this role by society?

Adolescence as problematic

A popular view of the distinctive health and social problems of adolescence is that all or most adolescents face serious problems in the transition to adulthood, problems

*This is discussed in Book III, *The Health of Nations*, Chapter 3.

†Mental disorders are discussed in detail in Book VI, *Experiencing and Explaining Disease*, Chapters 6–9.

that, for a few, can have catastrophic consequences. Adolescence in general is therefore portrayed as a difficult period of life. There are two broad types of theory as to the specific causes of this general problem. One sees it in terms of individual psychology, whereas the other points a finger at special social or economic circumstances.

We shall consider the psychological theory first. There is a long tradition of thought in psychological and psychiatric analysis that the transition from childhood to adulthood with all the major biological, emotional and social changes involved is a necessarily stormy passage. Writers in the *psychoanalytic tradition* have been particularly influential in fostering this view. Anna Freud, for example, wrote that:

> Adolescence is by its nature an interruption of peaceful growth and ... the upholding of a steady equilibrium during the adolescent process is by itself abnormal ... the adolescent manifestations come close to symptom formation of the neurotic, psychotic or dissocial order and merge almost imperceptibly into ... almost all the mental illnesses. (Freud, 1958, cited in Rutter, *et al.*, 1976, p.35).

Similarly, K.R. Eissler, another psychoanalyst, has argued that adolescent behaviour is not only abnormal but that its disorders take a characteristically varied and unpredictable form:

> ... (adolescent) psychopathology switches from one form to another, sometimes in the course of weeks or months, but also from one day to another ... the symptoms manifested by such patients may be neurotic at one time and almost psychotic at another. Then, sudden acts of delinquency may occur, only to be followed by a phase of perverted sexual activity. (Eissler, 1958, cited in Rutter, *et al*, 1976, p.35).

In this highly influential tradition, adolescence is characterised as a period of alienation and inner turmoil as the adolescent tries to come to terms with the demands of adult life, trying out a whole range of behaviour, some of it highly deviant, before finally settling down. Thus the standard American system for classifying psychiatric disorders, includes a specific *adolescent 'identity disorder'*. This is defined as severe subjective distress going on for longer than three months, due to an inability to reconcile different aspects of behaviour and personality into a relatively coherent and acceptable sense of self. Typical worries, of which the adolescent must have at least three to be classified as suffering from the condition, include serious distress over the following: long-term goals, career choice, friendship patterns, sexual identity and behaviour, and religious beliefs.

Given such premises, it is argued that because adolescent identity is so precarious, parents and teachers have a very special responsibility. A family or school that puts too much pressure on a child at this delicate stage may precipitate a crisis, as may those who offer too little support or understanding. This tradition therefore seeks the root of adolescent problems both in the peculiarly vulnerable status of adolescent identity and in the dynamics of family interaction. Parents who are absent or divorced — above all those who have not sorted out their own identity problems — render their children especially vulnerable. (Note that the debate about the effects of maternal employment and parental divorce examined in Chapter 9 in relation to *young* children, rages no less hotly over adolescents.)

Such a view seems plausible. Commonsense acknowledges that some people are mature and responsible, others less so, and that the passage from immaturity to maturity is a difficult one. There is, however, a major critique of the psychoanalytic theory of adolescence which, while it agrees that the transition to adulthood is indeed difficult in contemporary society, sees this as due to particular economic and social structures. Rather than trying to solve adolescent problems by probing the psyche of the individual teenager and his or her parents, proponents of this view argue that we should instead look to social and economic reforms.

There are numerous ways in which society might be the root cause of problems in adolescence.

□ Can you list some of them?

■ It may be that the roles we offer young people are in themselves a source of stress: for example, could social expectations about 'manly' behaviour have something to do with reckless motor cyclists or football hooliganism, and hence the accident and delinquency rates? A similar case could be argued for the pressure to be slim as part of the 'feminine ideal', and hence the prevalence of anorexia. An entirely different social explanation might lay the blame at inadequate schooling, or a shortage of jobs.

An even more subtle type of social explanation argues that contemporary society has brought the 'adolescence problem' on itself by segregating young people from the adult world.

□ Can you think of some examples of this?

■ Industrial societies place adolescents in rigidly age-graded compulsory education which is separated from the adult world, and impose a large number of formal legal rules governing the transition to adulthood: when you can marry, have sex, buy a drink, vote, leave school, and so on.

In Chapter 7, we considered the arguments of the French historian, Philippe Aries, that our view of childhood is a modern creation. The British sociologist and anthropologist, Frank Musgrove, has applied a similar argument to adolescence:

> The adolescent was invented at the same time as the steam-engine. The principal architect of the latter was Watt in 1765, of the former Rousseau in 1862 ... the tailor, the publisher, the social reformer and the educator came to Rousseau's assistance: they began in the latter eighteenth and early nineteenth centuries to cater for a specific age-group of 'young persons', neither children nor adults. Instead of wearing imitation adult clothing, young people at the end of the eighteenth century had their distinctive uniform, including 'long trousers', which actually anticipated the grown-up fashions of the future ...
>
> Reforms of the penal system and of factory conditions also distinguished 'young persons' from children on the one hand and from adults on the other ... The Youthful Offenders Act of 1854 enabled magistrates to treat young offenders and adult criminals differently. The Factory Acts of 1833 and 1847 distinguished the age-group 13–18 as needing protection from the full rigours of the adult world and restricted their hours of labour. Social legislation and changing social conventions *made* the adolescent. Areas of experience and knowledge were now designated 'adult' from which the less-than-adult must be shielded. (Musgrove, 1964, pp.33–34)

The transition from this 'twilight zone' to fully adult status tends to be associated with certain key events. As we noted in Chapter 2, you could remain 'a boy' in pre-war rural Ireland as long as your father stayed alive, and marriage for the eldest son could only follow attaining his inheritance. Changes in the significant indicators of adult status over time have been examined by the American historian, John Modell, and his colleagues. They defined five key transition points for the entry into adulthood: leaving school, entering the workforce, leaving home, getting married and setting up a new home. They then compared data from the 1870 Census for Philadelphia with that of the 1970 Census for the whole of the USA, calculating the mean age at which each of these transition points was accomplished in 1870 and 1970 and the length of time it took for the majority of the cohort to accomplish these acts (see Figure 10.7).

□ Examine Figure 10.7. What are the differences between 1870 and 1970 in the age at which young people entered the labour force, and got married?

■ Both males and females entered the labour force at a slightly later age in 1970 than they did 100 years earlier, but at the same time they also married much younger and much sooner after finding a job. As a result, whereas in 1870 in Philadelphia there was no overlap at all for either sex between entering the labour force and getting married, there was a very significant overlap in 1970. Some people were getting married *before* they found work.

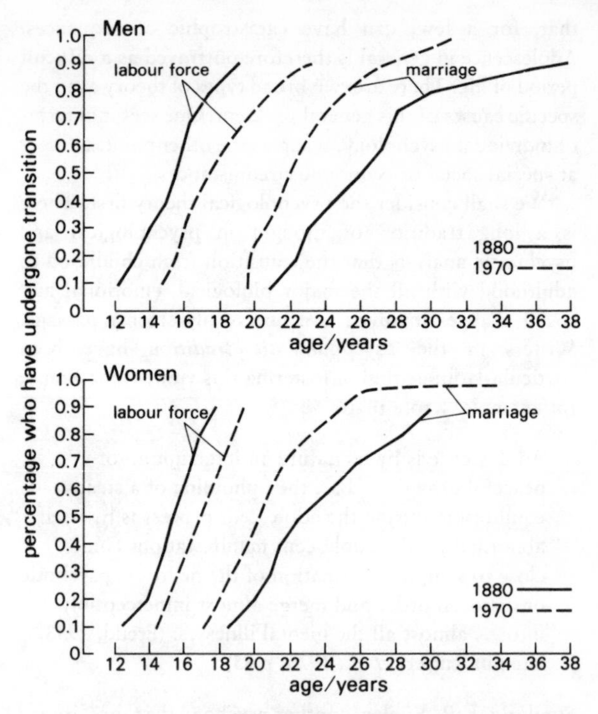

Figure 10.7 Range of the ages during which the transitions into the labour force and into marriage were made in 1880 and 1970, by sex. (Data from Modell *et al.*, pp.20–21)

□ There are, however, a number of problems with generalising from this study. What are they?

■ First, Philadelphia may not be representative of the rest of the USA in 1870. Second, the meaning of adulthood may have changed over this period — perhaps marriage now does not represent quite the same kind of transition that it did then. Third, what if the researchers were now to compare 1980 with 1870? The economic depression of the last decade seems likely to have affected certain key transitions, in particular that into the workforce. Cross-sectional data like this ignores the impact of the economic and birth cycles discussed in Chapter 3. At one point there might be relatively few teenagers and many jobs, at another there might be masses of adolescents and very little work.

Such changes since 1870 have been put forward to explain the problematic nature of becoming an adult in the modern industrialised world. For example, the two transitions external to the family (leaving school and entering work) started earlier in the nineteenth century and required less time for the cohort to pass through. By contrast, the three familial transitions — leaving home, getting married and setting up one's own home — all started at a later age in 1870 and took a lot longer to complete than in 1970. In the twentieth century, the extension of the *school-leaving age* and the growth of higher education appears to have lengthened the early stages of the transition to adulthood but, at the same time, the later stages, such as getting married and setting up one's home, have dramatically contracted. The transition from youth to adult status would, therefore, seem to be far more rapid in the USA in 1970. Moreover, whereas in 1870 individuals moved into adulthood at markedly different speeds, by 1970 almost the entire age-group is moving at roughly the same point in time. Thus, for example, the potential labour force is swelled by an influx of school leavers at the same time each year, making the search for work that much more difficult.

In summary, we may draw four possible conclusions about the social status of contemporary adolescents and the social and economic factors that shape their transition to adulthood, each of which may have important consequences for their health. First, the segregation of adolescents may cause considerable disaffection with the adult world; second, given that segregation, a rapid shift afterwards into adulthood may also cause problems; and third, what is the effect upon adolescents who have been segregated and trained over many years, if, at the end of the day, there is no work for them when they are finally free to join the adult world? And, finally, if the gender roles to which adolescents must conform contain destructive elements, these can also be a source of problems. Others, however, have cast a much more sceptical eye over the debate.

Adolescence as normal

Consider, for example, the viewpoint of the *Oxford Textbook of Psychiatry*. Out of more than 750 pages, its authors devote only three pages specifically to adolescence, and open with the firm statement: 'There are no specific disorders of adolescence.' (Gelder, *et al.*, 1983, p.677). This assertion is based on three arguments. First, although there is some strain and stress in the transition to adulthood, this has been very much overstated and does not result in any specific psychiatric problems. Second, although some adolescents do have psychiatric problems, these represent either the continuation of childhood psychiatric disorders or else the start of more adult kinds of problem. For example, anorexia nervosa should not be seen as a specifically adolescent disorder but one to which both adolescents and adults are prone. And third, it is mistaken to equate juvenile delinquency with psychological disorder. Most delinquents show no sign of such disorder, and conversely, many psychiatrically disturbed adolescents are not delinquent. On this analysis, juvenile delinquency is largely a social, not a psychological, problem.

To assess the validity of such a viewpoint, we need to take a closer look at some evidence about what is normal, or otherwise, in adolescence. In particular, how do people actually experience this period and the transition to adulthood? Two British sociologists, Frank Musgrove and Roger Middleton, were interested in what people saw as the significant stages and turning points in their lives, and to investigate this, they held lengthy informal interviews in 1981 with 24 people, mostly men, in three occupational groups: professional footballers in their twenties, schoolteachers in their thirties, and retired Methodist ministers and their wives.

None of those interviewed saw adolescence as a difficult stage in life. 'I was always happy at home with my mum and dad', said one footballer. 'My Mum never put a curfew on me', said another. 'She thinks I'm a big boy and can look after myself'. 'I had a very happy home life,' said a teacher, 'We didn't really have any major conflicts. Well, there were differences, of course. Smoking and drinking, that sort of thing. But adolescence was not the traumatic experience for me that it may be for others'. One of the footballers suggested that his lack of problems was due to the indifference of his mother. 'My mother has never been particularly interested in anything I've done. It sounds terrible, but it isn't really. She just left it all up to me.' (Musgrove and Middleton, 1981, p.43).

Likewise, one of the women teachers, a geography graduate, now in her thirties, commented:

> I came from a very working-class background, but the sort of working-class area where children are encouraged to get on . . . I missed out on adolescent development because I didn't have any sort of conflict with my parents. No conflict of any sort. They encouraged me. I was a bookwormish little lady.' (op. cit., p.44)

There are obviously problems with generalising from such a small, predominantly male sample, all in relatively high status occupations, who are looking back on past events. But the view of adolescence as generally unproblematic except for minor conflicts about 'smoking and drinking' has been borne out by a much larger study in the Isle of Wight. In 1970, Michael Rutter and his colleagues published results from a study of a large number of children whose psychological state was assessed by questionnaire at several points in time. When children were questioned at 14 years of age, it emerged that major rebellion and alienation from parents was unusual. There was, however, some support for the theory of inner turmoil: about half of all these adolescents reported periods of misery and self-deprecation, but these seldom lasted long and, apparently, were seldom noticed by adults. Finally, it was noted that as adolescents got older, rebellious behaviour did become more common and some became estranged from school during their last year. However, rebelliousness is not usually an indication of psychiatric disorder.

Finally, note that the key judgements involved in the assessment of adolescent behaviour as problematic are made by members of a different age-group who themselves have an interest in the outcome. Perhaps it is sometimes the case that the adolescents' behaviour is normal and the problem lies with the adults. The dominant view of what constitutes a poorly adjusted adolescent is itself also a social construct, determined partly by adult tastes in clothes, music and leisure activities; adolescents who do not conform to adult ways may easily be seen as rebellious or delinquent.

What conclusions can be drawn from all this? Is adolescence a period of intense inner conflict and social pressures — or has too much been made of stress in the transition to adulthood? We have summarised the arguments and some influential research studies, to which you will no doubt add your personal experience, but as with so many debates about health and disease there is no clear-cut answer. Critics of the view that adolescence holds special problems argue that the task of constructing an identity — a coherent sense of self — goes on throughout life. Indeed, the final chapter of this book considers the possibility that every major event in a person's life causes disruption to that sense of self, and requires a period of reconstruction thereafter. Furthermore, in a society such as ours where a fairly rigid system of age-grading chops up a lifetime into recognisable stages, the transition between one stage and another will create tension, no matter what the person's age. In later chapters we shall discuss other points of transition that are difficult for many people, for example, the menopause and retirement from work.

However, arguments such as these do not detract from the reality that for some adolescents and young adults very serious health problems arise which seem to bear some relationship to age. What has been omitted up to now has been a detailed consideration of such problems; we shall therefore conclude the chapter with two case studies — anorexia nervosa and motor cycle accidents.

Understanding anorexia

> All I want is to become thinner and thinner. It is this eternal tension between wanting to become thin and not give up eating that is so exhausting. In all other points I am reasonable, but I know on this point I am crazy. I am really ruining myself in this endless struggle against my nature. Fate wanted me to be heavy and strong but I want to be thin and delicate.

Anorexia nervosa is an eating disorder that is thought to affect up to 1 per cent of all adolescent girls and young women, but which is uncommon in young men. People with this condition are excessively thin (less than 75 per cent of normal body weight) but want to get thinner. They believe that they are grossly overweight and that eating normally will make them fatter. Although starving is a characteristic of anorexia, there may be periods of 'binge eating' or eating apparently normal meals, though this is usually followed by taking laxatives or forced vomiting, through sticking fingers down the throat. In this way, sufferers may be able to conceal the reason for their steady weight loss. Other common symptoms caused by starvation are cessation of menstrual periods, excess growth of body hair, a dry or scaly skin, coolness of the hands and feet, and an increase in tooth decay. Some anorexia patients have died as a result of starvation.

Newspaper accounts have tended to portray anorexia as a modern scourge that inexplicably strikes down young women. But closer inspection reveals a much more complex picture: for example, working-class girls are less likely to suffer from it than those from middle- or upper-class backgrounds; some boys develop anorexia, as do some adults, and, far from being a modern phenomenon, the condition was described as long ago as the seventeenth century. Theories that it is caused by some biological malfunction, possibly of the hormonal system, have not been able to explain all the features of the disease, particularly its class distribution. Most researchers, therefore, favour an explanation in terms of either the internal psychological state of the sufferer, or the effects on their mind of external social factors such as their family, the pressure of school or work, or the type of role society expects them to play.

Consider the two descriptions of anorexia below, the first written in 1689 by Richard Morton, the first doctor to describe anorexia nervosa; the second from a recent autobiography by Sheila MacLeod, who suffered from the condition for two years during her adolescence.

> Mr. Duke's daughter in S. Mary Ax, in the year 1684 and the Eighteenth year of her Age, in the Month of July fell into a total suppression of her Monthly Courses from a multitude of Cares and Passions of her Mind, but without any Symptoms of the Green-Sicknesse following upon it. From which time her Appetite began to abate, and her digestion to be bad; her Flesh began to be flaccid and loose, and her Looks pale, with other symptoms usual in Universal Consumption of the Habit of the Body ... she was wont by her studying at Night, and continual poring upon Books, to expose herself both Day and Night to the Injuries of the Air, which was at that time

> extremely cold, not without some manifest Prejudice to the System of her Nerves ... I do not remember that I did ever in all my practice see one that was conversant with the Living so much wasted (like a Skeleton clad only with Skin) ... (Morton, cited in Halmi, 1980, p.1882)

> [After a description of her happy childhood] In order to arrive at the truth behind the idyll, I must return to the matter of attributions. As I remember, the three adjectives applied to me most consistently throughout my early childhood were 'clever', 'good', and 'healthy'. Achievement, especially academic achievement, was what being clever was all about. I was destined for great things — Oxford or Cambridge, a string of letters after my name, a successful academic career, and would no doubt end up being the first woman Prime Minister. This sort of thing was impressed upon me by my whole family ... I thrived on the praise and admiration, loved to show off, and secretly (or not so secretly) thought myself superior to older children who had not yet acquired my special skills. But even more secret, so secret that I could scarcely admit it to myself, was my sense of inadequacy. I read and read, but increasingly, as I grew older, understood very little of what I read. (MacLeod, 1981, pp.31–32)

□ What are the similarities and differences in the explanations offered for anorexia in these two accounts?

■ Both accounts see anorexia as a predominantly 'mental' rather than a biological disorder, and both share an obsession with studying and academic achievement as part of the overall picture of the disease. However, Morton sees the 'poring upon Books' in the same light as 'exposing herself both Day and Night to the Injuries of the Air' — as *consequences* of the patient's disordered mind; MacLeod sees her obsession with studying as directedly implicated in the *causes* of the anorexia, in particular the discrepancy between her family's high expectations and her secret feelings of inadequacy.

MacLeod's emphasis upon the role of the family has been shared by many other writers. Some nineteenth-century psychiatrists advised that it was best for the anorexic patient to be separated from her family, and the most influential theory in current American psychiatry has recently been summarised as follows:

> The patient comes from an upper middle class, highly achievement-orientated family that values slimness and physical exercise. Mother and perhaps others in the family are constantly vigilant about weight. The family presents a facade of psychological health, but certain conflicts lurk below the surface between the parents. Because of lack of fulfilment as a couple, the parents find themselves striving for fulfilment in other areas: the mother in her children and the father in his occupation. The family communicates along few, narrow lines (among which is food). There is a channel of concern towards the pre-anorectic child so that the mother might become excessively involved with her. The mother might be over-directive, yet fail to acknowledge the child's individuality, and at the same time fearful of the child's impending or beginning adolescent psychosexual development and separation from the home and family. The over-directed child pursues the high-achievement orientation so valued by the family and becomes more concerned with external approval than with internal satisfaction. The pre-anorectic child feels that there are very few areas for real self-determination and self-control and develops a fragile self-image ... At a point of family disequilibrium ... the anorexia nervosa syndrome develops. (Yager, 1981, p.378)

Thus the child becomes afraid to 'grow up', starves herself so that womanly curves and menstrual periods disappear, and exercises control over the only thing left to her — the intake of food. In some accounts she uses this as a weapon against the oppressive mother; in others, by staying a child she believes she holds together a maritial relationship that survives only as long as there are dependent children. Such a pattern has also been observed in the family backgrounds of the occasional male adolescent with anorexia. For example, consider the following case history:

> The patient's eating difficulties started when he was aged 11. At this time his mother was admitted to hospital for a hysterectomy. This coincided with intense pressure from his father with regard to the patient sitting the 11-plus exam. The patient rapidly developed obsessional symptoms, including rituals of dressing and eating, which so affected his behaviour that they precluded him from attending school at all ... his obsessional symptoms persisted and his weight remained at approximately the same level and did not increase as he grew older. He was eventually admitted to the Maudsley [Hospital] at the age of 17 years ... He denied having any sexual interest and reacted in a childish fashion to the attentions of adolescent female patients ... (Beaumont, Beardwood and Russell, 1972, p.220)

However, there is a flaw in the explanation of anorexia as resulting solely from pressures within the family.

□ What does this theory not explain about the distribution of anorexia in the population?

- It does not explain why girls should suffer from the condition so much more often than boys; nor does it wholly account for the class distribution, since unfulfilled marital relationships and parents who want their children to achieve academic excellence are not confined to middle-class families.

Most conventional psychiatric theories of anorexia pay little systematic attention to this fact. There is, however, a variety of feminist arguments, all of which stress that the explanation for anorexia lies ultimately in the gender roles that girls and women are conventionally supposed to fulfil — roles summarised in the following quotation from a poem by Tennyson:

> Man is the hunter; woman is his game;
> The sleek and shining creatures of the chase,
> We hunt them for the beauty of their skins ...
>
> Man for the field and woman for the hearth:
> Man for the sword and for the needle she:
> Man with the head and woman with the heart:
> Man to command and woman to obey:
> All else confusion.
> (Tennyson (1809–92), *The Princess*, lines 147–149, 427–431)

According to MacLeod, it was the tension between this conventional subordinate vision of womanhood and her family's statement that she was clever and would have a great career, that provoked her anorexia:

> It is easy to see how an assumption of male superiority on the part of society at large can lead to psychosomatic disorders of an educated female population which has been freed from a round-the-clock drudgery of physical labour but has not yet been allowed to participate fully and on equal terms with men in the more psychologically satisfying occupations outside the home. (MacLeod, 1981, p.22)

This in itself does not explain the obsession with food. Another feminist writer, this time a psychotherapist, Marilyn Lawrence, has however pointed to the centrality of food in women's lives. Most women are, as Tennyson suggests they should be, in some sense tied to the hearth:

> Women are the prime and generally exclusive targets of all the propaganda about food, both medical and commercial. Food in our society and in most others it seems is regarded as the responsibility of women. It is one of the few areas of life in which we are expected to be in control. Responsibility for the provision of food does not just mean that we do the cooking (although within the home this is usually the case). Women spend very large amounts of time thinking about food, shopping, planning meals, studying the nutritional pros and cons of different foods and trying to reconcile these with other people's preferences, our own time and, of course, the constraints of the family budget ... (Lawrence, 1984, pp.28–29)

Finally, many commentators, feminists and non-feminists alike, have argued that anorexia is in large part a product of Western notions of female beauty. Whereas in poorer, more traditional societies, fatness is often highly valued (thus a traditional Punjabi compliment is 'you look fat and fresh today'), in richer industrial countries, there is now a major emphasis on thinness as the ideal bodily form for women. Such a view is given credence by the fact that by 1984 only two cases of anorexia nervosa had *ever* been reported among black Africans in the English-language medical journals (Nwaefuna, 1981). Similarly, a survey by Neil Buhrich in 1981 of 17 out of the 18 psychiatrists practising in Malaysia in 1978 showed that of the approximately 60 000 new referrals they had seen since they became consultants, only 30 were cases of anorexia.

There is some evidence that the 'ideal' shape for Western women has become thinner; for example, in the slimness of fashion models chosen in the 1960s (some will recall Twiggy). A study of American 'beauty queens' and Playboy centrefolds by David Garner and colleagues in 1980 revealed that their average weight declined during the 1970s. Note also that Miss America winners from 1970–78 weighed only 82.5 per cent of the average weight of American women of that age, and also weighed significantly less than the average for losing contestants. Feminist writers have argued that it is precisely because women are hunted 'for the beauty of their skins' that they are vulnerable to such changes in fashion and the problems of self-worth that may result.

There are, therefore, a variety of theories that attempt to explain anorexia nervosa: hormonal imbalance — though relatively few researchers hold this view; tensions within the family that place intolerable pressure on particular children; and several complementary theories that seek the answer in women's social role — the obligation to be beautiful and the idealisation of slimness; the central role of food in women's lives; the extreme pressure involved in striving for a career in a world still dominated by men.

These theories need not be mutually exclusive — indeed, such a range of explanations is necessary to account for the range of individuals who suffer from the condition — including boys and men, adult women who showed no tendency towards anorexia in adolescence, people from families where academic achievement was not a goal. It may be a mistake to consider anorexia nervosa as a single unified condition — it could be a response to various kinds of pressure.

A major stumbling block to a better understanding of anorexia nervosa is the fact that most research has been in the form of retrospective studies of the life history of patients, with little attention paid to adequate control groups with which they may be compared. For example, despite a century of claims that the family of the anorexic patient is also disturbed — and this is currently the standard theory in American psychiatry — no one has yet compared the behaviour of such families with that found in other families without anorexic children.

Likewise, a good deal has been made of the finding that anorexic women considerably over-estimate their body width. However, when such experiments were also conducted on non-anorexic women of similar age, there were no significant differences between the two groups; both over-estimated their body size. No one has checked to see if men also exhibit this phenomenon.

There has also been remarkably little attention paid to the unusual class distribution of this condition, its rarity among the people of Third World countries, and its relationship to other eating disorders that predominantly affect women. For example, consider Figure 10.8:

□ What do you notice about these data?

■ Obesity is far more common among working-class schoolgirls in America than among their middle-class counterparts.

Obesity is no less a health problem than anorexia; it is far more common, does not tend to disappear as the person gets older, and is associated with numerous types of ill-health and increased risk of premature death, especially from heart or blood-vessel deterioration (*cardiovascular diseases*). Of course, obesity is not an exclusively female problem, but adolescent girls are far more likely to be overweight than boys.

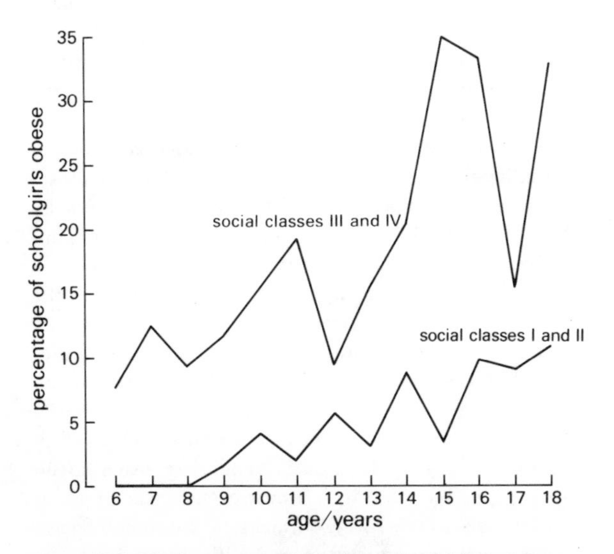

Figure 10.8 Obesity among 3 344 white schoolgirls in 3 Eastern American cities by social class. (Data from Stunkard *et al.*, 1972)

And the list of eating disorders to which women are especially prone does not end there. Another condition, known as *bulimia nervosa*, was definitively identified only in the 1970s yet seems to be at least as common as anorexia. It has attracted less attention because unlike anorexia, the sufferer is of normal weight and instead of starving herself alternates in the extreme form between bouts of uncontrollable or 'binge' eating in which large quantities of food are consumed, followed by deliberate vomiting and the use of laxatives in an attempt to control weight gain.

In 1984, two British psychologists and a psychiatrist (Peter Cooper, George Waterman and Christopher Fairburn) published a study of 364 women attending a family-planning clinic. It revealed that over 25 per cent of the women admitted to occasional bouts of binge eating, and 7.4 per cent said this happened more than once a week.

In addition, the historian and general practitioner Irvine Loudon has recently pointed out that there is yet a further major eating disorder to which anorexia may be related. Richard Morton in his description of Mr. Duke's daughter cited earlier, distinguished her case from that of 'Green-Sicknesse' or *chlorosis* as it was more technically known. Chlorosis seems to have disappeared or perhaps to have been re-classified, but around 1800 it was one of the most prominent of medical conditions, accounting for between 1 and 5 per cent of all cases seen in hospital out-patient departments. Patients were predominantly female, had a reduced food intake, depression and cessation of menstrual periods. They also suffered from *pica*, the craving for strange foods that some pregnant women experience. One nineteenth-century physician said that their tastes were

> ... directed to something dry and tasty — something that will endure mastication and make a pleasant crackle. I believe there are very few young women that do not eat rice or unground coffee; more rarely, hard herring uncooked, or salt, mortar, chalk, cinders, sealing-wax, and other dry, tasty, crackly edibles. (cited in Loudon, 1980, p.1672)

Whether pica should be seen as a 'disorder' is dubious, but it is one of a range of obsessional behaviours relating to food that predominantly affect women. They cannot all be explained by over-ambitious families pressing adolescent girls towards academic achievement, and we are forced to reconsider the central place of food in the lives of women, and cultural ideals that exert pressure on what a woman can eat. It may be that under the pressure of certain family or cultural expectations, some men react rather similarly to women but are much less likely to be seen as 'sick'. An article by two American psychiatrists and a psychologist

(Alayne Yates, Kevin Leehey and Catherine Shisslak) points to the similarity between anorexic women and those they term '*obligatory runners*' — long distance runners, usually men, who are obsessed with running, with their body-weight, with the special dieting that such running involves and who often run against medical advice. They conclude:

> Cultural ideals contribute to the two disorders: the runner aspires to athletic prowess and the dieter to slimness. From an early age both are strongly reinforced by society for their mastery, autonomy and bodily control. However, when dieting or physical activity becomes an intense and exclusive focus, the woman tends to be categorised as anorexic, which connotes sickness, whereas the man will be viewed as an unusually dedicated athlete. (Yates, Leehey and Shisslak, 1983, p.254)

This is strongly reminiscent of arguments put forward elsewhere in this course; that women are more likely to be seen as 'sickly' or to attract a diagnosis of mental disorder than are men.* When men take risks with their health, they are more likely to be seen as 'brave' or 'athletic' — a subject to which we now turn.

Understanding motor-cycle accidents

Almost a quarter of all fatal and serious injuries sustained in traffic accidents occur to motor cyclists and their passengers. Moreover, fatalities from *motor-cycle accidents* account for more than half of all road accident deaths in the 17–19 year age group. The majority of these deaths and injuries occur to young men.

Motor bikes are the most dangerous of all forms of road transport. Not only are they capable of very high speeds, but they are often hard for other road users to spot, and they offer little protection if an accident does occur. A study by the Transport and Road Research Laboratory which surveyed all the motor-bike accidents reported to the police in the Berkshire area in 1974 showed that 75 per cent of the riders struck their head on something during the accident, and 62 per cent of all severe injuries were to the legs. Of the 450 injured motorcyclists, 5 died and 95 were classified as receiving severe injuries. The age distribution of these motor cyclists is shown in Figure 10.9.

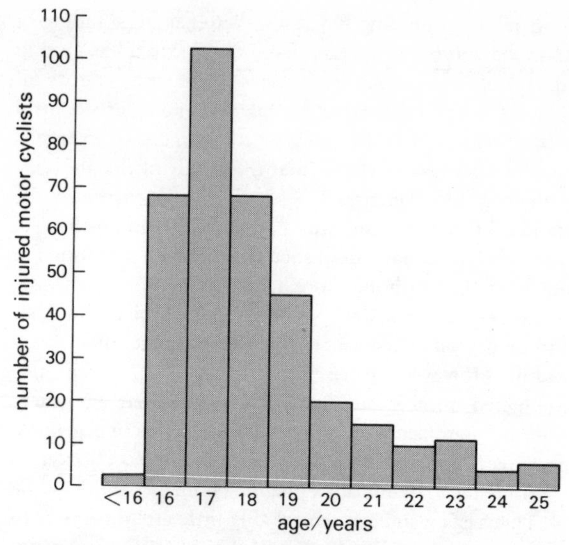

Figure 10.9 Age distribution of 450 injured motorcyclists in Berkshire area, UK, 1974. (Data from Whitaker, 1980, p.26)

□ Why should the motorbike accident rate be so high in the 16–20 year age-group?

■ There are several possible explanations. One is that it relates to teenage rebellion or identity crisis. Another is that people of such ages are still learning how to drive safely on roads. A third possibility is that young people lack the money to afford safer means of transport such as cars.

All of these theories may have some truth in them. However, none of them explains why it is young men rather than young women who should be particularly vulnerable in this respect. How can we account for this?

The reasons underlying motor-cycle accidents have been researched far less than the causes of anorexia nervosa, but it is interesting — if speculative — to consider whether *male gender roles* have some bearing on the matter.

Just as a good part of the answer to anorexia may lie in conventional notions of female duty and beauty, so cultural expectations about masculinity, particularly the criteria by which 'manhood' is judged, may explain the preponderance of young men who sustain injuries while riding a motor bike. This type of argument was put forward by the American essayist and social commentator Tom Wolfe, writing about the extraordinarily high rate of fatalities suffered by US Navy fighter-pilots in peacetime — one in four die in plane crashes!

To test the theory we want you to read an extract from Wolfe's book, *The Right Stuff*, and then listen to an audiotape we recorded with motor cyclists talking about their attitudes to this form of transport. We shall then ask you to point out similarities and differences. First, the fighter pilots.

*See Book II, *Medical Knowledge: Doubt and Certainty*, Chapters 8 and 9 for a discussion of hysteria; Book III, *The Health of Nations*, Chapter 9 for a discussion of consultation rates among women; Book VI, *Experiencing and Explaining Disease*, Chapter 8 for a discussion of the prevalence of depression among women.

'Bikers' (Photo: J. Allan Cash)

From *The Right Stuff* by Tom Wolfe, 1981

... simply taking off in a single-engine jet fighter of the Century series, such as an F-102, or any of the military's other marvellous bricks with fins on them — presented a man, on a perfectly sunny day, with more ways to get himself killed than his wife and children could imagine in their wildest fears. If he was barreling down the runway at two hundred miles an hour, completing the take off run, and the board started lighting up red, should he (a) abort the take off (and try to wrestle with the monster which was gorged with jet fuel, out in the sand beyond the end of the runway) or (b) eject (and hope that the goddamned human cannonball trick works at zero altitude and he doesn't shatter an elbow or a kneecap on the way out) or (c) continue the take off and deal with the problem aloft (knowing full well that the ship may be on fire and therefore seconds away from exploding)? He would have one second to sort out the options and act, and this kind of little workaday decision came up all the time ... (p.26)

... A young man might go into military flight training believing that he was entering some sort of technical school in which he was simply going to acquire a certain set of skills. Instead, he found himself all at once enclosed in a fraternity. And in this fraternity, even though it was military, men were not rated by their outward rank as ensigns, lieutenants, commanders or whatever. No, herein the world was divided into those who had it and those who did not. This quality, this 'it', was never named, however, nor was it talked about in any way.

As to what this ineffable quality was ... well, it obviously involved bravery. But it was not bravery in the simple sense of being willing to risk your life. The idea seemed to be that any fool could do that, if that was all that was required ... No, the idea here (in the all-enclosing fraternity) seemed to be that a man should have the ability to go up in a hurtling piece of machinery and put his hide on the line and then have the moxie, the reflexes, the experience, the coolness, to pull back in the last yawning moment ... and ultimately, in its best expression, do so in a cause that means something to thousands, to a people, a nation, to humanity, to God. Nor was there *a test* to show whether or not a pilot had this righteous quality. There was, instead, a seemingly infinite series of tests. A career in flying was like climbing one of those ancient Babylonian pyramids made up of a dizzy progression of steps and ledges, a ziggurat, a pyramid extraordinarily high and steep; and the idea was to prove at every foot of the way up that pyramid that you were one of the elected and anointed ones who had *the right stuff* ... (pp.18–19)

> At every level in one's progress up that staggeringly high pyramid the world was once more divided into those men who had the right stuff to continue the climb and those who had to be *left behind* in the most obvious way . . . (p.19) And in what test had [the washout] been found wanting? Why it seemed to be nothing less than his *manhood* itself. Naturally, this was never mentioned either. Yet there it was. *Manliness, manhood, manly courage* . . . (p.22) . . . To talk about it in so many words was forbidden, of course. The very words, *death, danger, bravery, fear,* were not to be uttered except in the occasional specific instance or for ironic effect. Nevertheless, the subject could be adumbrated in *code*, or by *example*. Hence the endless evenings of pilots huddled together talking about flying. On these long and drunken evenings (the bane of their family life) certain theorems would be propounded and demonstrated — and all by *code* and *example*. One theorem was: there are no *accidents* and no fatal flaws in the machines; there are only pilots with the wrong stuff (i.e. blind Fate can't kill me) . . . (p.27)
>
> Once the theorem [was] understood, the Navy's statistics about one in every four Navy aviators dying [in peacetime] meant nothing. The figures were averages, and averages applied to those with average stuff. (p.28)

Now compare Wolfe's analysis of the culture of American fighter pilots with the comments about motor cycling made by some keen British 'bikers' who are interviewed on the audiotape 'You just live for your bike' (Cassette AC805, Band 2). Play the tape now and note the main similarities between Wolfe's description of the pilots and the remarks made by the bikers.

The most obvious similarity is that the bikers emphasise the allure of what Wolfe refers to as 'putting your hide on the line'. Thus one biker comments, 'The end of it is you are gambling that your skill, ability, luck will last out long enough. Your good judgement, this is the main thing behind it. What you are actually putting down on the line is your life.'. There is also an emphasis in both groups on fraternity, on the benefits to be gained from talking and mixing with fellow pilots or bikers. '. . . the other thing is the comradeship . . . you can always talk about bikes to a biker.'. A distinction is made between 'real' bikers and those who simply ride bikes for transport or are 'posers' — this is strongly reminiscent of pilots who have 'average' or the wrong 'stuff'.

Both groups normally avoid the subject of death, and, when the subject is raised, they have highly elaborate ways of distancing themselves from it. The pilots stress that the statistics mean nothing for they only apply to those with average stuff; the motor cyclists minimise the threat by arguing that death is not to be feared since we do not know what it means: 'If it happens, it happens. Nobody has yet come up with an absolutely cast-iron idea of what happens on death or after death. So it's nothing I'll know until I try it.'

Finally, although the motor cyclists do not discuss why the majority of 'real bikers' are male, their description of the special qualities required are very similar to Wolfe's perceptions about 'manliness' and 'manly courage' being the basis of the 'right stuff'. For example:

> You have to be able to think fast, reflexes.
>
> You can forget drugs — at speed on a bike, you're the closest to flying you're ever likely to get.
>
> There are times where it might have been wiser to slow down, yeah . . . but you just think, what the hell — go for it.
>
> There's a certain more animal, the bigger bike you've got . . .
>
> When I first got my 750 I was practically scared of it — now I like to think I can throw it into all sorts of corners, get it in, make it do what I want it to do.
>
> There's a lot more risk in town. I suppose it's a mentality of wanting freedom, devil-may-care in some respects . . . you've got to be, some might say, screwball in the head.
>
> If I die, it's my business.

According to these young men, girl bikers either use a little bike to get to and from work, are 'obviously posing' or use a big bike the same way anybody else would use a car. The very rare girls who are real bikers have to be 'dedicated to say the least' because of all the pressure against women riding fast bikes, especially by parents. And real bikers are always young — older men do not have what it takes to ride in such a devil-may-care fashion even when they really enjoy riding their bikes, and these interviewees foresaw the possibility that they might have to slow down in the future when they had responsibilities to a wife and children.

□ Do you notice any differences between Wolfe's description of the fighter pilots and the motor cyclists' account of their way of life?

■ Unlike the pilots, the bikers are an informal group. They have not had to climb a formal bureaucratic ziggurat to qualify — many people can afford a motorbike. Nor is biking anywhere near as dangerous as being a Navy fighter pilot. Further, whereas the pilots are members of a highly prestigious elite, bikers are often viewed as a deviant minority who are a danger to the rest of the public — the two motor cyclists interviewed therefore spent some time distinguishing themselves from Hell's Angels. Also, the bikers are in competition with other types of road user, particularly car drivers; the pilots are on their own. But perhaps most importantly, the bikers stress that genuine 'accidents' can happen; the bike itself can malfunction; and the rider has an obligation to wear sensible protective clothing, and more or less observe speed limits — Wolfe's fighter pilots, on the other hand, considered that 'there are no accidents and no fatal flaws in the machines; there are only pilots with the wrong stuff'.

These differences are largely in the degree to which the dangerous activity is pursued despite the risks. Biking offers, in a relatively cheap and accessible form, some of the thrills and the danger that being a fighter pilot offers to an elite of men. And both express in their different ways a central aspect of the conventional male role. Tennyson ascribed the 'sword' to men and called them 'hunters'. Shakespeare wrote of 'seeking the bubble reputation even in the cannon's mouth'. Of course, not every man aspires to heroism, just as not every woman aspires to 'beauty' or home cooking. Nonetheless, every member of each sex feels some pressure in the direction dictated by cultural expectations, and some pursue (or flee from) these ideals with great fervour, sometimes to the detriment of their health. In both cases, it would seem, it is those on the verge of adulthood who feel the greatest pressure. But the main cause would seem to lie not so much in the strains of that transition as in the nature of the adult identities on offer. Heroism and beauty have their casualties as well as their rewards.

In the next two chapters we shall look at two other sources of stress and anxiety that are commonly experienced in adult life — the consequences of sexual relationships for health, and the effects of the 'working day'.

Objectives for Chapter 10

When you have studied this chapter, you should be able to:

10.1 Describe the major physiological changes that occur during puberty and outline the principal sources of anxiety for adolescents relating to these changes.

10.2 Discuss the health of adolescents with reference to: (i) mortality and morbidity data for this age group; (ii) theories that adolescence is either particularly problematic or no more difficult than other periods of life; (iii) historical shifts in the measures of adult status.

10.3 Discuss the various explanations that have been put forward for the predominance of anorexia nervosa among young women, and motor-cycle accidents among young men.

Questions for Chapter 10

1 (*Objective 10.1*) One of the letters reprinted from the problem page of a girls' comic was a complaint from a 12-year-old that her mother refused to tell her about periods, the need for a bra or the use of a deodorant. In what ways might the girl's anxiety be related to her *age*?

2 (*Objective 10.2*) Anna Freud regarded 'disharmony within the psychic structure' as a basic fact of adolescence. However, what are the social factors that, rather than individual psychological development, might cause disharmony in this age-group.

3 (*Objective 10.3*)

> When a fighter-pilot was in training ... his superiors were continually spelling out strict rules for him, about the use of the aircraft and conduct in the sky. They repeatedly forbade so-called hot-dog stunts, such as outside loops, buzzing, flat-hatting, hedgehopping and flying under bridges. But somehow one got the message that the man who truly *had* it could ignore these rules — not that he should but that he *could* — and that after all there was only one way to find out — and that in some strange unofficial way, peeking through his fingers, his instructor halfway expected him to challenge all the limits ... every unofficial impulse on the base seemed to be saying: Hell, we wouldn't give you a nickel for a pilot who hasn't done some crazy rat-racing like that. It's all part of the right stuff. (Wolfe, 1981, pp.24–25)

How might such an attitude explain the high rate of motor-bike accidents among young men in the UK, and could it be used to explain other types of adolescent 'deviance'?

11 Sex and reproduction

This chapter builds on the discussion of the reproductive system in Book IV, *The Biology of Health and Disease*, Chapter 10.

Sex and *reproduction* play an important part in the lives of most adults in this, as in other, societies. The commencement of sexual relationships is seen as a significant step towards adulthood — one that *heterosexuals* may not take legally in the UK under 16 years of age; male *homosexuals* do not reach the legal 'age of consent' until 21. Just as our society tries to exclude some of its members from sexual activity on the grounds of youth, so too it considers that people above a certain age are (or should be) 'past it'. In between fall the fertile years when to remain celibate for long often attracts pity or ridicule, unless it is part of a religious dedication. Rearing children is (among many other things) a statement to the world for some people that they are fertile, heterosexual and mature — indeed, couples who choose to remain childless may be branded as selfish or immature, while the failure to conceive can sometimes bring with it a crushing sense of inadequacy.

The fact that we have called this chapter sex *and* reproduction demands some comment. Sex *without* reproduction, that is sex 'for its own sake', has often been considered immoral in Western society. Even though most heterosexual couples nowadays are encouraged to 'plan' their families, it is considered natural by many that sexual activity should lead to reproduction at some point in an adult's life, and for some religious groups the use of contraceptives remains forbidden. Taboos against sexual relationships that have no intention or possibility of reproduction may underly society's attitudes against young or old people having sex, and against homosexual activity.

The interaction between sex and reproduction has become even more complex in recent years with the perfection of *artificial insemination* and *in vitro fertilisation** techniques, so that reproduction is now possible without sexual contact between the 'parents'. In studying

*The technique of fertilising an egg outside a woman's body, and allowing it to begin cell division before reimplanting it in her womb. *In vitro* is Latin for 'in glass', meaning in a laboratory flask or dish.

the material in this chapter you should bear in mind that although sex and reproduction can be biologically divisible activities, cultural attitudes often see them as inseparable.

For many people sex and reproduction should, ideally, be sources of pleasure and fulfilment, but everyone feels anxiety about one or both these areas of human experience at some time in life, and for some people they represent major sources of distress and/or physical illness. The medical profession has had a lot to say about sex and reproduction since its influence began to edge aside the monopoly of the Church during the sixteenth century. Today, most people would be more likely to consult a doctor than a priest for help in solving difficulties in these two areas.

□ List the sorts of sexual or reproductive problems on which people might seek medical advice.

■ There are three main areas: first, there are reasons to do with reproduction itself, such as obtaining contraception, routine care during pregnancy, seeking an abortion or dealing with difficulties in becoming pregnant. Second, there are problems resulting from the transmission of certain diseases through sexual activity. Third, people may seek medical advice concerning sexual activity itself; they may, for example, have sexual problems, such as an inability to maintain an erection or to achieve an orgasm, or they may be anxious or worried because their sexual behaviour is not what others would accept.

Concerns about sex and reproduction are not unique to any one age-group, even if society frowns on sex above or below a certain age. For the adolescent, there may be anxieties about one's own sexual development, and fear and concern stemming from ignorance about, for example, sexual activity and contraception. In early adulthood, there may be anxieties about conception and pregnancy. For the older adult, there may be worries about declining sexual capabilities or the menopause.

This chapter is about five common sources of anxiety: sexual activity and sexual preference, contraception, abortion, sexually transmitted diseases, and infertility. We have chosen to focus on *problems* that have repercussions for health and wellbeing rather than air the joys and benefits of sexuality and parenthood. In doing so we aim to expand on three major themes of this book — first, that each phase of life has unique features which affect the health and wellbeing of that age group; second, that these features are simultaneously biological, social and personal in origin; and third, that an historical perspective enables us to view the current situation with more detachment, taking less for granted. In covering such a wide range of topics, however, we cannot include a detailed historical account of each of them — this aspect of the discussion will rest mainly on the history of contraception.

Sexual activity and sexual preference

Despite the apparent 'liberalisation' of sexual attitudes in recent years, many people are reluctant to seek help or even discuss difficulties associated with sexual activity, and those that do may not be representative of the population as a whole. Systematic research into the incidence of sexual problems has been sparse in the UK, but even in America, where 'sexology' is a recognised academic discipline, research samples are rarely representative and as a result we know rather more about the sexual activity of white, heterosexual, middle-class Americans than about other groups. Bearing these sampling biases in mind, the consensus is that problems such as impotence, premature ejaculation, difficulty in achieving or maintaining sexual arousal, lack of orgasm, and sexual contact that is too seldom, too frequent, too rapid or too slow for one or other partner are exceedingly common. There is a recognition among GPs that many patients who come to see them initially with minor ailments are plucking up courage to seek help about their sex lives.

Sexual problems can cause acute distress and a sense of personal failure. In recent years, however, there has been some attempt to provide sexual counselling for people who seek help, although this provision is very limited within the NHS. Most people will get no further than consulting their GPs, most of whom will have had little training in dealing specifically with sexual problems. One counsellor suggested that the principal cause of many sexual problems is ignorance of how our bodies work sexually:

> Often sexual problems, such as lack of erections, too quick ejaculation, lack of orgasms or responsiveness, have a simple common denominator: lack of information, education and experience ... there is no set time before which ejaculation is premature, for example, it is premature if it is too fast for *you* and your partner. Nothing else counts. (Marshall, 1979)

The response of many people to sexual problems is simply to view them as 'personal' rather than medical or social, as something to be put up with, however distressing. In response to a questionnaire in a survey of women's sexual behaviour, one older woman observed:

> I am living in friendship with my sixty-six year old husband. I am and always have been sexually anaesthetised and believe I always will be. I enjoy sex psychologically ... but I have no way of knowing what sex *with* orgasms would be like, to compare it to. I feel extremely unique, sexually isolated, and disgusted. (from Hite, 1977, p.116)

Another source of worry and anxiety for some people are sexual feelings towards members of one's own sex. Homosexual activity is considered sinful or 'against nature' in many religious traditions, just as sexual activity between men and women which cannot lead to reproduction (for example, oral or anal sex) is often morally prohibited, and in some places is against the law. This religious prohibition is summed up by the sixteenth-century term for sodomy — *non nominandum inter Christianus* — that which is not to be named among Christians. However, there are numerous cultures in which sexual acts that cannot result in conception are considered normal, and this includes homosexual activity. For example, a review of anthropological literature by C.S. Ford and F.A. Beach (1952) found that homosexuality between men was seen as normal and acceptable for certain members of society in two thirds of the 76 cultures whose sexual practices they reviewed. Far fewer cultures openly approved of female homosexuality, but since Ford and Beach's study, more examples have been discovered. However, we cannot assume that the same meaning is attached to homosexual activity in the many different cultures in which it is approved.

A similar diversity is apparent in our own culture. Homosexual men and women tend to be viewed as a homogenous group, in much the same way as 'blacks' or 'the disabled', ignoring the fact that (for example) a white, Jewish middle-class lesbian may have little other than her sexual preference in common with her black, Christian, working-class counterpart. In addition, it is far from clear what we mean when we categorise someone as 'homosexual' or 'heterosexual'. Very large numbers of people have engaged in sexual activity with a member of their own sex at some point in their lives — does that make them a homosexual? And what about those people who have never engaged in homosexual acts, but sometimes wish they could?

Whatever the difficulties in categorising the range of human sexual experience into two mutually exclusive groups, many people come to see themselves as homosexual even when this is a highly stigmatised identity.* This can produce a special kind of identity problem:

> Until very recently all homosexual women and men have had to fight every inch of the way for accurate information about who we were and what we might become. We picked our way through a morass of hostilely written, ill-informed, deeply harmful books which told us we were mad, maladjusted, a social menace, hormonally imbalanced, externally damned, emotionally retarded, genetically damaged and a permanently doomed psycho-sexual mess. (Alison Hennigan, 'Raid on the Articulate', *New Statesman* 27 April 1984, p.28)

□ How does this situation differ from that experienced by people coming to terms with a heterosexual identity?

■ First and foremost, heterosexual activity is considered more 'normal' and thus has not attracted the public hostility, the research into causes and 'cures', and the legal penalties that homosexuals have suffered. Conversely, the unquestioned 'naturalness' of heterosexuality has resulted in neglect and ignorance. There is little help offered to young heterosexuals struggling to make sense of their sexuality, and sex education usually focuses on biology rather than relationships. (Freud pointed out that the 'exclusive interest felt by men for women is a problem that needs elucidation and is not a self-evident fact' but little attention has been paid to this proposition since.)

The way in which homosexuality has been viewed over the past few centuries reflects the rise of scientific explanations for health and disease. Before the sixteenth century, it was most commonly considered sinful or *morally* deviant, but as homosexual behaviour (along with many other types of sexual activity) began to be redefined as a medical rather than a religious problem, so explanations shifted towards *biological* or *psychological* deviance. The search was on for some naturalistic cause, and, as the quotation from Alison Hennigan's article records, there were numerous candidates. As with anorexia nervosa, an influential argument has been that homosexuality is a rejection of conventional gender roles as a result of disturbed relationships within the family. For example, homosexual men have sometimes been described as 'effeminate' — a condition that is supposed to result from having 'too close-binding and intimate' a mother.

□ There is no clear-cut evidence to support such an assertion, but can you discern the attitude towards homosexuality that underlies it?

■ It starts from the premise that homosexuality *is* deviant or unhealthy, yet unlike anorexia (a condition also attributed by some to maternal pressure) it is not life-threatening and is a source of happiness and wellbeing for at least some of those who experience it. (As for the intimate mother, one writer has expressed the following: 'What is wrong with such a mother unless you happen to find her in the background of people whose current behaviour you judge beforehand to be pathological?' (Davison, 1976, pp.157–162).

Sexual pressure of some sort is common to just about everyone, but homosexual men and women who are broadly satisfied with their sexual lives still have to cope

*Stigma is discussed in Book VI, *Experiencing and Explaining Disease*, Chapter 13.

with discrimination and hostility. In recent years this has eased a little as the Gay Rights movement has expanded, but it remains a source of distress in many people's lives. Attempts to alleviate this distress have tended to split into treatments aimed at 'curing' homosexuality (for example, the experimental use of psychoanalysis, electric shocks, drugs and 'aversion' therapy on a minority of homosexuals, mainly in the 1950s and 60s), and those that aim to help the person feel more at ease with their sexuality. This division is illustrated by the experience of these two homosexual men:

> They taught me to cope with whatever causes my stomach to kick up, to face issues rather than to avoid them. I used to have to go to hospital about twice a year for stomach trouble and I don't go anymore.
>
> It made me depressed. He brought out the disadvantages of homosexuality and it made me unhappy and depressed. He just wanted to reform everybody. (quoted in Bell and Weinberg, 1978, pp.205–6)

In Bell and Weinberg's study in America, homosexual men were more likely to report feelings of depression than were the heterosexual men to whom they were compared — a difference that was more marked among black than among white men in the sample. Perhaps because of reactions like depression, far more of the homosexual men had sought professional help than had their heterosexual counterparts. Women, by contrast, did not report significantly more depression if they were homosexual than if they were not; a finding confirmed by other studies.

A gradual increase in the acceptance of homosexuality within society has been detectable since the 1970s, and this has been echoed in the medical literature, as experimental evidence for significant biological or psychological differences between homosexuals and heterosexuals has not been found — 'The modern tendency is away from any pathology, to lesbianism as a normal variant of human sexuality, or as an alternative lifestyle.' (Kenyon, 1980, p.366). However, it is interesting that when the American Psychiatric Association voted in the early 1970s to remove homosexuality from the list of mental illnesses and re-classify it as a disturbance, the vote was 5 800 for and 3 800 against.

Homosexuals are not the only group in the population to suffer discrimination. People with certain physical impairments, particularly those that affect movement and co-ordination, report that they are additionally 'disabled' by a society that refuses to see them as sexual adults.

> 'How could you do it?' was a question which had many nuances and was put to me by many people, during and after my pregnancy. The GP wondered how I could have had intercourse in my 'predicament' ... you see, not only was it immoral to be an unmarried mother, but it was doubly immoral to be an unmarried mother AND a severely disabled person daring to produce a child — a normal, healthy beautiful child. (quoted in Campling, 1981, p.67)

There are major problems to cope with when trying to maintain a sexual relationship despite physical impairments, as one 25-year-old, paralysed from the waist down after a car accident, describes:

> In intimate relationships there is also that first moment when the mechanics of your bladder management are revealed. This is the major test. How will he react to a mature women who wears plastic knickers, pads and requires help when going to the loo? ... Even when sexually aroused, the spontaneity can soon disappear when your partner has to help empty your bladder and carefully clean and position you. Over-exhaustion, especially if orgasm is achieved, can make the disabled woman feel inadequate. (quoted in Campling, 1981, p.17)

Sexual problems can certainly be a source of unhappiness, even if they do not necessarily lead to ill-health, and do not always provoke people into seeing doctors. In the rest of this chapter, we will be primarily concerned with issues that typically involve medical consultation.

The association between sex, reproduction and the medical profession raises ethical questions that can only be briefly touched on here. Some problems relating to sex and reproduction involve people in making essentially *moral* decisions which, although to some extent private, become public as soon as they involve medical consultation. These issues include, for example, abortion, the provision of artificial insemination by donor (including to homosexual couples), surrogate motherhood (i.e. a woman bearing a child on behalf of another), and, for some people, contraception itself. Seeking an abortion, for example, involves not only the woman herself in making a moral decision, but also the doctors. Is it ethical for doctors to provide services such as abortion or artificial insemination by donor? Sex and reproduction includes several such areas of controversy. For example, a century ago fertility control by contraception was the focus of controversy specifically on moral grounds and in certain religious traditions remains so today.

Contraception and birth control

In the United Kingdom today, the majority of people expect to be able to exercise some control over the birth of their children by using some form of contraceptive device, sterilisation or sexual abstinence, at least at certain times.

Once the decision has been taken to use contraception, it is taken for granted that a choice of methods is available. Later in the chapter, we shall consider whether or not we really are free to make such choices, and what other factors influence them.

Giving birth used to be a hazardous business, as you read in Chapter 6. In earlier centuries, frequent pregnancies took an enormous toll on the health and welfare of women, as this working-class mother described in the late nineteenth-century:

> I do not think I was very different in my pregnancies to others. I always prepared myself to die, and I think this awful depression is common to most at this time. And when bothered by several other children, and not knowing how to make ends meet, death in some cases would be welcome, if it were not the dread of the children ... After the first three living children, I had three stillborn children. I was six months advanced when I fell downstairs over a stair-rod, which killed the child, which was born after forty-eight hours labour. After a lapse of two years I had another seven-months baby born dead, and again, after another two years, a five-month stillborn child ... I had a miscarriage after this of two months, and when I was thirty-five years old had my last baby. (quoted in Davies, 1978, pp.166–67)

It is thus scarcely surprising that women should want to restrict the number of pregnancies in some way. Although rather few of the correspondents quoted in Davies' book *Maternity: Letters from Working Women* made reference to means of prevention, these letters indicate that many women would have welcomed greater knowledge of how to prevent the endless round of pregnancies. Inevitably, knowledge of the risky methods of abortion was quite common among working-class women, who took a variety of drugs, including lead compounds, some of which were not successful and may have been fatal for the woman herself. Some managed to obtain more reliable information:

> As a result of this knowledge, I had no more babies for four and a half years ... My health improved, and people said I looked years younger ... I had a fight with my conscience before I used a preventative. But I have no qualms now. I feel I have better health to serve my husband and children, and more advantages to give them; while if another comes along, we will hail it with pleasure, as we did our last, instead of looking on it as a burden. (quoted in Davies, 1978, p.4)

Most of the more effective means of contraception that are used today are fairly recent inventions. The pill, for example, was first marketed at the end of the 1950s. That does not mean, however, that prior to this century there were no available means of contraception. Throughout recorded history, there have been attempts to prevent pregnancy and/or to limit the number of children by a variety of means, including abortion and infanticide.

□ From general knowledge of contraceptive methods, can you suggest how people may have tried to limit pregnancies before modern technology was available?

■ Coitus interruptus (withdrawal) has been practised for centuries. Other methods include the use of magic, sometimes combined with herbal potions. Many of these were probably ineffective, although some herbs may have contained drugs having contraceptive action. The most effective forms of contraception were those that we would now call *barrier methods of contraception* — attempts to provide a barrier between sperm and egg.

Modern barrier methods include the sheath and the diaphragm, both of which have a long history. The sheath, for example, was first described in the sixteenth century, being made of linen or part of the gut of animals. Initially, it was used as a preventative against sexually transmitted diseases, although by the eighteenth century, it was also used as a contraceptive. Casanova used the sheath for both purposes, referring to it as 'preservatives that the English

Figure 11.1 Extract from the Ebers papyrus, Egyptian, 1550 BC, which contains the earliest known reference to the use of pessaries with sperm-killing chemicals. (Courtesy of the Wellcome Institute for the History of Medicine)

have invented to put the fair sex under shelter from all fear' (cited in Himes, 1970, p.195).

Attempts to prevent conception by blocking the entrance to the uterus are even older, and references can be found to these in ancient Egyptian papyri (Figure 11.1) and in the medical writing of ancient Greece, which refer to the possibility of smearing the mouth of the womb with oil, honey or cedar gum (which would have had the effect of reducing sperm mobility). Putting linen rags, or even wooden or metal objects, into the vagina were also quite common. Some of these methods were probably not very effective; others, such as the use of half a lemon as a diaphragm, probably were. Casanova also reported the use of lemons in the eighteenth century. Not only did they act as a diaphragm, but the citric acid they contain acted as a spermicide (that is, it kills sperm).

☞ It is well known to the public ſhe has had *thirty-five years experience*, in the buſineſs of making and ſelling machines, commonly called implements of ſafety, which ſecures the health of her cuſtomers: ſhe has likewiſe great choice of ſkins and bladders, where apothecaries, chymiſts, druggiſts, &c. may be ſupplied with any quantity of the beſt ſort.—And

To guard yourſelf from ſhame or fear,
Votaries to Venus, haſten here;
None in my wares e'er found a flaw,
Self preſervation's nature's law.

Extract from an advertisement for Mrs Philip's 'implements of safety'. (From F. Grose, *A Guide to Health and Beauty*, London, 1796, pp.10–11). (Courtesy of the Wellcome Institute for the History of Medicine)

Although recent technology has changed the methods somewhat, we know that the *desire* to limit pregnancies is very old, but there has been a change in the extent to which people know about the methods available. During the nineteenth and early twentieth centuries, specific information about contraceptive methods began to be increasingly widespread. Norman Himes, in his *Medical History of Contraception*, written in 1936, suggested that:

> Contraceptive knowledge always has been, and still is to some extent the possession essentially of the upper, more privileged classes ... this information has, at an accelerating rate (now) spread to the working and less privileged classes. *This is the most important new aspect of birth control.* (emphasis in original, 1970 edn., p.210)

However, the spread to the working classes took many years, and in the meantime the toll on children's lives and the health of the women who bore them was considerable:

> What I would like to know is how I can save having any more children as I think that I have done my duty to my country having had 13 children, 9 boys and 4 girls. I have 6 boys alive now and 1 little girl who will be 3 years old in May. I burried a dear little baby girl 3 weeks ago who died from the strain of whooping cough, the reason I rite this is I cannot look after the little ones like I would like to as I am getting very stout and cannot bend to bath them and it do jest kill me to carry them in the shawl. I have always got one in my arms and another clinging to my apron and it is such a lot of work to wash and clean for us all ... if I was only thin I would not grumble and as my husband and myself is not so very old I am afraid we should have more children yet I was only 39 on the 19th of February just gone by ... I was 19 when I married so you can see by the family I have had that I have not had much time for pleasure and it is telling on me now I suffer very bad with varrecross vaines in my legs and my ankles gives out and I just drops doun. (quoted in Stopes, 1923, p.33)

□ Given that human populations have probably always *desired* to limit births, why do you think that it was not until the nineteenth and early twentieth centuries that knowledge became more widely available?

■ There are probably many factors, for example: the suppression of information by religious bodies prior to the eighteenth century; the impact of industrialisation, which brought more people into the urban areas, thus facilitating the spread of information; increased freedom for women; the effects of *Malthusianism*.*

Malthus' predictions of demographic change floundered as a result of his failure to anticipate the possibilities of increasing food production to meet the growth of population. He also failed to recognise the impact that contraception might have on population growth, concentrating instead on advocating later marriages and moral restraint as appropriate checks on population. His ideas did, however, contribute to the changing realisation during the nineteenth century that population growth was as much a product of economic and social factors as biological ones, and would need to be checked.

As early as 1797 (a year before Malthus published his essay) Jeremy Bentham, a 'liberal' philosopher, had suggested that contraception might be used to reduce the birth rate among the poor. It was, however, during the nineteenth century that such ideas became more prominent, particularly in the context of Malthus' advocacy of checks on population growth. Several people attempted to publicise ideas of contraception during this period, particularly to the working classes, although their attempts aroused considerable controversy. Francis Place

*Discussed in Book III, *The Health of Nations*, Chapter 6.

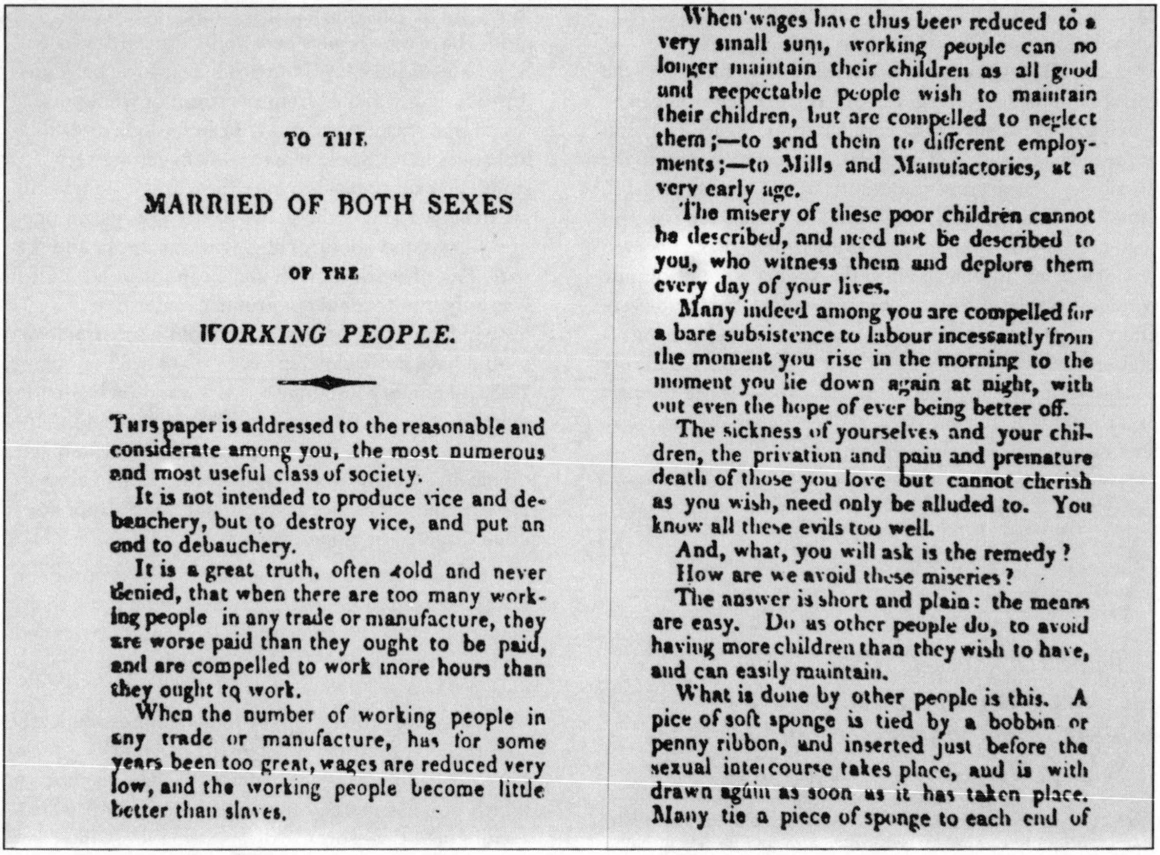

TO THE

MARRIED OF BOTH SEXES

OF THE

WORKING PEOPLE.

THIS paper is addressed to the reasonable and considerate among you, the most numerous and most useful class of society.

It is not intended to produce vice and debauchery, but to destroy vice, and put an end to debauchery.

It is a great truth, often told and never denied, that when there are too many working people in any trade or manufacture, they are worse paid than they ought to be paid, and are compelled to work more hours than they ought to work.

When the number of working people in any trade or manufacture, has for some years been too great, wages are reduced very low, and the working people become little better than slaves.

When wages have thus been reduced to a very small sum, working people can no longer maintain their children as all good and respectable people wish to maintain their children, but are compelled to neglect them;—to send them to different employments;—to Mills and Manufactories, at a very early age.

The misery of these poor children cannot be described, and need not be described to you, who witness them and deplore them every day of your lives.

Many indeed among you are compelled for a bare subsistence to labour incessantly from the moment you rise in the morning to the moment you lie down again at night, without even the hope of ever being better off.

The sickness of yourselves and your children, the privation and pain and premature death of those you love but cannot cherish as you wish, need only be alluded to. You know all these evils too well.

And, what, you will ask is the remedy?

How are we avoid these miseries?

The answer is short and plain: the means are easy. Do as other people do, to avoid having more children than they wish to have, and can easily maintain.

What is done by other people is this. A pice of soft sponge is tied by a bobbin or penny ribbon, and inserted just before the sexual intercourse takes place, and is withdrawn again as soon as it has taken place. Many tie a piece of sponge to each end of

Figure 11.2 Extract from *The Diabolical Handbill*, 1823 — one of the first leaflets produced in a campaign to educate the public about birth control. (From C. Wood and B. Snitters, *The Fight For Acceptance*, MTP)

(1771–1854) is generally held to be the first significant writer to attempt to distribute birth-control information. The first post-Malthusian publication providing practical instruction in contraception was the 'Diabolical Hand Bill' (as it came to be called) of 1823, published anonymously. The author, however, is generally regarded as being Francis Place. There were, in fact, three such handbills, widely circulated in London and the industrial districts of the North.

□ Fig 11.2 shows an extract from the 'Diabolical Handbill'. What is the main argument used in favour of birth control?

■ Economic. The author stresses the economic privation resulting from too many children and the consequent need for incessant labour.

The two methods advocated in the Handbill were the use of a vaginal sponge, and coitus interruptus.

Attempts to assist the spread of contraceptive information did not go unopposed, and many vitriolic attacks were made on the use of contraception, both in medical and in popular literature. Nineteenth-century medical writers warned women of the terrible dangers of contraceptive practice, which would, it was claimed, induce such horrors as galloping cancer, sterility, nymphomania, and death. Although Francis Place's pamphlets did not encounter legal opposition, later attempts to hand out pamphlets on contraception did, and in 1876 Charles Bradlaugh and Annie Besant were prosecuted for distributing a pamphlet outlining methods and advantages of contraception, which was judged to be obscene. Bradlaugh and Besant did, however, win the case and obtain rights to publish. The

GEORGE'S "COMPACTO" WHIRLING SPRAY.

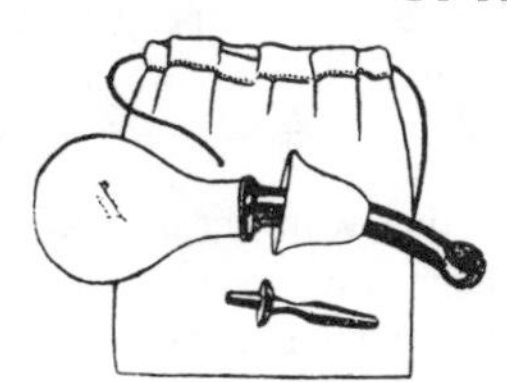

Can be used as an injection bottle or a Ladies' Whirling Spray. Disconnects and packs in small waterproof bag.

No. 67.—The ideal Spray for travelling. Price, complete with Bag, **12/6** each, post **6d.**

No. 65.—**The Marvel Whirling Spray.**—The original Spray that whirls. Nothing to get out of order.

Price complete **15/-**, postage **6d.** extra.

No. 66.—**The Omega Spray.** — Fitted with Raines Patent Vulcanite Mount. Produces two distinct sprays by single pressure of the bulb. The patent mount unscrews for cleaning purposes.

Price complete **15/-**, postage **6d.** extra.

Figure 11.3a Advertisements of the 1920s for contraceptive devices. (W. George, 10 and 21 Green St., Leicester Square, London, WC2)

Figure 11.3b Three types of diaphragm (cap) *c*.1925. (Courtesy of the Wellcome Institute for the History of Medicine)

Figure 11.3c Marie Stopes' clinic in a caravan, London, late 1920s. (Courtesy of the Wellcome Institute for the History of Medicine)

furore over the whole affair gave widespread publicity to arguments in favour of birth control, and the demand for information increased enormously over the next few decades. This period saw, too, the invention of a variety of devices aimed at contraception, including the modern rubber diaphragm, rubber sheaths, spermicidal pessaries, inter-uterine devices (IUDs) and vaginal douches. By the 1920s, devices were widely advertised, and some were obtainable from the birth-control clinics opened by Marie Stopes (see Figures 11.3a, b and c).

The birth-control movement that followed the publication of Place's handbills was motivated in part by a desire to alleviate the sufferings induced by too-frequent childbearing. It was, however, also motivated by what was seen as the future of the British race. Only planned parenthood, it was argued, could guarantee the quality and future of British children. The '*Eugenics*' *movement*, as it was called, played an influential part in the public debate until fairly recently.* Sir James Barr, the ex-President of the British Medical Association, writing in the foreword to a book on contraception written by the birth-control campaigner, Marie Stopes, commented:

> No one is responsible for his appearance on this earth and however undesirable his appearance may be, we may and perhaps should allow our altruistic feelings to minister to his comfort and survival, but we have no moral right to allow him to perpetuate his kind, and thus saddle the next generation with the maintenance of a race of degenerates. While the virility of the nation was carrying on the war, the derelicts would be carrying on the race. Our sentimentalists and would-be philanthropists at other

*Eugenics refers to the planned 'improvement' of the human race by selective breeding, brought into disrepute by the Nazi State in Germany in the 1930s and 1940s.

people's expense are crying upon these derelicts to produce more babies to replace the real nobility of manhood who perished in the war; this is the kind of material with which we are recruiting the next generation. (quoted in Stopes, 1923, p.xv.)

The birth-control movement rested on several inspirations. It drew as much on white, middle-class fears about uncontrolled breeding among the lower working-class or ethnic minorities as it did on concern for female equality or for the poverty and misery which frequent childbearing brought.

Eventually, the pressures brought by the contraceptive movement effected change, albeit slowly. By 1948, there were 65 'family planning' clinics in the UK and this grew to 400 by 1963. Family planning was still only available to married women, however, and it was not until the end of the 1960s that the clinics began to dispense advice to all women, regardless of their marital status.

Many of the methods of contraception mentioned above (such as vaginal douches) have largely disappeared, to be replaced by the *contraceptive pill*, the *intrauterine device* (IUD, or coil) and *sterilisation* or *vasectomy*.

□ Which do you think is the most widely used method of pregnancy prevention in the UK, and worldwide, at this time?

■ In the UK, the contraceptive pill is the most widely used, although a large number of people use the *sheath* (see Figure 11.4 which shows statistics for 1979). On a worldwide scale, though, prolonged breastfeeding (i.e. for several years) is still probably the most important since ovulation (the production of a fertile egg during each menstrual cycle) is commonly suppressed by lactation. However, in well-nourished women in the industrialised countries, ovulation may still occur during breastfeeding.

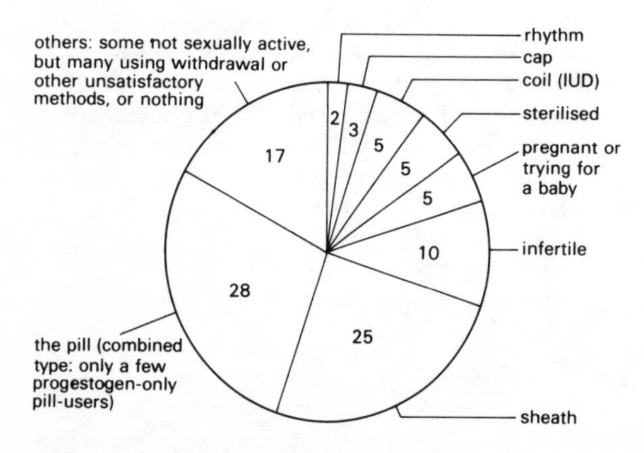

Figure 11.4 Use of different contraceptive measures, UK, 1979 (Family Planning Association estimate).

Although the types of contraception available have changed over the last four decades, the decision as to which one to use remains a problem for many people. This difficulty is a consequence of the numerous factors that may influence someone's choice.

I'm not allowed the pill and they won't fit the cap or the coil because I haemorrhage at my periods, and I don't like Durex—can't stand them, and we don't get on with the withdrawal method. I expect we shall try and use it though. (Cartwright, 1976. p.48.)

□ This extreme, though not rare, example of a woman's experience illustrates some of the factors influencing the decision about which method to use. What are those factors?

■ Factors illustrated in the quotation are: (i) the medical view — 'not allowed the pill'; (ii) past experiences — heavy bleeding which could be made worse by the coil; (iii) the aesthetic acceptability of the method to the user — 'I don't like Durex.'

□ Can you suggest any other factors that might influence the decision about which method to use?

■ There are several that you may have thought of, including:

(i) the views of the male partner — for example, prejudice against vasectomy or the sheath;

(ii) the known risks to health of different methods;

(iii) the effectiveness of different methods in relation to a person's needs — for example, only someone whose family is complete will opt for permanent contraception (sterilisation or vasectomy);

(iv) knowledge of available methods;

(v) economic considerations — someone might risk a method of lower effectiveness but greater aesthetic merit if they know that they can afford to look after a child;

(vi) religious beliefs or moral objections to certain methods — for example, the coil allows fertilisation to take place but prevents the egg from implanting in the womb.

These different factors fall into three main categories, relating to the person or couple (such as personal preferences), to the method itself (its reliability and safety), and to its availability (will doctors prescribe it?). Each of these categories need to be considered in greater detail.

Personal factors

A person's decision as to which method to use will be influenced not only by their past experiences, but by current

Table 11.1 Use of different methods of birth control by women of different ages in the UK, 1976

Method	Per cent using this method in different age-groups				
	under 20	20–24	25–29	30–34	over 35
oral contraceptive pills	62	52	41	23	11
female sterilisation	—	1	5	10	20
male sterilisation	—	2	4	6	11
diaphragm	—	1	3	2	1
coil (IUD)	2	5	8	7	4
sheath	15	20	24	24	25
withdrawal/rhythm/others	5	9	9	13	14
none	16	10	6	15	14

(Data from Cartwright, 1976)

factors, such as how often they are having intercourse, and their future plans for having children. Clearly anyone wanting to have children in the future would only consider a reversible method, as opposed to an irreversible method such as sterilisation. The personal influence on deciding which method to use is associated with several factors, including age, social class, ethnicity and religion.

In a study carried out in 1976 in England and Wales, the sociologist, Ann Cartwright, found that the proportion of women using the pill declined with increasing age (see Table 11.1), and conversely, the use of the coil, the sheath and sterilisation increased as women got older.

Distinct differences have also been observed between social classes, though these have diminished since the 1960s. Table 11.2 shows the proportion of contraceptive use among married women according to social class.

□ In which social classes was the highest proportion of women who had ever used contraception?

■ In social classes I–IIIN: by 1975, 80 per cent of these women had at one time used contraception, compared to 65 per cent in social classes IV and V.

This class difference reflects a common trend in health care — the earlier adoption of innovations by middle-class than by working-class people. This happened with the pill: middle-class women were the first to use it, and have also been the first to give it up, so that by 1975 there was little difference between the classes.

Part of the explanation for differences in use between age-groups and social classes relates to knowledge of the methods available. For example, a study of *sex education* and practice among a sample of teenagers in England and Wales, conducted in the mid-1970s by Christine Farrell, found that approximately10 per cent of this age-group said that they had had only a single lesson in sex education while at school, and 9 per cent reported not having any. It was also evident from the study that a number of topics related to sex and reproduction were dealt with rather rarely; some of the results from a sample of 16–19 year olds, are shown in Table 11.3 (overleaf).

Table 11.2 Use of contraception by married women* under 41 years of age in 1970 and 1975 (figures in brackets) by social class (percentages)

Type of contraception	Social class			
	I, II and IIIN	IIIM	IV and V	All
pill	28 (42)	24 (43)	21 (39)	25 (42)
I.U.D. (coil)	6 (9)	5 (9)	4 (7)	5 (9)
cap	10 (5)	3 (2)	4 (1)	6 (3)
condom	38 (28)	35 (24)	36 (24)	36 (25)
withdrawal	12 (4)	23 (8)	22 (13)	19 (7)
safe period	8 (1)	6 (1)	3 (1)	6 (1)
abstinence	3 (2)	3 (1)	7 (1)	4 (1)
% women (or husbands) sterilised	(9)	(12)	(12)	(11)
Users of family planning services				
current users	32 (47)	24 (43)	21 (40)	27 (44)
ever used	62 (80)	51 (70)	49 (65)	54 (73)

Note Columns do not add up to 100 because some respondents reported using more than one, or no, method.
* Use by married women who were neither sterile, pregnant nor planning to be pregnant.
Numbers of women in the samples were 1913 and 2220 respectively.
(Reid, 1981, Table 5.10, p. 173)

These data also show that the 'personal' dimension of sex education is relatively neglected. You will probably notice from this table that although a large proportion learn about the mechanics of reproduction, rather fewer learn about love and relationships. Less than half the adolescents questioned in this study had had a sex education that included mention of personal relationships, or of family and parenthood. Farrell also found that 58 per cent of the adolescents questioned had never had any lessons about contraception at school, although nearly all these adolescents knew of the existence of the most commonly

Table 11.3 Proportions of young people in mixed and single sex secondary schools reporting on sex education topics

	Pupils attending mixed schools/per cent reporting	Pupils attending single sex schools/ per cent reporting
animal reproduction	73	80
human reproduction	73	88
sexual intercourse	70	75
female puberty	73	77
male puberty	65	69
family and parenthood	44	42
personal relationships	46	49
masturbation	25	27
venereal disease	60	65
abortion	33	39
homosexuality	19	26
lesbianism	18	22
no sex education in secondary schools	10	7
number of young people (=100%)*	943†	451†

* Percentages add to more than 100% because more than one topic mentioned by some.
†11 young people excluded from this table because answers inadequate.
(Farrell, 1978, p. 131)

used forms of contraception by some means or another:

> I never learned anything at school about them, only from seeing things in pubs and barbers, and stuff about the pill in the papers. (Farrell, 1978, p.205.)

> [Sexual knowledge] just gets passed around. My parents never said anything to me, it just gets passed around with the friends, doesn't it? We never had any sex education lessons at school and that. Wish I'd been told properly at school. (ibid, p.167.)

However, even if they knew something about most methods, more than half of those questioned wanted to know more: 75 per cent, for instance, wanted to know more about the coil (or IUD) and 71 per cent more about the pill.

Although most methods of contraception are used by women, women do not always make the decision alone about the method to use. Occasionally a family planning group or doctor requires the permission of the husband or partner before issuing contraceptives to women (although his permission is not actually required by English law). Moreover, the partner may influence the woman's choices directly, or may refuse to consider male methods, as these two statements illustrate:

> I want to go back on the pill, but my husband won't let me. It took me quite a long time to catch on (i.e. get pregnant) ... that's why he won't let me. I could go on it, I don't want one till he's about three — if ever. But he thinks it takes too long when you come off, that's why he won't let me. (quoted in Roberts, 1981, p.14)

> She wanted me to have the knife, but I'm not too willing ... I'm not keen on that vasectomy. No, I know about three blokes that's had it done and two out of three haven't been very pleasant with it ... one bloke couldn't walk ... to me it isn't final yet. They don't know. I mean it's like landing rockets on t'moon. It's alright, they've landed them at one side and they ain't found nowt. But if they land them at t'other they might get devoured by summat. They don't know. I'd rather it was proved. (ibid, p.15)

However, initial reluctance by men to undergo a vasectomy has been replaced by long waiting lists at many NHS clinics. In a study of contraceptive methods used by 17 302 white married women in the Oxford area, 21 per cent reported that their husbands had been sterilised by 1981. This method was more commonly chosen by men from social classes I, II and III; less than 10 per cent of the men who had been sterilised were from social class IV or V, revealing a clear class bias in this highly personal contraceptive choice.

Reluctance to use one or more methods because they are 'messy' or interfere with intercourse can make the finding of a suitable method almost impossible for some people:

> Don't fancy the cap, I don't fancy mucking about with that. I don't fancy Durex, they've given us loads, we've got loads upstairs, and we can't give them away, can we? Give us one and a half dozen and we haven't used one. Don't fancy Durex at all, I think they're horrible ... you know, I hate this idea of stop, hang on, you know, this sort of thing. And what else is there? I didn't fancy the pill again. I've never been quite right, have I, since I went on the pill? (quoted in Roberts, 1981, p.2)

However, acceptability may itself depend on other factors, such as frequency of intercourse. Some people prefer to use a 'messy' method if they require protection only occasionally, rather than a method which needs to be ever-present (e.g. the pill or IUD), and which carries some health risks.

Finally, ethnicity and religious belief influence the choice of contraceptive method. In Ann Cartwright's study, mentioned earlier, she found that whereas 88 per cent of the Protestants she interviewed and 81 per cent of the Catholics favoured birth control in some form, this was only true for 54 per cent of the Muslims. The differences between

Catholic and other mothers interviewed in the survey in their current use of birth control methods were relatively small.

Menstrual bleeding confers social restrictions for orthodox Jewish, Muslim or Hindu women. For these women, and many others, the prolonged blood loss sometimes associated with the IUD, or the irregular cycle that sometimes occurs with the mini-pill or with injectible contraceptives weigh against the acceptability of these methods.

Reliability and safety of the method

Clearly, most people want reasonably effective methods of contraception, but do not want methods that are likely to make them feel uncomfortable or unwell, or to pose serious risks to their health. There is, however, no one method that is (a) perfectly safe in terms of health, *and* (b) 100 per cent reliable at preventing conception, so these two factors have to be weighed against each other.

Reliability depends not only upon the efficacy or *theoretical effectiveness* of the method in preventing pregnancy, but also upon how the user applies the method, that is, its *practical effectiveness*. For example, the oral contraceptive pill is, in theory, nearly 100 per cent effective, but pregnancies do occur because the user has not taken the pill consistently.

□ From general knowledge, can you rank the following methods of contraception from the most reliable (in practice) to the least? (a) sheath; (b) mini-pill (progestogen only); (c) rhythm (or safe period); (d) IUD (or coil); (e) combined pill (oestrogen and progestogen); (f) withdrawal (coitus interruptus); (g) sterilisation; (h) diaphragm.

■ The order of practical effectiveness is (with the approximate number of pregnancies occurring in 100 women per year in brackets): female sterilisation or vasectomy (0.3); combined pill (up to 1.0); mini-pill and IUD (3.0); diaphragm and sheath (5.0); rhythm and withdrawal (up to 25, although the rhythm method can be as low as 4.0 if used carefully and if the woman has a regular menstrual cycle).

If the health risks of each of these were the same, then most people would probably opt for sterilisation if family size was complete, or the combined pill if they wanted more children. However, as you probably know, this is not the case: not only are the health risks not equal, but they may also be affected by other factors related to a woman's individual history. For instance, the health risks associated with the combined pill are now known to increase with age and with smoking; the IUD is not commonly fitted in women who have never had children because of the greater risk of injury to the uterus.

There have been several epidemiological studies of the associations between different methods of contraception and ill-health. Two of the largest have been carried out by the Royal College of General Practitioners, and by Oxford University in conjunction with the Family Planning Association. The latter looked at the health of over 17 000 women from 1960 onwards in relation to the contraception used; the women's health was followed up seven years later according to whether they had been pill-users, IUD-users, or diaphragm-users. Some of the results of this survey are summarised in Table 11.4.

The association between pill use and *thrombosis* (the formation of blood clots in the circulatory system) has been confirmed by several studies, but other associations are less clear-cut, for example the association of the pill with cancers of the female reproductive organs. Despite the view

Table 11.4 Side-effects of some contraceptive methods on health

Type of contraceptive	Unwanted effects	Welcome effects
oral contraceptive	migraine	menstrual cycle:
	cardiovascular disease	— regular
	delayed return of fertility	— less painful
	erosion of cervix	— less heavy bleeding
	cancer of cervix (?)	fewer ovarian cysts and ovarian cancer (?)
	cancer of breast (?)	less benign breast disease
	skin disorders	
	thrombosis	
diaphragm	cystitis	fewer sexually transmitted infections
intra-uterine device (IUD; coil)	heavy bleeding	
	infection of uterus and Fallopian tubes	
	miscarriage, premature birth and stillbirth (if method fails)	

put forward in some newspaper reports, the evidence is far from conclusive. *Some* women may be at a slightly greater risk from cancers of the breast or cervix, but conversely the Oxford study suggested that use of the pill may even be associated with a *decrease* in the incidence of cancer of the ovaries. Both effects are likely to depend on the exact brand of pill used, the age at which pill use began and the length of time it continued.

Despite the equivocal nature of current research, bad publicity about the pill has influenced women's choice of contraception. In particular, the number of middle-class women using the pill has declined since 1975. In addition, few doctors now prescribe it to women over 35, particularly if they smoke. Originally hailed as a step forward in the liberation of women from unwanted pregnancies, the pill has come to be regarded with more suspicion.

Provision of contraception

Access to services providing contraceptive methods used by adult women in the UK is usually only a minor problem or inconvenience. This is less true, however, for many adolescents. Although some adolescents approach doctors or clinics readily, others worry about, or even avoid consulting a doctor, as the following teenagers suggest:

> Well, there's always a chance that he might tell your parents.
>
> Well, I don't like my doctor — he's very abrupt and I couldn't talk to him very well.
>
> It took me two months to pluck up courage. (quoted in Farrell, 1978, pp.190–91)

Whatever view you take of adolescent sexual activity, failure to use contraception adequately, for whatever reason, carries with it the risk of pregnancy, which may pose more problems for the young adolescent than it does for the majority of older people. However, even adults may encounter difficulties in getting the method they choose. Clinic doctors and nurses can clearly influence choices by, for example, suggesting one method and not another, or by suggesting that one type of contraception is not suitable without discussing it further. There are also instances of clinic staff in effect making choices *for* women — for example, in the belief that 'they cannot be relied upon to take the pill'.

One response to this belief is to offer the woman a *contraceptive injection*, such as Depo Provera (these work by preventing ovulation, like the pill, but are given once every three months). Such injections are occasionally prescribed in the UK but are more frequently used in the Third World. Their use in the UK has aroused controversy because they have sometimes been given to working-class or immigrant women, to whom the choice of other methods may not be offered fully. Some critics consider their prescription to be embedded in prejudice; for example, one Leeds woman, whose first language was not English, had this experience, described by her English teacher:

> They treated N. very badly, like an idiot; never explaining anything. The nurse constantly talked to me, not to N. She told me: 'These people have a low threshold of pain and can't be trusted to take pills regularly'. That's presumably why they got her on the injections. She's been on them for nearly three years now, with very bad headaches and back pain. She won't go to the clinic any more because they have been *so* unpleasant and rude, so she's stopped getting the injections. (quoted in Roberts, 1981, pp.82–83)

There is anecdotal (but not systematic) evidence that some gynaecologists refuse to carry out abortions on certain women unless they consent to having a sterilisation at the same time. Here, for example, is one case, reported by Wendy Savage, herself a gynaecologist, in an article criticising assumptions often made within gynaecology:

> Ms A.T., a 22-year old West Indian single parent ... requested reversal of her tubal ligation (sterilisation) done three years earlier. She had had two children by Caesarean section five and four years earlier in another hospital. When she presented for her third termination of pregnancy at the age of 19, the gynaecologist would not agree to an abortion unless she consented to sterilisation concurrently. At laparoscopy I found the left ovary adherent to the uterus ... but no tubes ... when I told her this she said 'They never said they were going to take my tubes away, only tie them', and insisted, 'I didn't sign for that'. This summer I finally did a hysterectomy, as her chronic infection, which appears to date from the combined abortion and sterilisation procedure, has made her life a misery. (Savage, 1982, p.294.)

Controversy never seems to be far away from the discussion of birth control. Modern methods of contraception, combined with much greater knowledge of their use, have transformed society. At the same time, they have confronted people with some difficult decision-making: whatever contraceptive is chosen is likely to have at least one disadvantage, and the decision about how to prevent unwanted pregnancies may have to be changed several times during adult life. Anxiety about pregnancy is a common aspect of adult experience.

Unwanted pregnancies and the issue of abortion

There are numerous reasons why 'accidental' pregnancy may occur, despite the availability of contraception. Some

Table 11.5 Number, per cent and rates of legal abortions performed to women of different ages, resident in England and Wales in 1983

Age/years	Number	Per cent	Rate per 1 000 women in that age-group
all ages	127 234	100	10.45
under 16	4 079	3.2	5.27
16–19	31 196	24.5	19.25
20–24	34 985	27.5	18.49
25–29	22 131	17.4	13.15
30–34	16 880	13.2	9.66
35–39	13 055	10.3	7.64
40–44	4 380	3.4	3.14
45 and over	442	0.4	0.33
age unknown	86	0.07	—

(Data from OPCS, 1984, Table 2, p. 1)

people still don't know enough about alternative methods (particularly if they are young) and others simply take risks believing that 'just this once won't matter'. However, 45 per cent of women who obtain a *legal abortion* are over 25 years old, as Table 11.5 shows, and it is therefore likely that problems in finding and using a suitable method of contraception underly many unwanted pregnancies, rather than simple ignorance or 'irresponsibility'.

Some pregnancies, though unplanned, will still be welcomed or accepted without distress. Others present the pregnant woman, and possibly her partner, with the dilemma of whether to seek an abortion or adoption of the baby soon after birth.

In the past, *infanticide* was an option that some historians believe was frequently used, but for which precise data cannot be obtained.* There are similar difficulties when trying to quantify abortions in the UK before the 1967 Abortion Act, which provided legal exceptions under which abortion might be performed up to the 28th week of pregnancy.† Figure 11.5 shows the incidence of legal abortions carried out in England and Wales between 1969 and 1983.

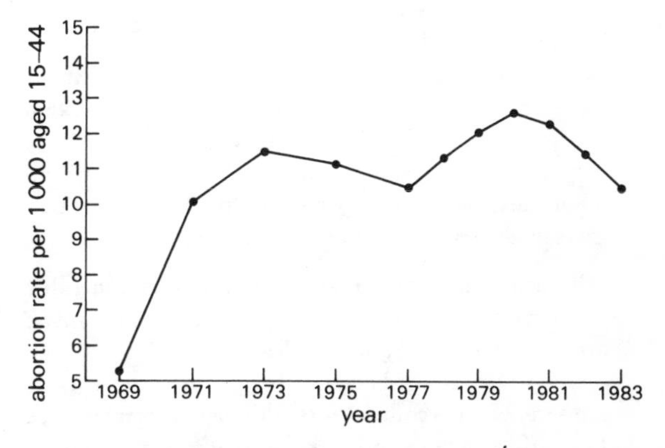

Figure 11.5 Legal abortions in England and Wales (resident women) 1969–81. (OPCS Monitor, 1984, Table 2)

□ What do you notice about the graph? Can you suggest reasons for its shape?

■ There are two distinctive features. First, the incidence rises steeply after 1969, until 1973, when it levels off. It then rises again after 1977. The main reasons that have been put forward for these two features are (i) the initial rise occurs because abortions were made legal, and (ii) the second use occurs because of changes in the use of contraceptives, particularly the shift away from the most reliable method of reversible contraception — the pill.

This illustrates two major influences on the incidence of abortion. First, the number of legal abortions varies according to the restrictiveness or otherwise of the law. This shifts the balance between legal and illegal abortions, as well as determining where and how people obtain abortions. Second, abortion is influenced to some extent by personal choices. This includes not only methods of

*The difficulties associated with assessing infanticide rates in previous centuries is discussed in Book III, *The Health of Nations*, Chapter 8.

†The 1967 Abortion Act provides that no offence is committed under the law relating to abortion when a pregnancy is terminated by a registered medical practitioner, if two registered medical practitioners are of the opinion, formed in good faith, that the continuance of the pregnancy would involve a risk to the life of the pregnant woman, or of injury to the physical or mental health of the pregnant woman, or any existing children of her family greater than if the pregnancy were terminated, or that there is a substantial risk that if the child were born it would suffer from such physical or mental abnormalities as to be seriously handicapped.

contraception, but also the beliefs and attitudes of the people involved towards abortion itself.

In some countries, state policy on abortion is partly related to population policy. Abortion has at times been made readily available or totally illegal by governments, in attempts to decrease or increase the birth rate, sometimes with tragic consequences. Following the introduction of a restrictive abortion law in Rumania in 1966, for example, people responded by turning to illegal abortions; abortion-related deaths among women rose from 50 a year to over 350 a year by 1971.

Since 1967, state policy in Britain has been that abortions are, under certain circumstances, legal, and obtainable within the NHS. However, in practice the provision of abortion facilities has often been haphazard.

□ Table 11.6 shows the percentage of abortions carried out in NHS hospitals for some Regional Health Authorities in England in 1983. What conclusions can you draw from these data?

■ The most obvious point about the data is that the proportion of abortions carried out within the NHS varies markedly from region to region. In the West Midlands, for instance, only 15.7 per cent of all abortions were carried out within the NHS compared to, say, 99.3 per cent in the Northern region.

So the availability of an abortion varies considerably depending on where you live. If a woman cannot obtain an abortion from the NHS, the only legal alternative is to seek one at a private clinic. Fees are charged by the charitable organisations to cover their costs (although they are waived in cases of exceptional poverty), so that having a private abortion usually requires money, and this further restricts availability.

The lack of provision in many parts of the UK may be due to legislation (as in Northern Ireland, where abortion remains illegal unless the woman's life is in immediate danger) or to lack of resources (such as insufficient hospital beds or medical staff). However, the main restrictions on provision are the attitudes of the doctors, who, under the 1967 Abortion Act, have to agree to the procedure being performed. Doctors' attitudes on the moral aspects of abortion vary widely, as illustrated by the following quotations from GPs obtained by the sociologist Jean Aitken-Swan in a study conducted in Scotland and published in 1977.

Table 11.6 Percentage of legal abortions performed in NHS facilities on women resident in six Regional Health Authorities in England in 1983

Region	Percentage of abortions in NHS facilities
Northern	99.3
East Anglia	97.3
Trent	61.1
Mersey	42.3
Yorkshire	38.2
West Midlands	15.7
average for England and Wales	47.7

(Data from OPCS, 1984, Table 4, p. 3)

> I suppose I'm old-fashioned in the respect that once a baby is conceived, to me it's a baby and I think there's something morally wrong in this attitude that you just go in and get rid of it as though it was some sort of garbage. (quoted in Aitken-Swan, 1979, p.57)

> I don't have much in the way of objections. I do have objections to abortion on demand by promiscuous people who will demand it again and again and I do have objection to abortions of convenience. (ibid, p.58)

> I'm a believer more or less in abortion on demand. I've never felt that a woman who found herself pregnant and didn't want to carry on with this pregnancy should have to. (ibid, p.59)

□ Contained in these quotes is the key issue of who should decide whether or not a woman has an abortion. Summarise the views expressed by these three GPs.

■ The first two GPs consider that they, rather than the woman, should decide, whereas the third GP felt it should be the woman's decision.

The attitudes expressed by the first two GPs can be seen in the following experiences of some young women who had been refused an NHS abortion in a study conducted in the south of England:

> [The GP said] 'you've made your bed and now you've got to lie in it . . . you ought to have it; it'll buck your ideas up a bit; it might be the making of you.' (Age 22; unemployed; relationship steady until pregnant. Quoted in Ashton, 1980, p.205)

> [The GP said that] 'at 2½ months you are too far gone'. He said that there was no reason why she should not marry and have the baby. (Age 15; schoolgirl: relationship steady. Ibid, p.205)

> The family doctor had refused to prescribe oral contraception despite the parents' permission. The consultant had told her 'you don't tell me you have come for an abortion — I decide whether you can or not'. After examining her he said she was healthy enough to have it and would have it whether she liked

> it or not. He said that she 'could have the child adopted if I did not want it'. He said 'I was going to have it and in his hospital'. (Aged 15; schoolgirl: relationship steady until pregnant. Ibid, p.208)

Becoming pregnant for these young women inevitably faced them with difficult, at times impossible, ethical and practical choices. In the cases quoted above, none of them had a source of income, so, financially at least, trying to look after a baby would be very difficult. In 1981 there were 144 000 unmarried mothers in England and Wales, of whom 93.7 per cent were receiving Supplementary Benefit — a means-tested benefit available to people living in relative poverty. Even if abortion is decided upon, it may be difficult to achieve, or it may be followed by doubts and regrets: for all these reasons, it is rarely an easy decision for anyone to make. For some women, abortion remains unacceptable in all but the direst circumstances; as two respondents in the study by Ann Cartwright (referred to earlier) commented:

> It's a life. It's killing. I think it's murder. (quoted in Cartwright, 1976, p.68)

> A lot of people have them (abortions) in desperation and must suffer a lot afterwards thinking what they've done. It must always be with you. It's murder whichever way you look at it. (ibid, p.68)

About 9 per cent of respondents took this view. In contrast, almost half emphasised the woman's freedom to choose for herself whether or not to go on with the pregnancy: 'If she wants it — everyone to their own opinion. You must decide for yourself.' (quoted in Cartwright, 1976, p.67).

For women who do not find abortion totally unacceptable, a determined effort will usually succeed in terminating the pregnancy legally; if an NHS abortion is unobtainable, then they will go to the charitable organisations until they get one. This is what women have been doing for centuries: women with unwanted pregnancies in earlier ages still made difficult choices and sought abortions at times. The fundamental difference is that a much greater number of them died in the process.

Sexually transmitted diseases

Another unwanted consequence of sexual activity is the risk of infectious diseases. *Sexually transmitted diseases* (previously known as *venereal diseases*; a term no longer used as, strictly, it only applies to a few such infections, including syphilis and gonorrhoea) have always occupied a unique position in both medical and lay attitudes. Whereas respiratory or gastrointestinal infections have been treated with sympathy and concern, people suffering from sexually transmitted diseases (STDs) were ignored or treated with hostility in earlier centuries. This can be seen in the evidence given, for example, by Dr Samuel Solly, President of the Royal Medical and Chirurgical Society, to a Government Committee in 1868: 'Syphilis was self-inflicted, avoidable by refraining from sexual activity, intended as a punishment for our sins, and we should not interfere in the matter.' (quoted in Adler, 1980, p.206).

The refusal by doctors to 'interfere' persisted into the early years of this century. One doctor was reported as writing to a patient, 'You have had the disease one year, and I hope it may plague you many more to punish you for your sins and I would not think of treating you.' (quoted in Royal Commission on Venereal Diseases, 1916).

Although the view that disease is a justified punishment for immoral behaviour is less widely held today, it does persist. In her study of adolescents' sex education, Christine Farrell noted that 20 per cent of the adolescents interviewed thought that such diseases were caused by immoral behaviour, or promiscuity.

> They said that it was if you met a boy and if he kept going from one girl to another and then had intercourse with you, he might know about it and wouldn't care and you would end up with it as well. (quoted in Farrell, 1978, p.50)

Farrell suggests that parents often echo the view that STDs are a punishment for immorality; two thirds of the parents interviewed issued warnings about the dangers of STDs:

> ... that it can ruin their lives and will stop them having a happy married life if they catch VD when they're young. (op. cit., p.96)

> [They should be] frightened by the thought of babies deformed at birth. She saw it at Madame Tussaud's at Blackpool. I think it frightened her. (ibid, p.96)

In addition to the belief that the disease is a suitable punishment, two other beliefs have become established over the last few decades — that the incidence of STDs has dramatically increased, particularly amongst the young, and that there are new, more serious diseases. These beliefs go hand in hand with ideas about the so-called 'sexual revolution' which hold that sexual morality and practice have undergone a dramatic 'liberalisation'. What evidence is there to support these views?

As you will be aware from numerous discussions in this course, routine morbidity data are often unavailable or inadequate. This is true of information on the incidence of STDs. The only routine data available concern the number of people attending specialist clinics for these diseases. The number of new cases attending each year in England and

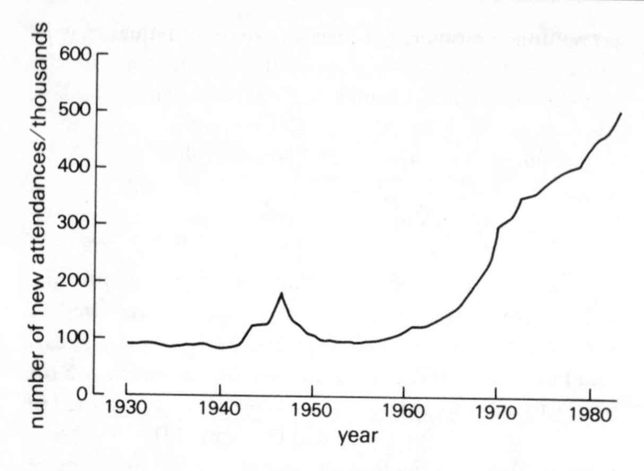

Figure 11.6 New attendances at STD clinics, England and Wales, 1925–82. (Communicable Diseases Surveillance Centre, Report, 8 March 1984, p.3)

Wales since 1925 is shown in Figure 11.6.

□ Can you suggest some factors which might have contributed to the five-fold increase in new attendances since 1950?

■ Some that you may have thought of are:

(i) The population has increased in size.

(ii) There are now more clinics, so there is better publicity and easier access.

(iii) More diseases are now classified as, or recognised as, sexually transmitted than in previous years.

(iv) People have gradually become more prepared to attend the clinics.

(vi) The incidence of STDs in the population has increased.

It is difficult to disentangle the relative contribution of each of these factors: for example, the shortage of accurate, routinely available data prevents any straightforward assessment of the influence of demographic changes. What of the possibility that more diseases are now classified as sexually transmitted?

□ Which diseases do you think of as sexually transmitted?

■ Most people would include syphilis and gonorrhoea; you might also have thought of AIDS (Acquired Immune Deficiency Syndrome) which has recently spread through parts of the male homosexual community in the USA and reached Western Europe by 1984.

It is now increasingly recognised, however, that a number of other diseases can be spread through sexual activity. In 1981, for example, only 12 per cent of people treated at STD clinics were suffering from classical venereal diseases. The remaining 88 per cent included such conditions as non-specific urethritis (often referred to as NSU, the cause of which is uncertain), candidiasis (or moniliasis, which is caused by a fungus, more usually known as thrush), trichomoniasis (caused by a protozoan — a single celled animal) and genital warts and herpes (both caused by viruses). In practice, although syphilis and gonorrhoea can be very serious if not treated, they can quite readily be cured if detected early. On the other hand, some of the other conditions that we have just listed can be quite difficult to cure, such as NSU and herpes.

Increases in the *attendance rate* for these conditions largely reflect a change in the medical view of STDs. Conditions such as trichomoniasis and thrush have only been recognised as potentially sexually transmitted quite recently. Thus part of the increase has resulted from the clinics taking over conditions that were previously either unrecognised (such as herpes) or were treated by other practitioners (e.g. GPs treating vaginal infections). In addition, the clinics have recognised that some of these conditions are not always spread by sexual activity, although they can be (e.g. thrush). This change of emphasis was officially recognised by the UK Department of Health in 1974 when it approved the change in the name of the speciality from venerealogy to genito-urinary medicine. It is also worth noting that 25 per cent of attenders at such clinics do not require medical treatment, but are seeking information, advice or reassurance.

Another factor that we might consider is that people are now more prepared to attend the clinics. VD clinics, as they were originally known, were often housed in the basements of old inner-city hospitals and reached along dark back alleys. The clinic work was regarded as low status by medical personnel. As the Chief Medical Officer mentions in his annual report for 1982, 'the old-fashioned clinics discourage patients from attending and make it very difficult to attract staff to work in them'. The other discouragement to patients was, and still is to some extent, the stigma attached to STDs. On the other hand, as more and more people attend for less serious diseases, then the stigma is likely to lessen. The greater readiness to seek specialist care has been another contributing factor in the increased number of clinic attendances.

Finally, there is the suggestion that the incidence of STDs has actually risen. Again, the necessary evidence for or against this is lacking. The number of clinic attendances is not an accurate indication of the population incidence of these conditions, particularly since some are still treated by other practitioners. In addition, we would need to know *age-specific rates*, given that there are now more young adults than there were in previous decades. The only relevant information that is available shows that the attendance rate for new cases of gonorrhoea and syphilis was either unchanged or actually fell between 1970 and 1981 in those aged 16–24 years. Whether or not other conditions, such as herpes, trichomoniasis, and so on, have actually increased is hard to determine. Currently, the two conditions attracting most attention are herpes and AIDS. Genital herpes is certainly not a new disease. Its increased recognition stems largely from the development of new laboratory techniques for the study of viruses. Before such facilities existed, people suffering from herpes infections would have been classified under conditions of unknown cause.

In contrast, AIDS may well be a new disease in North America and Europe. *Acquired Immune Deficiency Syndrome*, a frequently fatal condition, was first described in the USA around 1980. The immune system of sufferers is severely unbalanced, making them vulnerable to overwhelming and often unusual infections, and the development of a rare form of skin cancer. Few sufferers survive more than two years. The causes of AIDS had not been absolutely identified at the time of writing in 1984, but a virus in combination with certain aspects of lifestyle seem to be implicated. The prevalence of AIDS among male homosexuals has already had an effect on sexual behaviour: fear of the condition in the USA is reported to have reduced the frequency of sexual contacts among the homosexual male community. Whether this change in behaviour in turn affects the spread of the disease remains to be seen.

Infertility, miscarriage and stillbirth

Finally, we return to the reproductive consequences of sexual activity. Earlier in this chapter, we were concerned primarily with the decisions that have to be made to prevent conception. A rather different set of choices may, however, face adults when they are *trying* to conceive.

To begin with, most couples assume that, sooner or later, they will conceive as planned and give birth to a healthy baby. But that does not always happen. For some, it may be difficult (*subfertility*), or even impossible (*infertility*); for others, conception may take place but be followed by *miscarriage* or *stillbirth*. Living with events like these can be very painful. There may be a profound sense of failure, and of exclusion from social groups of parents, as these two women found:

> It's such a personal thing, a secret I was harbouring. My body didn't belong to me and I didn't like it. My self-image was badly dented through all of this. I turned in on myself. I felt as though I wasn't a proper woman. (quoted in Pfeffer and Woollett, 1983, pp.22–23)

> This is a very suburban area. Being childless here means you are different. I'm not part of their world, and not because I don't want to be. (ibid. p.17)

For women, the sense of failure has to do with the failure to become a mother. For men, the sense of failure may be associated with a feeling of sexual inadequacy. One woman did not want to tell her husband for this reason:

> If I thought that there was nothing that could be done for my husband I'd rather that he didn't know. I know it's not so, but if only it could be put across that it isn't a sign of sexual deficiency, if you don't produce enough. (ibid. p.30)

Sometimes, people facing infertility may assume that it is the woman who cannot conceive; learning that an *infertility investigation* usually involves the man too can then be a bit of a shock:

> After the sperm count, the doctor said send your husband down. I was prepared to bare my tubes to the world so I was utterly shocked and amazed. I had somehow automatically assumed that it was my fault because I didn't have regular periods. (ibid. p.29)

Doctors may have to deal with these feelings of inadequacy carefully:

> When we went to the clinic the doctor said, 'I don't want to worry you and I don't want you to think any the less of yourself, but we consider your sperm count is slightly below average'. The way he said it made me think that he didn't know what to say, but also that he was telling us the way he would feel if that were him. (ibid. p.64)

Trying to conceive can begin to take over your whole life. Women often begin to worry about whether their body is working properly. The feeling of need to have a baby can become obsessional:

> I feel that whilst you're doing it, your life's in limbo. Jobwise, I haven't done the things I would have wanted because I spent so much energy thinking; Oh, I'm not going to be here long. I'll be pregnant soon, it's not important. (ibid. p.26)

> I go through different phases about whether I can bear to look at a mother and a baby walking down the street. I want to stare at them, or snatch them away out of prams, and at other times I just avoid looking at them altogether. (ibid, p.32)

The average time taken to conceive by couples is about five months, and 80 per cent will conceive within one year. The proportion of couples who cannot conceive is not known, although it may be as high as 10 per cent. There are many different causes, including problems in the production of ova or sperm; conditions affecting their passage through the reproductive system, such as blockage of the Fallopian tubes; and difficulties with sexual intercourse. All these possible causes are thoroughly investigated by subfertility clinics. One of the less pleasant things that people undergoing subfertility investigations have to face is the interference with sexual pleasure. Sex becomes mechanical. Not surprisingly, some people find this rather hard to cope with:

> I regarded my body as a machine, a bit of clockwork. I forgot all about him. I took the tablets, I used the douche, and then expected him to do his bit. He was very, very upset by the whole thing and couldn't cope with it all being divorced from feeling. (Pfeffer and Woollett, 1983, p.38)

> It was hard enough having sex to fit with my cycle, but getting up at six o'clock to masturbate was more than my husband could manage. But I found it difficult to be sympathetic because it would mean missing an appointment and prolonging the agony. (ibid, p.42)

The sense of failure, inadequacy and depression that often accompanies difficulty in conceiving a child is also experienced when a pregnancy ends in miscarriage. The poet Sylvia Plath, describes this in this extract from her poem 'Three Women'. The setting is a maternity ward.

> Parts, bits, cogs, the shining multiples.
> I am dying as I sit. I lose a dimension.
> Trains roaring in my ears, departures, departures!
> The silver track of time empties into the distance,
> The white sky empties of its promise, like a cup.
> These are my feet, these mechanical echoes.
> Tap, tap, tap, steel pegs. I am found wanting ...
>
> It is a world of snow now. I am not at home.
> How white these sheets are. The faces have no features.
> They are bald and impossible, like the faces of my children,
> Those little sick ones that elude my arms.
> Other children do not touch me: they are terrible.
> They have too many colours, too much life. They are not quiet,
> Quiet, like the little emptinesses I carry.
>
> I have had my chances. I have tried and tried.
> I have stitched life into me like a rare organ,
> And walked carefully, precariously, like something rare.
> I have tried not to think too hard. I have tried to be natural.
> I have tried to be blind in love, like other women,
> Blind in my bed, with my dear blind sweet one,
> Not looking, through the thick dark, for the face of another. ... (Plath, 1971, pp.41–42)

Both miscarriage and stillbirth evoke powerful emotions, as with other bereavements:

> The miscarriage was also a bereavement, in the real sense of the word. I'm approaching the time when it would have been due, and as that gets closer, I get more and more sad and depressed about it. (Pfeffer and Woollett, 1983 p.110)

In the case of a stillbirth, the bereavement may be easier to cope with if the dead baby has actually been *seen*. Contrast the experience of these two mothers:

> I have a recurring dream that I'm in that hospital searching for him. I just assumed that they burned him. I look over at the hospital chimney all the time. I can see it from my window and I can see the smoke coming out ... If you say to me: 'Stand up and tell me what you're about', I'd stand up and say to you: 'My name is Sandy and what I'm about is stillbirth'. I feel it is the most important event in my life. And yet, it is a terrible nothingness. (quoted in Lovell, 1983, p.758)

> They wrapped Bill (the stillborn baby) in a blanket. We didn't look at his body ... just his little face. I held him and Michael (baby's father) sort of hung on. The nurse left us. Then she came back and took Bill away. Afterwards, she brought us a cup of tea. It was an amazingly good thing to have done. (ibid, p.757)

In recent years there has been a shift away from the practice of whisking away the tiny corpse without contact with the parents, and more stillborn babies are now given a funeral.

In this chapter, we have touched on a number of topics related to sex and reproduction, and their relationship to health. Although this chapter has been concerned with adults in general, the topics we have considered affect people throughout life, but undergo a gradual evolution as life progresses. Contraception, for example, raises different sorts of problems at different ages: an older person who does not want any more children may solve the problem in a different way from a younger person who wants children in the near future. Similarly, someone who has sexual intercourse intermittently may choose a different solution from someone who is in a permanent relationship. Abortion is something that might be more readily chosen by young single women for whom pregnancy would be a greater burden than it would be for many older women. Sexually transmitted diseases are arguably more of a risk for younger people, and are certainly more of a risk to those having multiple sexual relationships. Finally, we turned to a topic that affects particularly those in their twenties and thirties — the childbearing years, when failure to achieve a longed-for pregnancy can be particularly difficult to bear. This final topic serves to remind us that, although sex and reproduction can be sources of great joy, they can also be sources of great anxiety and pain.

Objectives for Chapter 11

When you have studied this chapter, you should be able to:

11.1 Outline ways in which sex and reproduction may be related to health and disease via biological, social and personal factors, and indicate how this relationship might change throughout a lifetime.

11.2 Discuss the various influences on the choices people make about limiting pregnancy, and the degree to which people are free to make such choices.

11.3 Consider critically the evidence for the view that there is a current 'epidemic' of sexually transmitted diseases and abortions.

Questions for Chapter 11

1 (*Objective 11.1*) In what ways might the decision to terminate a pregnancy by a legal abortion be influenced by biology, society and personal history, and how might these differ between, say, a woman of 20 and one of 40 years?

2 (*Objective 11.2*) Read the following extracts from two newspaper articles, reporting on the same day on the same research study published in the *British Medical Journal*. Then answer the question below:

> GIRLS ON PILL 'FACE HIGHER CANCER RISKS'
> (*Daily Telegraph*, 26.6.81)
> Girls who start taking contraceptive pills in their teens may face an increased risk of breast cancer in later life, a medical study report says today... It says that the effect of the Pill on breast cancer may take as long as 30 years to become apparent.

> PILL FEARS 'PARTLY ALLAYED'
> (*Guardian*, 26.6.81)
> Fears that the contraceptive pill may be linked with breast cancer are partly allayed by reports... published in the *British Medical Journal* tomorrow. The Royal College of General Practitioners study... reports 'no convincing evidence of any adverse effects of oral contraceptives on breast cancer'.

What influence might such media coverage have on the choice of contraceptive method and the extent to which a person is free to choose?

3 (*Objective 11.3*) During the 1970s, the number of legal abortions obtained by women aged 15–19 years rose from 9.1 per 1000 women in this age group to 16.8 per 1000 by the end of the decade. In the same period, the live birth rate to women in this age group fell from 50.4 to 31.0 per 1000. Do these data support the view that increased sexual permissiveness and the availability of abortions has resulted in more unplanned teenage pregnancies?

12
Work and health in adult life

This chapter builds on the discussion of poverty, housing and work (with special reference to women) and their relationship to health (Book III, *The Health of Nations*, Chapter 10); defining and measuring stress (Book IV, *The Biology of Health and Disease*, Chapter 15); hormones and stress (Book IV, Chapter 6); and the discussion of family structure and roles in Chapter 4 of this book.

For most people, getting their first job is a major turning point in life. This is widely seen to be the beginning of adulthood — indeed, school leavers who fail to find work are often not considered 'adults' at all, and unemployment later in life brings with it considerable loss of adult status. The subject of *unemployment* and its effects on health has been discussed fully in another book in this course, so we shall not consider it further here.* Instead we shall focus on the working day, and the way it is experienced by different groups of workers.

If childhood is seen as a time of freedom — to play, to learn, to explore — then adulthood is seen as the time to shoulder one's responsibilities and settle down to many years of steady work. The majority of adults live in families; feeding, clothing and housing not only themselves, but also their children and, increasingly, elderly relations. State benefits and pensions help with the financial cost of this task, but the majority of the money required is earned by paid labour. A person in full-time employment can now expect to work about 40 hours per week, 49 weeks of the year for 40 or 50 years until retirement. Throughout this period, very considerable physical work must also be performed daily within the home — work that has no fixed hours, scheduled days off, or date of retirement.

There are many dimensions to the subject of work and health. Two important ones are the chemical and physical hazards to which workers inside and outside the home are exposed, and the variation in such hazards between different occupations.† In this chapter we shall consider the health consequences of the way in which work is organised — the hours worked and the pace of work — and the different effects of this on the work experience of men and women, and disabled people of both sexes. We shall do

*Book III, *The Health of Nations*, Chapter 11.

†These are discussed in Book III, *The Health of Nations*, Chapter 10.

this, as elsewhere in this book, by drawing on the personal statements of individuals reflecting on their working lives, as well as on quantitative research.

Health and the organisation of paid employment

Many different aspects of the way in which work is organised may have implications for health: standing or sitting all day with little opportunity to rest or to 'stretch one's legs'; working to constant and inflexible deadlines; working at high speeds on a production line; working long and/or unsociable hours; work which involves too much responsibility or too little, or which gives meagre satisfaction. Although conditions such as these may be easily coped with by some workers, all of these dimensions of work have, like chemical and physical hazards, been associated with health problems. These problems may not be as dramatic as the loss of a limb, or a cancer, but they can be difficult to live with and they may have long term implications for health. Table 12.1 illustrates some of the reasons given by a group of men and women for absence from work of six weeks or more.

□ Make a list of the health problems mentioned in the table, and attempt to form them into groups of related conditions.

■ The most obvious groupings are: (i) *injuries* — slipped disc and broken ankle; (ii) *respiratory problems* — asthma, bronchitis, pleurisy, cough, catarrh; (iii) *problems with digestion* — ulcers, stomach trouble; and (iv) *nervous complaints* — strain and stress.

□ What causes of ill-health are suggested by the people quoted in Table 12.1?

■ Some of the suggested causes relate to the physical conditions of the work itself, such as injury resulting from moving heavy loads (Examples 1 and 3), or illness resulting from working conditions, such as poor ventilation (Examples 2, 5 and 9). Others mentioned factors relating to the organisation of work, such as irregular hours or shift work (Examples 4, 7 and 8), or that the work imposed psychological stress and strain (Examples 6 and 7).

What is the evidence that the illness or injury could have been caused by the factors mentioned? It would seem likely that the back injury reported in Example 1 *was* related to lifting heavy loads at work, but it is often much less easy to establish a connection between, say, the organisation of work and illness. 'Stress and strain' are often given as reasons for people's illness, but *stress* is hard to measure, and it may be difficult to say how much stress results from the work itself. The article by Mildred Blaxter in the Course Reader (Part 1, Section 1.5), which was recommended reading in Chapter 7, looked at how a group of Scottish women explain the causes of diseases. Many of them made reference

Table 12.1 Reasons for being off work sick for more than six weeks

Worker*	Reasons for absence
1 Man, 55, cleaner in bakery	Moving large barrels caused a back injury (also chronic asthma and bronchitis).
2 Woman, 55, textile worker	My doctor said it was because there was poor ventilation in my place of work. I have a weak chest and it brings on a bad cough.
3 Man, 53, builder's labourer	I had a heavy job and was doing a lot of lifting. I slipped a disc and had to have an operation. (Registered disabled)
4 Man, 22, bus driver	I got ulcers or some kind of stomach trouble through irregular meals.
5 Woman, 41, greengrocer's assistant	The draught might have caused my pleurisy.
6 Woman, 21, tarpaulin proofer	The job was going for my nerves. My doctor advised me to leave.
7 Woman, 38, packer in cardboard factory (then factory worker 'stretching alloys')	I slipped and broke my ankle. In my other job I worked shift hours and the strain gave me nervous trouble. (Evidence of consultations with GP and ten visits to hospital out-patients.)
8 Man, 54, superintendent engineer (of corporation)	I was called out during the night to mechanical breakdowns and I got ill.
9 Woman, 26, boxmaker	All-electric factory dried atmosphere, and increased catarrh.

* These are nine examples selected from 53 in Townsend's book.

(Data from Townsend, 1979, p. 447–450)

Figure 12.1 The pressures of working on a factory production line (The Photo Source)

to 'stress' and one woman explained her stroke as follows:

> I'd an awful lot of stress with my husband dying, and looking after my mum, and I went out to work... I wisnae home here until evening and by the time I did housework and bed — I was up early in the morning again. I think it just began that it got too much. (Blaxter, 1983, p.64)

□ What factors does this woman suggest were contributing to the 'stress' she experienced?

■ The illness of her husband, the care of her mother, paid employment outside the home, long working days and housework.

If this woman is right, and stress contributed to her subsequent illness, then conditions associated with her paid employment were only part of the contributing factors, a point which should be borne in mind in the subsequent discussion.

One way of attempting to quantify stress at work would be to measure particular features of a person's physiological state, such as heart rate or blood pressure, and see if they vary with different working conditions.* The effects of stress on the human body cover a wide range of physiological changes, but research has most often been concentrated on changes in the level of certain hormones in the bloodstream, particularly adrenalin. This hormone is released from the adrenal glands just above the kidneys whenever additional energy is required: for example, on getting up in the morning, running for a bus or when faced with a sudden emergency. Adrenalin acts on several parts of the body, but in particular it causes an increase in glucose levels in the blood as a source of energy, and makes the heart beat faster. The adrenalin level also increases when a person feels anxious, for example, when taking an examination, and seems to be associated with getting the body ready for *'fight or flight' reactions*.

Managers and other professionals in positions of responsibility at work have been shown to have higher than average levels of adrenalin in their bloodstream during the working day, and this has been assumed to contribute to the high rates of conditions such as stomach ulcers and heart disease that this professional group suffer. However, a number of studies have shown that, at least as far as adrenalin levels are concerned, these 'top jobs' are not the most stressful occupations. For example, in 1980 D.A. Jenner and colleagues found that adrenalin levels were highest in people doing repetitive manual work, like those in Figure 12.1. Whether or not such changes are related to specific diseases is an issue we return to later in the chapter.

*Physiology is the branch of biology concerned with the integrated functions of tissues and organs within the body, maintaining the optimum internal state despite fluctuations in external conditions. Details of this can be found in Book IV, *The Biology of Health and Disease*, Chapter 5.

Figure 12.2 The pressure of office work. (Photo: Ron McCormick)

However, it has also been shown (at least in experimental animals) that if there is action available to the organism under stress, this has an effect on its physiological state. So, for example, rats given mild electric shocks to which they could react by jumping onto a platform showed fewer physiological signs of stress than rats given the same number and duration of shocks from which there was no 'escape'. This type of research is relevant to the stressfulness of working conditions, since manual workers are less able to 'escape' the production line than are managers, for example, who can take a short break without jeopardising their jobs.

□ Read the following accounts of production line work and comment on how the pace of work is controlled and what this implies about the workers' opportunity to respond to the pressure they may be under.

> It is widely recognised on the shopfloor that technological change has resulted in a frantic work tempo for those who remain. At the Triumph Plant in Coventry it is reckoned that a human being is 'burned up' in ten years when working on the main track. (quoted in Cooley, 1980, p.13)

> The women ran the line but we were also appendages to it. Its discipline was imposed automatically through the light, the conveyor belt and the bonus system. We just slotted in like cogs in a wheel. Every movement we made and every second of our time was controlled by the line... it is impossible to put over in writing the speed of the line, the pace of the work, and the fiddliness of the job we had to repeat all day long as tray followed tray down the line. We were physically geared up, straining to get it down as fast as we could and the atmosphere was frantic. Everything was rushed, work, breaks, drinking tea, reading the paper. We were so speedy that we rushed at everything. (quoted in Cavendish, 1982, p.111)

■ These extracts suggest that the *pace of work* is controlled to a large extent by external factors, particularly the speed of the machines, and to some extent by the bonus system, which puts pressure on workers to 'keep up' so as not to jeopardise the bonus of fellow workers 'on the line'.

Three of the workers quoted in Table 12.1 referred specifically to problems caused by hours of work — irregular mealtimes, nightwork and the strain of *shiftwork*. The potential health effects of shiftwork have in fact been the focus of increasing attention, as the number of people involved in shiftwork and the speed at which people are expected to 'rotate' between different shifts have increased. There are now around 3 million full-time shiftworkers, 20 per cent of whom are women. In addition, many of the 3.5 million part-time workers — the majority of whom are women — work early morning or evening shifts.

Most shiftworkers are in manual jobs, but in the health service, for instance, all grades of staff do shiftwork, and many shiftworkers report considerable disruption in their lives.

□ Look at the quotations below from full-time shiftworkers, and list the problems they identify.

Shiftwork disrupts your whole social life... you can't go to a dance or go fishing at weekends. (quoted in Gallie, 1978, p.72)

On shifts you don't see your wife for a day at a time and then at odd hours. You don't see your children for a week on some shifts. You're a stranger to them. (ibid. p.72)

It's hopeless on the nightshift... I never get more than four hours sleep... but even after a long sleep I still feel fatigued. (quoted in GMWU, 1980, p.14)

On days I go to the toilet regularly... on shiftwork I take to the Epsom Salts. (ibid, p.14)

Most shiftworkers take medicines for stomach troubles... the food from vending machines doesn't help. (ibid, p.14)

■ The quotations suggest that social life in general, and family life in particular, can be severely disrupted; the length and quality of sleep are affected, and this may cause chronic fatigue and possibly increase the risk of accidents; eating patterns are also disrupted, causing digestive problems.

These people experience their work as stressful, but what is the evidence that such stress contributes to disease? Several studies have found disrupted sleep patterns and raised levels of hormones such as adrenalin in shiftworkers, which might provide physiological evidence of stress. However, evidence to link these changes to increased ill-health among shiftworkers is limited and confused. There does appear to be good epidemiological evidence that shiftwork is associated with an increased incidence of gastric and duodenal ulcers, although it is not clear whether shiftwork causes, or simply exacerbates, these problems. Some studies suggest that accident rates are in fact lower among nightworkers than day workers, but that accidents at night are more severe. Sickness absence rates are also frequently found to be lower among shiftworkers than among day workers. (It should be noted that most of the research in this area has been concerned with male shiftworkers.)

Obviously, the extent to which shiftworking disrupts social and biological systems will depend to some extent on the pattern of shiftwork involved. It may even be advantageous for some workers — both men and women — if, for example, they have school-aged children. In one study, 20 per cent of male shiftworkers felt that their contact with the family had actually improved since they had gone on shifts and 75 per cent felt that their health had not been affected at all (see Harrington, 1978, for a review of research in this area). But research suggests that workers in 'poorer' health may in fact be selected out of shiftwork.

For all but a few, shift work is undertaken voluntarily. Those who are unable, for whatever reason, to adapt themselves to its demands usually manage to find a job on day work... In studying [the mortality of] shift workers with 10 years or more experience, we are looking at a survivor population and, moreover, one that is largely self-selected in the first place. (Taylor and Pocock, 1972, p.206)

Given that many shiftworkers experience considerable disruption in their lives, we need perhaps to ask why they work the hours they do. There are many possible explanations.

□ Can you suggest what some of these might be?

■ 1 The job might demand it — nurses and doctors, for instance, are required to be on duty at all hours; some types of equipment (e.g. smelting furnaces) require constant attention.

2 Economic decisions in a particular industry might make 24-hour operation the most profitable method of production.

3 People might be unable to find a full-time day job.

4 People may actually prefer shiftwork, either because some of it pays higher rates for unsociable hours, or because it fits in with other family commitments, or they might just prefer the hours.

For both men and women, *patterns of work* are closely related to their family responsibilities. Although there is little information about this in relation to men, a survey of male shiftworkers conducted by the National Board for Prices and Incomes in 1970 found that 62 per cent had dependent children compared with only 38 per cent of day workers. The most important reason given by these men for doing shiftwork was the financial advantage it involved. According to a survey of shiftworkers in 1983, they received an average of 26 per cent more than basic rates. However, the influence of family responsibility on women's employment is much more pervasive, affecting not only the hours they work, but whether or not they work at all and even the type of employment they are able to take. In one survey of women and shiftwork, for example, over 70 per cent of all women engaged in part-time evening work had children under five. In another study of women in factory work, by Sylvia Shimmin and her colleagues in 1981, such work was often seen as the only job possible in the circumstances and entered into more from necessity than choice. But in contrast to male shiftworkers, few women workers receive additional financial premiums for working shifts. Rather, they work the hours they do in order to fit employment in with their responsibilities for childcare and housework.

This division of labour within the home, with women retaining prime responsibility for domestic labour and childcare, reflects the deeply held beliefs about the proper role of men and women in the family which were referred to in Chapter 4. These, in turn, rest on unproven assumptions that women are physically weaker than men, that they have instinctive childrearing abilities and that they are innately more suitable than men for work that involves providing a service and caring for others. Such assumptions have profoundly influenced the way in which the *labour market* operates, generating legislation and trade union and employers' practices that effectively bar women from certain kinds of jobs; social security regulations and systems of taxation that force women to be dependent on men; levels of pay that continue to assume men are earning the 'family wage' while women work for pin money; and a sexual division of labour in the formal labour market whereby women not only have predominantly part-time, low paid jobs, but they are largely concentrated in service occupations — nursing, teaching, cleaning, cooking, etc. Thus, as British sociologist Hilary Graham puts it, women are '... doing on a larger scale for society what they traditionally have done on a small scale for their families.' (Graham, 1984, p.64). However, we are not primarily concerned here with why such divisions exist, but rather with what the health implications of these divisions might be.

Health and the sexual division of labour

In our society men on average die younger than women, and male mortality rates are higher than female mortality rates at all ages. There are also important differences between married and single men and women: married men and women live longer lives than their single counterparts (though the difference is much greater among men than among women). In contrast to mortality rates, morbidity rates are higher for women than for men for several conditions, most notably depression and certain chronic conditions such as rheumatoid arthritis. For most other conditions, male and female morbidity rates are very similar. Women also have higher consultation rates for certain services related to health, particularly visits to GPs. Caution is needed in interpreting morbidity data because some of the differences might be explained by differences in diagnostic behaviour, illness behaviour or in access to services. But Hilary Graham argues that these differences in mortality and morbidity between men and women,

> ... like differences between social classes, reflect in part differences in the ways the sexes live, differences in particular in the working conditions of men and women. In general terms, it appears that it is the particular kind and pace of men's work which makes men as a sex more vulnerable to premature death. Similarly, it is the kind and pace of work which women do which makes women more vulnerable to illhealth. (Graham, 1984, p.75)

Women's paid work involves less risk of accidental death than men's — few women are employed in those industries where mortality rates are high such as construction, mining, and engineering. But, just like all workers in low paid, low status jobs, they are exposed to hazards and stress. Traditional female employment often involves exposure to both chemical and physical hazards: laundry work, for example, involves exposure to detergents and hot water. However, many women are also exposed to the additional health hazards associated with work in the home and with the need to combine family responsibilities and paid employment — the '*double day*', as it is often termed. Sociologists such as Hilary Graham argue that this is a significant factor in the extent of ill-health suffered by women.

Housework may involve quite serious hazards to health. Many houses are in poor condition, and damp and structural problems pose a greater threat to the mental and physical health of women, who spend longer in the home, than to the health of men. Housework also involves the risk of accidents, particularly from burns, chemicals, electrical appliances and falls. One fifth of all accidents in the home occur to women between the ages of 20 and 64. And of course housework and childcare never stops!

> I think men have got more spare time 'cos (when) they're away from their work so what they do then really it's up to them. I mean if they don't want to help the wife ... nobody can force them to and they can just sit down all night if they want to ... Whereas a woman ... they've still got to cook the tea and do anything else that needs doing. Like if one of the children make a horrible mess of the room ... or tip something on the floor, then they can't say 'Oh, it's gone five o'clock ... it'll stop there now until nine o'clock tomorrow morning'. They've got to clean it up. (quoted in Hobson, 1978, p.88)

Given the constant and often unpredictable demands of housework and childcare, it is not surprising that combining such responsibilities with paid employment may impose considerable strain, certainly sufficient to undermine any idea of women as the weaker sex! Consider the demands on the woman quoted below:

> I get up about quarter to five, make the children's lunches up, get the children up about half past six, get breakfast, do their hair and everything and then I go

to work about ten to seven. My husband takes them next door and then he goes out about quarter past seven. I get home at lunchtime, make the beds and do the housework. I just sort of make a drink of tea and a sandwich and I keep going while I'm eating because if I sit down I don't feel like working. I pick the children up from school, go swimming one night and then it's their tea time. I make the dinner, get the children to bed, and that's it really. I never really sit down... I go to bed between 10 and 11 otherwise I can't get up for work. (quoted in Shimmin *et al*, 1981, p.347)

Given these sorts of pressures why do women continue to combine paid work and domestic responsibilities? Research suggests that financial reasons are important, particularly for those mothers with sole responsibility for children and for women whose partners are low paid. But there are other reasons.

□ Read the quotations below and list the positive aspects of paid work identified by these women.

... to me just packing all night is boring... but the girls are okay, you have a bit of a laugh. You're not talking about children all the time, you're talking about general things so it gets you off that subject. If you're at home all day you get like a cabbage. I like the independence of working. (Liff, 1980)

Working gives me my own spending money and it makes me a little more independent of my husband. If something should happen and I have to take over supporting the family, I'm ready for it. I'm not just locked in the dark, not knowing what to do and where to turn. (quoted in Dabrowski, 1983, p.44)

I really do need to work... Everybody has inner feelings about who they want to be. They want to feel a little important by being somebody or doing something. It is really not possible to do this by being in the home. (ibid, p.44)

■ These women are suggesting that for them employment provides social networks and interests outside the home, a degree of independence and a sense of worth.

These sorts of factors help to explain why, for men and women, employment can be psychologically supportive even when conditions are poor. For example, it certainly appears to protect some women from depression.* But how do we reconcile these positive attitudes towards work and the fact that it may actually promote mental health in some cases, with the effects of the considerable burden that the

*Depression is discussed more fully in Book VI, *Experiencing and Explaining Disease*, Chapter 8.

Table 12.2 Percentage of women workers likely to have poor mental health as estimated by a self-completion questionnaire

Hours worked	Percentage estimated to have poor mental health
full-time	47.8
morning shift	38.2
afternoon shift	31.6
evening shift	26.8
all part-time	30.8

(Data from Shimmin *et al.*, 1981, p. 348)

'double day' may involve? One research study on the mental health of women factory workers helps to answer this question.

Table 12.2 shows the percentage of women working different hours who had a high score on a '*General Health Questionnaire*' — a self-completion questionnaire which is a standard device used in the detection of psychiatric problems in General Practice. It focuses on recent health and is thought to detect mainly depressive and neurotic illness: the higher the score the greater the likelihood for that individual to have poor mental health. As the table shows, a far higher proportion of full-time women workers had poor mental health on this measure compared to part-time employees. The lowest proportion of women with poor mental health were found among women working the evening or 'twilight shift'. Possible explanations for these differences are, first, that all part-timers are likely to have more hours available for their domestic work and, second, that women on the evening shift are likely to have less difficulty with childcare as partners or other relatives are around while they are at work. The researchers on this project also found that full-time women workers were under the greatest financial pressure and felt unable to leave the job even when they did not like it.

An American study of heart disease by S. Haynes and M. Feinlab (1980) found a similar pattern, reporting a significantly higher incidence of heart disease among employed married women compared to employed single women and non-employed married women. But when the results were analysed on the basis of family responsibility, married women with larger families were more prone to heart disease than those with fewer or no children.

In summary, family responsibilities are shared disproportionately between employed men and women in most British families. The health consequences of this 'double day' for women are most prominent where material circumstances are poor. Let us now conclude this chapter by reviewing the experience of another group who have particularly acute difficulties with work, people with a physical impairment.

The 'disabled' worker

People with a *physical* or *mental handicap* obviously face hazards at work as do able-bodied workers, but a disproportionate number who wish to work fail to find employment. Of those who have a job, the majority receive relatively low pay. This bias in the labour market, reminiscent of the situation faced by most female workers, is reflected in the proportion of disabled people who live on or near the margins of poverty. In 1976, for example, 46 per cent of people with physical impairments were living on incomes at or below the supplementary benefit level, compared to 12 per cent of the general population. This poverty is directly related to difficulties associated with work, as the following statement illustrates.

> In the final analysis the particular form of poverty principally associated with physical impairment is caused by our exclusion from the ability to *earn* an income on a par with our able-bodied peers, due to the way employment is organised... In our view, it is society which disables physically impaired people. (Union of the Physically Impaired Against Segregation and the Disablility Alliance, 1976, quoted in Humphreys, 1979, pp. 11–12)

□ What do you think is meant by saying it is 'society which disables'?

■ The implication is that the attitudes within society towards people with a physical impairment, both in relation to work and other areas of life, give them a second-class status, and it is this which constitutes 'disability'.

The statement goes on to explain: '*Disability* is something imposed on top of our impairments by the way we are unnecessarily isolated and excluded from full participation in society'.

As the statement indicates, the *organisation of work* can contribute to the exclusion of people with impairments. They may, for example, have problems with mobility. This can result from the way work is organised to take place at specified times: for example, lack of transport at certain hours may make shiftwork impracticable. There can also be difficulties in mobility at the workplace. Like most other buildings, workplaces are not designed to cater for people with impairments, even though there is provision by Act of Parliament for public money to be made available under certain circumstances to install ramps and other 'aids'. One young woman teacher described the difficulties she faced:

> One's self-confidence is subjected to much unintentional battering by the public at large, too. Suddenly one discovers that one is imbecilic ('does your wife take sugar?') and quite possibly unemployable. I had been a teacher of English... when I broke my back in 1972. I was shattered when they asked me to resign because it was going to prove too difficult to arrange for me to teach in one room on the ground floor. I felt totally rejected, not only was my body impaired, but it seemed that even my mind was no longer of any use. (quoted in Campling, 1981, pp.40–41)

Work of any kind can be particularly tiring if you are physically disabled, thus imposing additional strains. Two disabled women describe the difficulties they face doing housework (see Figure 12.3).

> With a large house, I have to work to a method to cope with my housework. I miss being able to walk into a room, look around to see if the room is tidy or not. I have to go into the room and feel all around it... This takes time and energy, even if the room does not need cleaning...
>
> A question I am often asked... is, 'What is it like being blind?' and I always reply by saying, 'It is very tiring'. I think this is more true of a woman than a man, and being a blind housewife and a mother is an added strain. (quoted in Campling, 1981, pp.93–95)

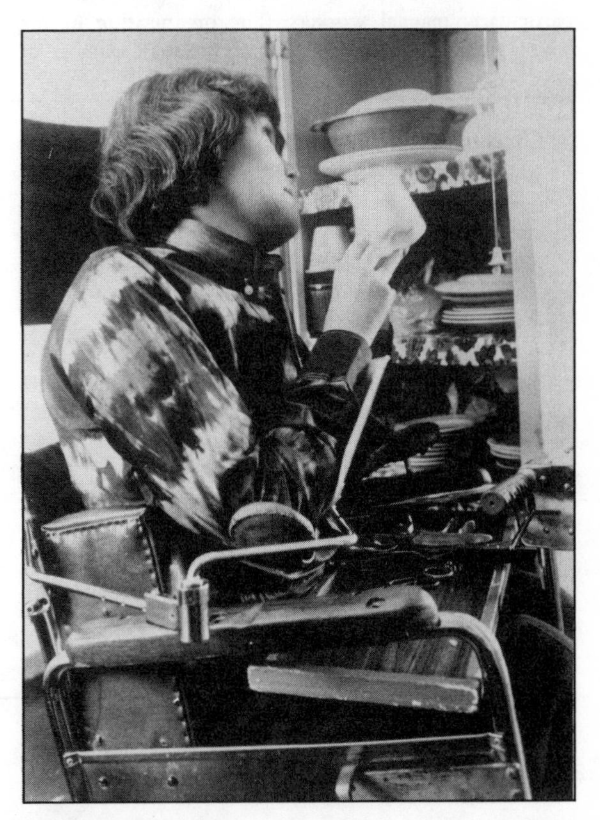

Figure 12.3 The difficulties of housework when physically impaired (Photo: Chris Steele-Perkins)

> I cannot twist my wrist and arm to dust, washing a cup is painful and it is impossible for me to push a vacuum cleaner or carpet sweeper... When I have managed to do the washing (by machine) I am in terrible pain for the following two days and nights... I can just about cook a dinner with my husband preparing the vegetables and straining them off and cutting the meat. Some days my legs won't hold me up and he has to take over completely. (quoted in Glendinning, 1980, p.37)

These women struggle daily to keep up with their commitment to work and to fulfil certain family responsibilities through physical labour. This reflects the key place work holds in the lives of British adults: everyone expects to labour either inside or outside the home, and the majority of women in families expect to do both. Fatigue and discomfort in paid and unpaid work may be particularly acute where the organisation of the working day is abnormally long (e.g. the 'double day'), entails disruptive shiftwork patterns, is repetitive and relentless, or where the worker has a physical impairment. As with other health hazards, disruptive working patterns are more common among lower paid sectors of the workforce, particularly manual workers. The organisation of the labour market means that a disproportionate number of employed women work in low paid jobs in industries that reflect society's view of women 'serving' the community at work and their families at home. Similarly, a disproportionate number of physically impaired people cannot find work, or can only earn low wages, because employment practices or work patterns exclude them from work or better paid jobs.*

This exploration of ways in which health is related to the organisation of work in adult life goes some way towards explaining the different mortality and morbidity experience of men and women. Men suffer higher mortality which is partly related to the chemical and physical hazards associated with their work, particularly in manual occupations. We can be less sure about the precise effects of shiftwork and 'production line' working methods, but they do appear to have some adverse consequences for health. Women's work also entails health hazards, particularly for those women who combine responsibility for home and children with paid employment. The higher rates of certain types of ill-health, particularly depression and other chronic conditions, suffered by women relative to men seem to reflect this. For both sexes, *any* hazards resulting from working inside or outside the home can be expected to exert pressure on a person's health throughout adult life.

Objectives for Chapter 12

When you have studied this chapter, you should be able to:

12.1 Discuss the ways in which the organisation of paid employment might be associated with ill-health in adult life and comment on some of the difficulties involved in assessing this.

12.2 Comment on how the sexual division of labour might contribute to an understanding of male/female mortality and morbidity differences.

Questions for Chapter 12

1 (*Objective 12.1*) It has been estimated that 37 million working days are lost in the UK each year through disorders such as headaches and depression, which may be related to stressful conditions at work. This is more than the time lost through accidents in the workplace.

(a) What aspects of the organisation of work *might* contribute to these forms of ill-health?

(b) Why is it very difficult to establish a causal connection between them?

2 (*Objective 12.2*)

> When I started work with two young kids, the agreement was he worked nights and I worked days. So, he agreed to keep the house straightened up in the daytime and take care of the kids. Then at night I would keep the house in order. Well it worked for about two or three days. After that it was all on me. (Dabrowski, 1983, p.41)

What differences in how work is organised for men and women are revealed by this couple's decision about which of them worked the night or day shift, and what implications for their health are there in this?

*Disability and social attitudes to it are the subject of an audiotape associated with Book VI, *Experiencing and Explaining Disease*, Chapter 13.

13

Change and crisis in mid-life

This chapter builds on the discussion of hormones and reproduction in Book IV, *The Biology of Health and Disease*, Chapter 10. In particular, you will need to know about the regulation of oestrogens and progestogen levels in maintaining the menstrual cycle. Reference is also made to randomised, double-blind trials and the placebo effect, both of which are discussed in Book I, *Studying Health and Disease*, Chapter 6.

> Is it true that women go crazy while going through the menopause? (A teenage girl, quoted in Weidger, 1977, p.206)
>
> What does a woman go through? Everything I've heard about seems to imply that after a woman has been through the menopause her sex life isn't satisfying. She turns frigid. (A teenage girl, ibid, p.219)
>
> Why does a rising corporation executive suddenly, in his early forties, quit his job and go off with his family to a new kind of life on a farm? What makes a seemingly happy husband leave his wife for a girl not much older than his daughter? Why do so many men, at about this time in their lives, begin to drink too much, become discontented and depressed for no clear reason, undergo what appears to be a distinct personality change? (quoted by Scarfe, 1977, p.302)

The transitions of middle age are often thought to be a time of turmoil and trouble. Women undergo what is sometimes ominously known as 'the change of life'; many men are held to experience a 'mid-life crisis', or even a 'male menopause'. How far are these stories true? Do most women experience painful physical and mental changes? Do men suffer from analogous problems? If so, are these the result of biological change, or the product of transformation in their social lives? These are the topics of this chapter, though we shall only attempt to answer some of these questions in detail. We shall focus principally on women and the *menopause*, for it is here that most research has been undertaken, and here too that an important and controversial form of medical treatment has been devised, that of hormone replacement therapy (increasingly known as HRT).

The most obvious outward sign of biological change in women in their forties is that menstruation becomes more irregular and infrequent, and eventually ceases altogether.

The ovaries cease to produce mature eggs (ova) at regular intervals, and the levels of hormones secreted by the ovaries gradually declines to about 20 per cent of that secreted in earlier years. The average age at which women in Britain today undergo the menopause is fifty-one years, although some women begin it long before that (for example, approximately eight per cent of women have a menopause before they are forty) and others continue to menstruate for many years after fifty-one. (You should note that we are referring here to a naturally occurring menopause, but there can also be a surgical menopause which occurs if the ovaries are removed as they sometimes are when a hysterectomy is performed.)

In men there are also changes in the reproductive system during middle age. The fundamental difference between the sexes is that the menopause for women is a relatively rapid affair, while changes in the male system occur over a much longer time. Male fertility, as measured by sperm count, declines somewhat as men approach later middle age (although some men remain quite capable of fathering a child until well into old age). The other major change in men is that hormone production from the testes begins to decline from the age of about 30 onwards, which in turn can have some effects on sexual performance (affecting erection time, for example). However, the changes in men occur slowly over several decades and may not even be noticeable until a man is much older.

The physiological changes associated with the menopause are, by contrast, relatively rapid. It was once thought that the menopause occurred as the ovary 'ran out of' eggs. At birth, the ovaries already contain all the eggs that a woman will ever have, but they are in an immature state, whereas men make new sperm continuously from puberty onwards. However, it is now known that, although *mature* eggs are not produced after the menopause, many immature ones remain in the ovaries after this point.

□ Can you suggest any advantages the menopause might have, in biological terms?

■ Since eggs are not newly made throughout life, there is an increasing risk that as the eggs age, they will develop genetic defects. For example, the risk of giving birth to a baby with Down's syndrome increases with the mother's age. The cessation of reproductive capacity is one way that such risks are reduced.

What causes the ovaries to stop producing a mature egg each month? The ovaries (and testes) are under the control of hormones produced by the pituitary gland, which in turn is controlled by parts of the brain. One possibility, then, is that the stimulus from the brain to the pituitary gland or from there to the ovaries ceases, rather than locating the cause within the ovaries themselves. This idea is reinforced by some animal experiments, in which 'old' ovaries were transplanted into younger animals. In the presence of a normally functioning pituitary gland, these transplanted ovaries did indeed begin to release mature ova again. As menopause begins, the stimulus from the pituitary gland to the ovaries declines, and the quantity of hormones that they secrete is reduced. It is this decline in hormones — particularly oestrogens — to which many of the unpleasant symptoms of the menopause have frequently been attributed.

The biological changes occurring in the middle years are, at least in women, quite profound, but there are also some major social changes during this time of life that can result in upheaval. For many people, middle age is a time of satisfaction. They may be well established and secure in their jobs, mothers who gave up paid work while their children were young may have returned to work, there may be more leisure time now that the children have grown up. Family life can bring new satisfactions, such as grand-parenthood. But for others, it can be a difficult time. Work may start to prove unsatisfactory. Old age, loneliness, chronic illness, and the threat of death and decline can suddenly seem very close, giving a sense of 'time running out', as these two middle-aged men observed:

> I tend to notice it in the newspapers nowadays when people of my own age die. Which is something you don't seem to remark on much when you're in your thirties. But then, people at that age die in accidents; in their forties they start to keel over from heart attacks... Where you say: 'God, in six years I'll be fifty'.

> I'm working in the business, hard. And I'm getting older, and the energy I started with is running out. Sooner or later I'm not going to be able to work as hard, and I really haven't gotten any place. As you get older, you begin to think of yourself as a man in a hurry. The years are going by, and you want to know your life meant something. (quoted by Scarfe, 1977, p.305)

Family life also changes, and, as children leave home, their mothers may feel that there is now little point to their own lives. Other children may disappoint parents' fond aspirations. Sick and elderly parents may become a burden. One woman, for example, felt that her life had only been happy when her children were at home; middle age was a time,

> ... when I had to break up and be myself, and be alone, and I'm just — I really feel that I'm not only not loved but not even liked sometimes by my own children... they could respect me. If — if they can't say good things why should they, why should they feel better when they hurt my feelings, and make me

cry, and then call me a crybaby, or tell me that I — I ought to know better or something like that. My worst thing is that I'm alone, I'm not wanted, nobody interests themselves in me... nobody cares. (quoted by Bart, 1971, p.167)

Women who have had to care for their families over many years may react to the loss in other ways: the following poem suggests how a woman's family responsibilities and role changed dramatically, and how she responded to this one day:

They call me Grace.
Yesterday I went
to the grocery store.
I had filled up
the cart
and was half way through
the check stand
before I realised
I had shopped for the whole family.
The last child left
two years ago.
I don't know what
got into
me.
I was too embarrassed
to take things back
so I spent the whole week cooking
casseroles.
I feel like one of those
eternal motion machines
designed for an obsolete task
that just keeps on
running.

(Susan Griffin, from her play, *Voices*, quoted in Grassman and Bart, 1982, p.185)

In middle age, there is a small but significant increase in the rate of petty crimes, such as shoplifting, committed by women.

□ Can you suggest possible reasons why some women should react like this, or like the woman in the poem?

■ One possible explanation is that it is related to the biological effects of the menopause, e.g. hormonal changes. However, as you have seen, middle age is also accompanied by many social changes: women may be feeling depressed, for instance, because of the loss of younger family members. The social changes of middle life may compound other problems, such as poverty, thus making the job of managing household budgets more difficult. We cannot readily separate all these out.

It is not only women, of course, for whom middle age brings potentially disruptive changes to their lives. Men, too, may experience dissatisfaction and problems, to which they may react in different ways. There is an increase in the incidence of alcoholism and suicide among middle-aged men, for example, which may reflect the stress experienced by this age-group.

Since these social changes coincide with biological changes of the menopause in women, it is perhaps not surprising that for some women the menopause itself is experienced as stressful:

Women's magazines tell you all the physical symptoms about hot flushes and feeling physically ill and yet they don't tell you about the mental stress and I think that's sad because it's the worst part. (quoted in Fairhurst and Lightup, 1980)

I didn't expect that I'd be like this and, like I've said before I like to feel that I'm a sensible, level-headed type and I'm surprised that it's happening to me. It's something that I can't control and I'm shattered. (ibid)

... until I knew this symptom of mental disturbance wasn't peculiar to me and it was all part of the menopause syndrome, I was even frightened to tell my own doctor... it can be a real terror, particularly if you considered yourself completely level-headed up till then and then you think you're the next one for certification. (ibid)

I have recently turned down a good post because I know that when I flush from the toes upwards, and feel like crawling into a corner, I just could not face a large office. So although I have the ability and could earn a great deal more, I stay in my safe little job and resign myself to that. (quoted in Cooper, 1976, p.75)

□ These women have spoken of some of the changes they experienced. What health problems have you heard of or experienced as being associated with the menopause?

■ Your list may have included some of the following: first, hot flushes and 'mental stress' were mentioned by the women quoted above. Others that are sometimes reported include excessive perspiration, tingling of the extremities, aches in muscles and joints, insomnia, dizziness, headaches, irritability, depression, difficulty with sex, pain when urinating, and backache.

As we noted above, many of these problems have been attributed to the decline in hormones from the ovaries during menopause. But how can we tell if hormone changes are responsible, given the large overlap of social and biological changes occurring in many women's lives at this time?

We shall consider three types of study, each of which takes a different approach to answering this question. The first approach is to check how far these symptoms are actually associated with the menopause. The second is to ask if these symptoms are also sometimes found in men as well as women. And the third considers the effectiveness of *Hormone Replacement Therapy* (*HRT*–taking oestrogens prescribed by a doctor). Does it really help women who suffer from the symptoms described above?

The first approach looks at the range of symptoms that are attributed to the menopause, and attempts to determine how far they are associated with the biological events of the menopause, or whether social changes also play an important role.

We shall consider two examples of this type of study. The first was carried out in 1974 by statistician Sonja McKinlay and sociologist Margot Jefferys, and used a postal questionnaire. Respondents were asked about their last menstruation, about the incidence of certain *menopausal symptoms* during the previous year, and some questions about their social background (e.g. marital status, school-leaving age and social class). The data were analysed by determining the frequencies with which different measures were associated in different women. The results were analysed using a method known as *cluster analysis*. In this method, the data can be presented as a graph in which the *distance* between any two points represents the strength of the association between these two measures (see Figure 13.1). If two points are very close together, these measures are highly correlated and occur together frequently in large numbers of women. The measure *menopausal status* near the bottom of the graph refers to whether or not the woman was premenopausal, menopausal, or just postmenopausal.

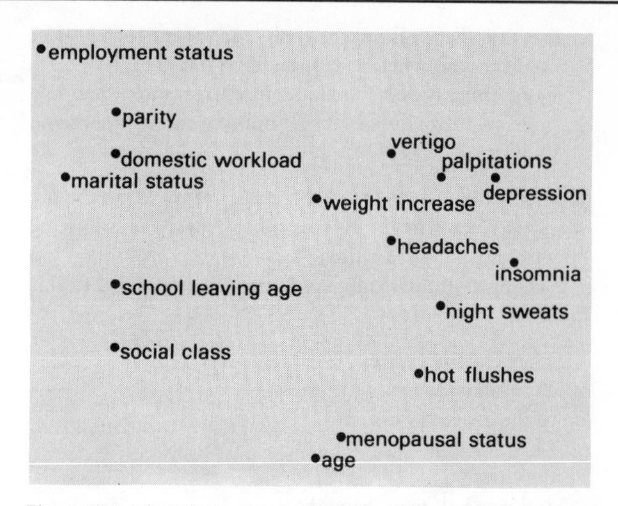

Figure 13.1 The relationship between the menopause, distressing symptoms and social variables (for explanation, see text). (McKinlay and Jefferys, 1974, Figure 1)

□ What conclusions can you draw from the data in Figure 13.1?

■ The nearest point to 'menopausal status' is age, indicating (not surprisingly) that these two measures are highly correlated. Menopausal status is also fairly closely correlated with hot flushes. However, none of the measures of social variables such as employment, parity or social class, had a close relationship to menopausal status; nor did the other 'menopausal' symptoms that were included in the questionnaire — vertigo, depression, headaches, and so on. However, the loose grouping of the latter suggests that they tend to occur together. This study, therefore, suggests that some of the symptoms *attributed* to the menopause showed no close relationship to it and remain, on this evidence at least, something of a mystery.

Now consider another study of the same type, but which focuses more closely on the relationship between psychiatric illness and the menopause. This study was conducted by a psychiatrist, Barbara Ballinger, in Dundee in the early 1970s. In it, 539 women between the ages of 40 and 55, all patients of six doctors in one group practice, were sent two postal questionnaires; one about menstrual symptoms and current family situation, the other the General Health Questionnaire (mentioned in Chapter 12). In this study, a total of 155 women (29 per cent) were identified as having 'probable' psychiatric illness; there were no significant variations with social class or marital status. Thus, women in this age-group showed a rather high prevalence of minor mental illness, which rose even higher during the menopause. This rise in psychiatric morbidity started in fact *before* the menopause but did not persist more than one year after the end of menstrual periods. At the same time, it was not related to two physical symptoms frequently attributed to the menopause, flushes and night sweats. However, there *was* a possible link to some social variables. The psychiatric 'cases' tended to have larger families and to be more likely both to have had a child who recently left home and to have mentioned family problems.

Now, let us turn to the second type of study. This looked at men as well as women, but relied, as before, on postal questionnaires. It was conducted in 1980 by Geoff Bungay, Martin Vessey and Klim McPherson. Their sample consisted of people drawn from General Practitioners' patient lists in the Oxford Health Region and contained 1 120 women and 510 men. Some of their results are shown graphically in Figure 13.2. Look carefully at these graphs, and then answer the following questions.

□ 1 How many of the symptoms shown here, with

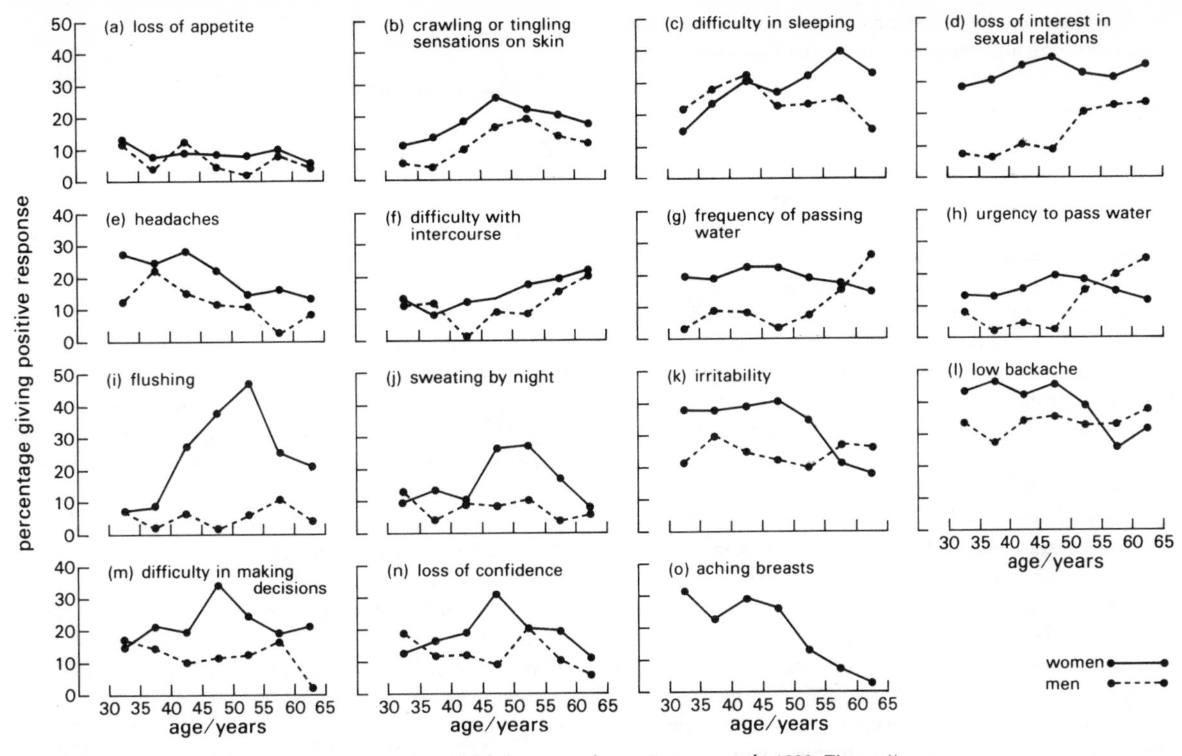

Figure 13.2 Patterns of distressing symptoms in mid-life by age and sex. (Bungay *et al.*, 1980, Figure 1)

the obvious exception of 'aching breasts', show a clear sex difference?

2 Which of these also shows an association with the age at which the menopause takes place (on average, 51 years)?

3 Do these graphs suggest any symptoms that are *clearly* associated with the menopause?

■ 1 The three graphs (a), (b) and (f) show symptoms that both men and women report with roughly equal frequency. All the other graphs show clear sex differences.

2 Graphs (c), (d), (e), (g) and (h) show some sex differences, but with no clear association with the menopausal period. The seven at the bottom (i-o) show some relationship to the age of menopause.

3 The responses shown in (i), (j), (m) and (n) were for symptoms that, for women, peaked around the age of menopause and then declined. However, of these, only flushing and night sweating were directly associated with menopausal age; the two behavioural effects (difficulty in making decisions and 'loss of confidence') actually peaked slightly before the age of menopause (i.e. between 45 and 50). (This fits well with Ballinger's finding of a significant rise in minor mental illness also beginning slightly before this point.)

What can we conclude from these studies? First, of all the physical symptoms that are traditionally associated with the menopause, only two — hot flushes and night sweating — retain this link on closer examination. Flushing affects up to 50 per cent of all women, night sweats up to 30 per cent. Second, the McKinlay and Jefferys study provides evidence that some of the traditional symptoms do cluster together, but they do not seem to be closely related to the menopause, or indeed to social variables such as class, domestic workload, employment or marital status. Third, although the McKinlay and Jefferys study found no close links between depression and the menopause, the Oxford and Dundee studies both suggest a relationship between minor mental illness and the 'change of life'. Rates of such illness are already high among women in this age-group and they seem to rise even higher just before the beginning of the menopause and dip again once it is over. Fourth, although men seem to suffer considerably less than many women from the classic menopausal symptoms, they do possess their own special physical problems, particularly the urinary problems that increase quite rapidly from the age of 50 onwards. Moreover, some men, though only a few, complain of hot flushes and sweating by night. Finally, in the Dundee study, women with a high level of psychiatric morbidity were those with larger families, who were more likely to report children leaving home, problems with those that remained, and problems with their husbands.

In general, these studies do not suggest that there are many symptoms that can unambiguously be attributed to the biological events of the menopause itself. Hot flushes perhaps come closest, but for most other symptoms there is no clear association with the menopause. Moreover, some of the findings suggest that other factors such as family size may also influence symptoms occurring during the menopause. As rather few symptoms are closely associated with the menopause itself, it seems unlikely that they could be interpreted as being caused solely by hormonal events. We should, therefore, consider the third type of study mentioned earlier, studies in which the effects of hormones (HRT) are investigated directly. What is the effectiveness of HRT?

One way to approach this question is by means of randomised double-blind trials in which the effects of oestrogens are compared with those of a placebo.* The results of such trials have been striking.

Hot flushes, which involve feelings of heat in the face and neck, accompanied by perspiration and sometimes shivering, as well as changes in heart rate (shown in Figure 13.3) seem to respond well to oestrogen treatment in most studies, and there is some evidence that these symptoms are experienced more severely by women who have low oestrogen levels before the menopause.

However, few of the other menopausal symptoms respond particularly well to oestrogens, and most show a strong '*placebo effect*'. Joint pains and backache, for instance, respond as well to placebo as they do to oestrogen. Similarly, various psychological symptoms such as depression and anxiety do not appear to be uniquely dependent upon oestrogens. In addition, some symptoms that appear to be improved by oestrogen treatment may be secondary to some other effects of the hormone: insomnia, for instance, appears to be alleviated by oestrogens, but this may itself be a by-product of the hormonally-related hot flushes which can interrupt sleep.

Given these results, there has been a controversy over the use of hormone replacement therapy as a treatment for women suffering from unpleasant symptoms during the menopause. Although oestrogens were prescribed for the alleviation of menopausal symptoms in the 1940s and 1950s their use dramatically increased in the 1960s and 1970s, following a campaign by some doctors and drug companies. An influential American campaigner for the use of HRT, the Brooklyn gynaecologist, Dr Robert Wilson, eulogised about the wonderful things that HRT could do for a woman, in his interestingly entitled work, *Feminine Forever* (1966).

*This type of trial is described in Book I, *Studying Health and Disease*, Chapter 6.

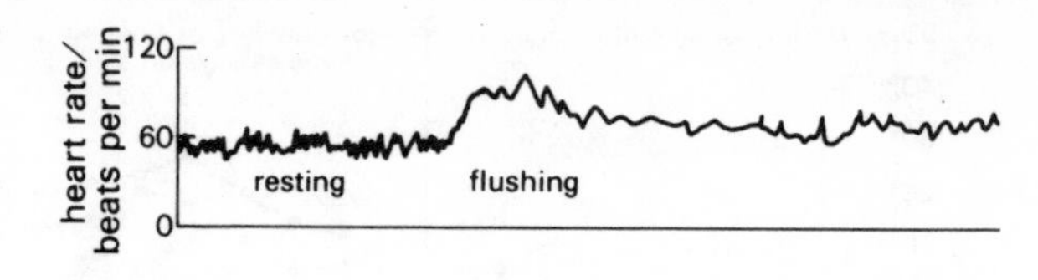

Figure 13.3 Physiological recording of heart rate (beats per minute) from one menopausal woman before and during a hot flush. (Sturdee *et al.*, 1978, p.80)

Partly as a result of such campaigns, HRT was enthusiastically taken up by American gynaecologists, and was popularised among middle-class women, partly through the medium of medical advice columns in women's magazines. During the 1980s, approximately 20 per cent of menopausal American women received HRT. Its impact in the UK has been rather less widespread, although the use of HRT increased considerably during the 1970s. Between 1971 and 1977, for example, the number of prescriptions for hormones to treat menopausal symptoms issued each year by GPs in Britain roughly trebled to about 1.2 million. Wilson's campaign for HRT in the USA has found followers here. Wendy Cooper, for example, writes the following in a chapter entitled 'Biological Lib':

> [Dr. Wilson betrays a] reverence for that mysterious core of womanhood which he calls 'femininity'. This quality, a subtle blend of the sexual and emotional rooted deep in our correct hormone balance could be, he believes, cruelly extinguished by what he terms the 'castrating' effects of the menopause, leaving a neutered and devalued creature, deserving man's pity rather than his passion. (Cooper, 1976, p.21)

As a result, women here are usually well aware of the existence of HRT:

> Well, I'd read all about it. I'd read all the literature and a lot of the symptoms that you could get and they say it does help . . .I went to the clinic before I actually had the menopause because I didn't know whether you needed it as soon as you started getting symptoms or whether you waited till the symptoms were well established. (quoted in Fairhurst and Lightup, 1980)

□ From the brief discussion of menopausal symptoms above, do you think it likely that there is evidence to support Wilson's claim that a woman's sexual and emotional life are 'rooted deep' in her hormone balance?

■ No. As we noted above, the changes in behaviour and mood (if those are representative of the 'sexual and emotional' factors to which Wilson refers) do not show a clear relationship to hormonal changes. There is certainly no evidence that oestrogens provide 'femininity forever', whatever that may mean. Graph (d) in Figure 13.2 shows that women's interest in sexual activity declines only very slowly after the age of 50.

Incredible claims aside, there has been some controversy surrounding the use of HRT, both in the USA and in the UK.

□ Bearing in mind the discussion in Chapter 11 about hormone-based contraceptives, what do you think the central issues of the controversy about HRT are?

■ The central issues are those of personal choice and possible hazards to health, particularly if a woman stays on HRT (as has sometimes been advocated) for many years.

There have been a number of reports that long-term HRT may pose increased risk of cancers of the female reproductive system and of cardiovascular disease, and much discussion of whether or not these risks are reduced by, say, combining the oestrogens with a progestogen. Long-term studies of health risks are still being conducted and no definitive answer can be given at present. In the meantime, a woman has to make her own choices. For some, the potential benefits of HRT far outweigh any possible risks to health. Many women who had severe problems during the menopause are very enthusiastic about HRT, and dislike being taken off it; something which can lead to real dilemmas:

> A gynaecologist has put me on oestrogen treatment. I have been feeling much better, but every time I go to my local GP for the tablets, he warns me that not enough is known about long-term results and whether it can produce cancer, which I am sure is no doubt very laudable, but naturally it disturbs me. My GP has made me very nervous but I feel so well, I just can't give up and go back to the misery of hot flushes and sweats. (quoted in Cooper, 1976, p.143)

Although prescriptions for HRT in Britain have increased, many doctors remain cautious and try to discourage patients from staying on HRT for long periods. Oestrogens are most commonly prescribed for a short period during the menopause itself and are less often given to women in later life. The long-term risks are still not adequately known, but there is no evidence that they can keep a woman 'feminine forever'. And there is still much to be discovered about the effect of *social* changes in middle age on the health of both sexes.

Objectives for Chapter 13

When you have studied this chapter, you should be able to:

13.1 Discuss the association of biological changes during the menopause with unpleasant symptoms and the implications of this for hormone replacement therapy (HRT).

13.2 Discuss the possible influence on health of the social changes that women and men may experience during middle age.

Questions for Chapter 13

1 (*Objective 13.1*) A General Practitioner sees three middle-aged women patients:

(i) the first has ceased her periods, but is suffering severe distress caused by hot flushes and sweating at night;

(ii) the second has also recently ceased her periods and is severely depressed;

(iii) the third is menstruating still, but says that she will be starting the menopause soon and wants to go onto HRT straight away. She has read all about the symptoms and certainly does not want to go through that.

The doctor is considering HRT for each of them. What is the evidence that HRT might help in each case?

2 (*Objective 13.2*) A fifty-year-old family man complains to his doctor that he has suddenly started to become irritable, and has become impotent. The patient wonders if this is due to a male equivalent to the menopause. Is there any evidence for this suggestion?

14

Growing older

This chapter is the first of three on different aspects of growing older. At the end of it, you will be asked to listen to the audiotape sequence 'When you get old' on audiocassette AC805, Band 3. You will need the Audiocassette Notes to help you analyse the interviews you hear.

As the years pass in adulthood, changes in our bodies which have been occurring gradually since birth, begin to show the signs that we recognise as 'old age'. Our appearance changes as we develop wrinkles and grey hair, we may feel our physical strength declining, and our risk of illness becomes greater. At the same time our role in society may change if our children become independent or our working life comes to an end. The transition to old age involves the loss of many attributes that are highly valued by our society; the gains are less universally accepted.

> Grow old along with me!
> The best is yet to be,
> The last of life for which the first was made.
> (Robert Browning, 1812–89, in 'Rabbi ben Ezra' (i))

> Do you know the worst of all vices?
> It is being over fifty-five.
> (Ivan Sergeyevich Turgenev, 1818–83)

These two quotations reflect some of the differences in people's views about what it means to be old. This is the question that we shall be discussing in the rest of this chapter – a pertinent one, since most of us will reach the age of seventy, if we have not done so already. We shall be looking not only at the health of the elderly, and their economic status, but also at society's attitudes towards older people. As you will see, all these factors are interrelated.

Before you start reading this chapter, you might like to write down what you think are the right answers to the questions below, and you can then see how far your attitudes and opinions match with what we think is the true picture. This is an important exercise because, as you will see, it is not only the physical process of ageing that alters people's lives, but the changes that they, and other people around them, expect.

□ 1 Are elderly people treated better or worse in the UK now than in the past?

2 How rich are old people? For instance, what proportion of old people are entitled to supplementary benefit?

3 How healthy are people over 65? For instance, what proportion of them need help in their daily life, and what proportion live completely independently of outside help?

Moralists are fond of saying that there's no respect left nowadays for the elderly, and politicians suggest that we no longer look after our elderly relatives as we did in the past (and ought to do now). Some demographers and historians have echoed this view of a cosier past, and suggest that demographic changes have led to changes in attitudes: when there were fewer old people around they had 'rarity value' and commanded more respect than they do now. It is certainly true that, though all societies classify some poeple as old and treat them differently because of this classification, there is considerable variation in the way in which they are treated in different societies.

China is one culture with a long tradition of giving high status to its older members — a situation which seems to continue to the present day, at least if judged by the age of its political leaders. In ancient China, wisdom was considered impossible to attain in youth; it was possible only after *long* study and self-discipline. There was a complex code of etiquette when a young man addressed an elder:

> In going to take counsel with an elder, one must carry a stool and staff with him. When the elder asks a question, to reply without acknowledging one's incompetency and [trying to] decline answering is contrary to propriety. (From the *Li Chi* — Book of Rites, first century BC)

There were times in Chinese history when it was the custom to honour a man who reached the age of eighty by freeing one of his friends from all government service: if he reached ninety, all the members of his family were similarly exempted.

In Europe we do not have such a tradition of codified respect towards our elderly. If we look at the literature of Europe since Greek or Roman times we find an ambivalence of attitude towards old age. Ancient Greek mythology is filled with tales of conflict between young and old, usually over property and power. Old age was sometimes considered a punishment: 'A lingering old age came upon Phineus, son of Agenor, for revealing the prophecies of Zeus' (quoted in Stahmer, 1978, p.34). Old age did command respect at times: 'It would be a hard thing if we were to put any slight on the eldest and best among us' (Homer's *Odyssey* XIII, 141–42). Yet Sophocles has his chorus despise 'the final lot of man, even old age, hateful, impotent, unsociable, friendless, wherein all evil of evil dwells' (*Oedipus at Colonnus*, quoted in Blythe, 1979, p.99).

In English literature the same ambivalence is found. Whereas biblical texts are cited giving honour to the aged, popular plays and novels do not portray such reverence. Shakespeare, in *King Lear*, describes how an aged king, tiring of the responsibilities of power, hands over his lands to two of his daughters, and is dismayed to find that they no longer treat him with love, respect or generosity. Jonathan Swift, writing in 1726, describes a race of aged immortals with disgust:

> They had not only all the Follies and Infirmities of other Old Men, but many more ... They were not only opinionative, peevish, covetous, morose, vain, talkative; but incapable of Friendship and dead to all Natural Affection ... (*Gulliver's Travels* quoted in Freedman, 1978, p.52)

Fifty years later Frances Burney wrote the best-seller *Evelina* in which the young bloods at a country house-party decide to arrange a race between two local women of more than 80 years. Bets are laid as the women are escorted to the race ground — the description does not suggest much veneration for old age:

> They set off, and hobbled along, nearly even with each other for some time, yet frequently, and to inexpressible diversion of the company, they stumbled and tottered; and the confused hallowing of 'Now Coverly!', 'Now Merton!' rang from side to side during the whole affair. (quoted in Freedman, 1978, p.55)

In the nineteenth century a somewhat more romantic view of old age emerged. William Wordsworth saw the possibility of 'An old age serene and bright/And lovely as a Lapland night.' But this optimism was not universal, as we see from the wry cynicism of the American essayist, Ralph Waldo Emerson, who wrote: 'We do not count a man's years until he has nothing else to count.' (*Journals*, 1840)

There is little documentary evidence from rural or early industrial societies as to the real treatment of the old. Property laws suggest there was often conflict between the ancient owner of land or house which his sons wished to inherit or be free to work. One French peasant wrote in passing: 'When, in 1891, after the death of my father, I became free to act as I wanted ...'. As you read in Chapter 2, in Ireland in the 1930s a 'boy' could not become a man until his father died. R.S. Thomas, a Welsh poet of this century, has described the effects of the power of the old tenant farmers in rural Wales and is scornful of the popular image of the happy extended family:

> Here, every farm has its
> Grandfather or grandmother, gnarled hands
> On the cheque book a long slow
> Pull on the placenta about the neck.

Old lips monopolise the talk
When a friend calls. The children listen
From the kitchen; the children march
With angry patience against the dawn.
They are waiting for someone to die . . .
(From R.S. Thomas, 'Tenancies', 1968)

It seems that in the UK today there is no such tradition of universal respect for old people as in China, and, as you will see in the next few pages, this shows in their average income and social conditions. First we need to consider how society defines old age.

□ When is old age generally considered to start in this country?

■ Although it is, of course, a gradual process, the major milestone is retirement from work, normally at 65 for men and 60 for women. Even people who have never had a job are classified officially as 'old' at these ages, when they may become eligible for an Old Age Pension, and are included in statistics on 'old age'.

Retirement is a new phenomenon. In most societies people change the type of work they do as they get older, but the idea of stopping work at a set age belongs to this century. In Western culture old age is defined not biologically, in terms of fitness or number of wrinkles, but by chronological age. Retirement means an enormous transition in someone's life. After forty years of doing a job every day, there is a farewell party and perhaps a retirement gift. Then he or she leaves the world of work and wages to become a 'Senior Citizen'. For most people, reaching the age of sixty or sixty-five means the end of any paid employment: in the UK in 1976 official records show that only 5 per cent of men and 4 per cent of women over sixty-five were working full time, and only 10 per cent of men and 4 per cent of women had part-time jobs.

□ What do you think a person loses when they leave paid employment?

■ There might be a loss of income, status and companionship; a loss of the enjoyment gained from work, and of the predictable routines which come with working.

□ What gains might retirement bring?

■ Increased leisure; an increase in freedom; stopping an arduous, unpleasant or boring job.

Obviously the way a person reacts to retirement will depend on the relative importance of what they lose or gain. Different researchers into the results of retirement have come to different conclusions. On the one hand, some suggest that 'blue-collar workers' find it harder to fill their time than 'white-collar workers'. On the other, some have found that people used to manual work find it easier to cope with retirement and enjoy it more than 'knowledge' workers, who miss the mental stimulation of their job. Most researchers note that the situation is different for women who continue their traditional role as home-maker, which maintains their sense of worth, as does the tradition by which women play a much greater role in the care of grandchildren. Nevertheless, a survey done by Age Concern in 1974 showed that only 26 per cent of their sample thought that it was difficult to fill their time after retirement, and only 10% per cent said they would like a paid job (Age Concern, 1974). There is also little evidence to show that people's health declines suddenly on retirement, despite the popular view that retirement often leads to illness.

Retirement brings many changes and it is not usually the extra leisure time that causes the greatest anxiety: research has shown that the over-riding concern about retirement in all age-groups and all types of work is the loss of income that it signals. Without money it is hard to take advantage of new-found leisure, and even harder to adjust to the loss of status that a job used to bring. It can be misleading to generalise about the poverty of old people. A few old people are, of course, extremely rich, and, on a lesser scale, a significant proportion of old people (about half of all elderly couples) have pensions from their former employer, or from private pensions schemes. Though retirement still usually brings a drop in income, their expenses may become relatively less as their families grow up and become independent. However, this is not the general situation. Consider the following statistics:

1 75 per cent of people over 65 live at or around the margins of poverty (this is generally defined as up to 140 per cent of supplementary benefit) compared to 20 per cent of people under 65.

2 40 per cent of retired couples, and 60 per cent of single retired households, are mainly dependent on state pensions for their income, (that is, at least 75 per cent of their household income comes from state benefits).

3 The single person's pension represents about 25 per cent of the average full-time worker's wage, and the married couple's pension about 40 per cent. (These figures relate purely to the UK. State pensions in other European countries such as France and Germany are relatively higher.)

4 The low levels of state pensions in the UK, and the numbers of people who are completely dependent on them, mean that nearly 50 per cent of all pensioners are entitled to claim supplementary benefit, although only 20 per cent do so.

□ Why do you think so few claim supplementary benefit?

■ This may be because of: (i) ignorance that benefits

exist; (ii) a dislike of the personal questions asked; (iii) a dislike of charity.

People over 65 in the 1980s lived through the 1920s and 1930s depression and the Means Test; some have unpleasant memories of government aid.

> With the dreaded Means Test in the 1920s officials would call to see if you had anything you could sell. Sons and daughters left home because they were expected to support their parents... Relief tickets created problems. Some shops didn't like them; they preferred cash customers. With coal tickets we were told if merchants had any coal left over we could have it but cash customers *first*. (quoted in Elder, 1977, p.65)

The queues and investigations of some social security offices do little to dispell the notion that supplementary benefit is a charity that it is humiliating to accept. Peter Townsend, a British social policy analyst, reports these responses from elderly people who were interviewed in the 1960s:

> I've never liked to cadge. I don't go running for help.
>
> I don't want to tell people all my affairs. They ask too many questions. I'm proud, I suppose.
>
> The pension is different. Everyone has a right to that. But the other, they have to come round every 6 months or so asking questions. (Townsend, 1963, pp.183–84)

Poverty in early life may mean that people are used to a low standard of living, and they may remember the old people of their childhood and feel that they are relatively well off. Ronald Blythe, an English author, who, in *The View In Winter*, recorded conversations with many old people, quotes an 84 year old retired district nurse who used to work in a country village, who remembered the extreme poverty of the elderly villagers:

> Poor old things, poor old things! They weren't what they are now. I can tell you when I looked after the old people before the war in the village round here, they had nothing at all. Nothing. You'd see them, the old ones, men and women alike, pulling sticks out of their gardens or out of the hedges along the lanes, pulling sticks, picking up sticks, to make a bit of a fire. (Blythe, 1979. p.58)

Life has improved since then for the elderly. State pensions do at least exist, even if they are not large. However, fuel consumes a large proportion of income for most old people. Single retired people mainly dependent on state pensions (often women over 75 years of age) spend 70 per cent of their income on housing, food and fuel. From a single person's pension of £34.05 per week (1984) this would leave £10.22p for all other expenses. It is perhaps not surprising that in one study 40 per cent of people over 75 felt they needed extra money in order 'to live without money worries and in reasonable comfort'.

The effect of the low incomes of the elderly is reflected in their standard of housing. For instance, 12 per cent of people over 65 live in houses with only an outside WC and this percentage increases to 15.3 per cent of those over 85. Because of inadequate housing and low incomes, many elderly people live in very cold conditions. A national survey in 1972 suggested that 10 per cent of their sample of old people had house temperatures that put them at risk from hypothermia.

Lack of money does not only affect bodily comforts: *relative poverty* demeans a person within a society.* John Galbraith, an American economist, has described relative poverty like this:

> People are poverty-stricken when their income, even if adequate for survival, falls radically behind that of the community. They cannot have what the community regards as the minimum of decency. Thus they cannot wholly escape the judgement of the larger consumer that they are indecent. They are degraded, for, in the literal sense, they live outside the grades ... which the community regards as acceptable. (quoted in Elder, 1977, p.18)

The relative poverty of the majority of old people makes it difficult for older people to acquire a higher status, and thus change attitudes to being old. We can deduce these attitudes, not only from the relative poverty of the elderly in the UK, but from everyday conversation, in which the word 'old' is used as a term of abuse — 'dirty old man', and 'silly old woman' are two of many phrases that are laden with prejudice against being old. This prejudice has recently been named 'ageism'. *Ageism* is defined by Alex Comfort, the well-known gerontologist, as: 'the notion that people cease to be people, cease to be the same people, or become people of a distinct and inferior kind by virtue of having lived a specified number of years.' (Comfort, 1977, p.35).

Examples of ageism are not difficult to find. In 1962, a British physician wrote in *The Lancet* that it is 'normal' for people over the age of 75 to be: 'frail and unsteady, dozing by day and wakeful by night, confused about people and places, forgetful and untidy, repetitive and boring, selfish and petty perhaps and consumed by a fear of death' (Kemp,

*The concept of relative poverty is discussed more fully in Book III, *The Health of Nations*, Chapter 10.

1962, p.515). And this advice for the elderly is contained in a *Dictionary of Symptoms*, by Joan Gomez (published in 1967):

> Make friends, but do not hanker after those in full flurry of activity ... if you are past seventy, the middle-aged may have minds too agile for you. Your own contemporaries tend to self-centredness, though they are worth cultivating. You will find the greatest of common ground with children.

Ageism depicts old people as a uniform group, decrepit and senile, incapable of looking after themselves, sexless and passive. Is there any truth in this? We will be discussing the physical and mental health of older people in the next chapter. For the moment you should note that the majority (75 per cent) of over-65s are physically and mentally fit enough to lead entirely independent lives, and half of all people over 65 and one-third of those over 85 report *no disabilities at all*. Prejudice against old age may be self-perpetuating. Dr Johnson, the famous eighteenth-century English writer, described how prejudice may affect the way that old people are perceived:

> There is a wicked inclination in most people to suppose an old man decayed in his intellect. If a young or middle-aged man, when leaving a company, does not recollect where he laid his hat, it is nothing; but if the inattention is discovered in an old man, people will shrug up their shoulders and say 'His memory is going'. (Samuel Johnson, 1709–84)

There is evidence to back up Samuel Johnson's suspicions: one study tried out a well-accepted *senility test* on a group of people over 65, and on a group of university students. The students emerged from the test with higher rating for senility than the elderly group (Carp, in Puner, 1974, p.87).

□ Does this mean that there are no changes in intellect between youth and old age?

■ No. To see exactly what it means you would have to know much more about this 'test for senility'. What it does mean is that senility, as defined by a test that was popularly used on old people, is not a characteristic unique to people over 65, but is found equally or more often in university students.

The over-65s are often considered, for official and statistical purposes, as a uniform group — 'the elderly' — but this presumes that they are an homogeneous group, despite the wide range of ages. Between people of 70 and 90 there is an age difference of one generation with probably just as much of a 'generation gap' as between teenagers and their parents. There have been amazing social changes in the last hundred years and people's experiences at formative times are radically different. Those who grew up in the 1930s Depression are most anxious about pension rights; First World War veterans still meet to talk about their past experiences; and women of 80 who did not get the vote until they were 25 may be more 'feminist' than their younger friends.

Finally, there is a cultural prejudice in the UK that old people should not, cannot, or do not have sexual intercourse. The words old and sexually attractive are considered incompatible: if a man or woman remains attractive in old age they are described as looking amazingly young for their years. There is disgust or amusement at the idea of old people dressing to look sexy. This prejudice is an old one, as you can see from this description of some old women from a popular play by Plautus, a Roman playwright of the second century BC:

> Those raddled old creatures who plaster themselves with perfume, toothless hags trying to hide their ugliness with make-up — what with scent and sweat together they smell like as if a cook's been mixing up too many different kinds of stew. You can't tell what they smell of, all you know is they smell horrible. (*The Ghosts*, quoted in Freedman, 1978, p.52)

Since then, both old men and old women have been portrayed repeatedly in plays and novels as comic because of their 'inappropriate' sexual desires. Popular wisdom also says (in ironic contrast) that men become impotent with advancing age and women lose interest in sexual intercourse, or do not enjoy it after the menopause. Studies into older people's sexual behaviour do not bear out these popular stereotypes, although there are changes in sexual physiology in both men and women as they get older. Older men and women usually become sexually aroused more slowly than when younger: for instance, a man may develop an erection over several minutes rather than in a few seconds, and some older men report that their erection feels less full and demanding than when they were young adults. Both men and women may find that the time between arousal and orgasm is usually lengthened, and they may feel less urgency to reach an orgasm. Some women find that their vagina is less well lubricated when they are sexually aroused than in their youth. These changes may alter the quality of sexual relations (for better or worse, depending on opinion) but they do not warrant the label of impotence or asexuality.

Studies such as the Kinsey Report in 1953 (in which older people were grossly under-represented) showed that average sexual activity gradually declines with age, but more recent longitudinal studies have shown that this average decline masks considerable variation between different people. Some people do stop having sex as they get older — the reasons given are usually a decrease in desire, illness, or the illness of a spouse — but others

Figure 14.1 Old Age Pensioners demonstrating for better pensions. (Photo: Michael Abrahams)

continue well into old age. One study questioned people aged between 60 and 93 years of age and found that 54 per cent were still sexually active. There was no fall off from previous levels of sexual activity until the age of 75; of those over 75, 25 per cent were still sexually active. Gerontologists have pointed out that this level of sexual activity occurs despite the prevailing preconceptions that old people do not have sex, and they speculate that attitudes will change considerably as people who are middle-aged now grow older, since they have spent much of their lives in a time when sexual desires are more openly admitted (Hendricks and Hendricks, 1978). Common preconceptions about old age, then, have less basis in fact than is popularly believed. What action have older people taken to counteract such 'ageist' views and to improve their standard of living? In Britain the action has been largely political.

□ What political pressure do you think elderly people could wield?

■ As the population 'ages', the proportion of elderly voters will increase. In 1984, a quarter of all voters were over 65, and this will go on rising.

Old Age Pensioners have organised together to fight for better conditions in groups which are often affiliated to the Old Age Pensioners Association — a Federation which states that they stand for: 'the principle that old age and infirmity shall no longer be subjected to utter despair . . .'. One of the founder members of Camden Old Age Pensioners Union, Betty Harrison, describes their aims like this:

> Our main aim is to increase the pensions for old people, with the ultimate objective of getting a pension related to the average earnings in industry. [. . .] We are working for this because we want to do away with people going to Social Security to ask for money to buy another blanket. We don't want them to have to ask for the telephone to be paid for, either, or the television licence. All these demands are also in our programme. But we are different from other organisations such as Care for the Elderly and Good Neighbours because we don't want these things as charity or hand-outs. We feel that the old age pensioner has earned them as a right, particularly this generation of OAP's who fought and won two World Wars for this country, who suffered unemployment

and came out of that, who fought for, and won, a Health Service and the Beveridge Insurance Plan. These things had to be fought for, too, they were not just handed out as a generous bonus. Now our generation of pensioners built up the wealth of this country in order to be able to do these things, and therefore we are entitled as a right to a sufficient pension to live a decent life in the community with dignity. (quoted in Carver and Liddiard, 1978, p.370)

On the health side, Alex Comfort suggests that three-quarters of all infirmities in old age are *culturally*, not biologically, determined — most people slow down only because they *expect* to slow down. Many geriatricians now stress the possibility of staying active and therefore 'young' into old age.

□ Can you think of any objections to this advice, to stay 'young' into old age?

■ If taken to excess, it tries to solve the problem of old age by avoiding it — it suggests that the only way to make old age bearable is to make it as nearly like youth or middle-age as possible.

Some religious thinkers and philosophers are trying to avoid this denial of the reality of old age. Some have tried to reverse their own conditioning and discover which aspects of growing old could be considered as advantages. For instance, loss of speed, or slowing up, and changes in appearance and memory, can be described positively as they are in this extract by two Americans, Sally Gadow (a philosopher) and Geri Berg (an art historian):

It may be that with age we realise time has the dimensions of depth as well as duration ... we slow ourselves then to explore experiences, not in their linear pattern of succeeding one another, but in their possibility of opening for us entire worlds in each situation and each person encountered. We slow ourselves to be more gentle with these experiences, to take care to let their possibilities, their rich density emerge ...

... one of the processes of ageing that we recognise most easily is the alteration of smooth surfaces and straight lines; skin wrinkles and roughens; posture becomes curved; memory is restructured; formerly unbroken stretches of clarity are marked by peaks and between them hollows called 'confusion'. What positive human meaning could such phenomena suggest?

It is as though, through these changes, body and mind express the greater intricacies, the finer articulations that are possible in the person for whom reality becomes many layered, folded upon itself, woven and richly textured, a reality no longer ordered in the more familiar linear fashion, but now a world filled with leaps, windings, countless crossings, immeasurably more intricate and perhaps also more true than the world of one-dimensional thought and self-evident distinctions. (Gadow and Berg, 1978, pp.85–86)

Other 'age liberationists' have pointed out that, since elderly people have usually retired from work, and no longer need to impress people and 'succeed' in the world, they are free to be themselves and behave as they wish. Some of the possibilities are described in this extract from a poem by Jenny Joseph about a young woman looking forward to the freedoms that she imagines old age could bring.

When I am an old woman I shall wear purple with a
red hat which doesn't go and doesn't suit me.
And I shall spend my pension on brandy and summer
gloves
And satin sandals, and say
We've no money for butter
I shall sit down on the pavement when I'm tired
And gobble up samples in shops and press alarm bells
And run my stick along the public railings
And make up for the sobriety of my youth.
(From 'Warning', Joseph, 1982, p.27)

It would be an unusual woman who could really throw off the 'responsible' and acceptable behaviour that she has learnt during her life, especially if her income is falling, she is beginning to feel the effects in her body of old age, and she no longer feels that the world sees her as attractive, but this poem does illustrate the opportunities that arise if people see old age as a time of gain as well as a time of loss.

For most of this chapter we have taken a fairly broad view of what it is like to grow older in the UK, in order to establish what are some of society's basic views towards ageing, and the health and economic status of the elderly.

□ What major problem is there in taking this 'broad view' of the elderly?

■ It obscures the enormous individual variation in the experiences of older people.

It is obvious that there are differences in people's experiences of old age. However, the reasons for these differences are not always so clear.

□ What factors do you think would influence a person's experience of their old age?

■ Sex, age, class, ethnicity, culture, economic status, marital status, family, health, philosophy, personality, past history, and anything else you can think of.

You should bear these factors in mind as you finish this chapter by listening to the audiotape sequence 'When you grow old' (AC 805, Band 3). This contains interviews with three old people on the advantages and disadvantages of being old. Try, as you listen, to see why they are happy or unhappy with different aspects of old age. Follow-up questions to help in your analysis are contained in the Audiocassette Notes.

Objectives for Chapter 14

When you have studied this chapter, you should be able to:

14.1 Discuss the role that society plays in defining which of its members are old, and the status of its old people in terms of their self-worth, health and standard of living.

14.2 Analyse some of the factors which may contribute to an individual's experience of being old.

Questions for Chapter 14

1 *(Objective 14.1)*

> I am no longer clerk to the Firm of, etc. I am Retired, At Leisure. I am to be met with in trim gardens. I am already come to be known by my vacant face and careless gesture, perambulating at no fixed pace, nor with any settled purpose. I walk about; not to and from ... (quoted in Blythe, 1979, p.41)

This was written by Charles Lamb in his nineteenth-century novel *The Superannuated Man*, one of the first books to describe the novelty of retirement, in this case, of a clerk who has worked 10 hours a day, 6 days a week for 36 years before being pensioned off as a reward for good services. What effects does he suggest this has on his life, and why?

2 *(Objective 14.2)*

> The first motor bicycle passes, the sun rises, cold and watery, perhaps, but sun. It is then that time stretches, time that you're free to spend exactly as you wish. You can eat what you like when you like, drink what you like when you like, or not at all ... you can spend a couple of hours dressing or slop around, not bothering to dress at all, reading passages from *King Solomon's Mines* or *Lady Audley's Secret*. Or wander about in what passes for a garden. There's time for everything. The intoxicating feeling of freedom repays you a thousand times for any loneliness you may have endured ... (Jean Rhys, novelist, in 1975)

What factors contribute to the author's enjoyment of old age?

15

Age, health and disease

This chapter deals with the biology of ageing and the common diseases of old age. It draws heavily on the discussion of ageing in Book IV, *The Biology of Health and Disease*, Chapter 4, and on the diseases, common in old age, that are described in Book IV, Chapter 16.

There is a wide variation in both fitness and health among old people. (Photo: Topix)

Although it is true that some of the changes associated with ageing are culturally induced, there are, of course, inevitable and gradual biological changes in the body throughout life. Ageing does not start at any one time, but the gradual accumulation of cellular and tissue changes over time have external signs and effects that become increasingly evident with age. These changes can result from a number of processes: the changes in cells themselves; in proteins in the fluids between cells (extra-cellular fluid); from 'degenerative' changes in whole organs, and because of the effects of distinct diseases. In this chapter we shall first look at these different factors in ageing and whether they can be prevented. We shall then look at how these add up to cause a loss in some physiological functions, and how these, with some diseases, may cause disability in the old. After this we shall move on to see how frequently these disabilities occur in old people. But first, back to cells.

The cell and age

All cells undergo some changes with *age*, though age does not necessarily mean the same thing for different types of cell. Some cells in the body rapidly die and are replaced by other cells, for instance skin cells and red blood cells. For these cells, ageing occurs over a few weeks — the cells change gradually in form and function and are eventually shed or destroyed. Other cells, such as nerve cells in the brain and muscles, do not divide, or divide only rarely, and last for most of a person's lifetime.

□ What changes are seen in older cells in mammals?*

■ There are changes in the proportions of fats and proteins in the cell. In addition, there is an increase in pigment granules in the cytoplasm, and an increase in the number of *lysosomes* — the small intracellular packets of enzymes and other reactive proteins in the cytoplasm.

*There are discussed in Book IV, *The Biology of Health and Disease*, Chapter 4.

It is not certain whether these changes in cells are actually signs of malfunction, but it is certainly true that pigment accumulates in a cell, and the cell becomes more likely to die as time passes. In tissues where there is not much cellular replacement during life this can lead to a gradual reduction in the weight of an organ and sometimes in loss of function. For instance, 50 per cent of nephrons (the filtration units in the kidney) are lost between the ages of 30 and 90 years; the average brain weight of a person of 90 is 1.36 kg compared to 1.5 kg when he or she was 30. These organs generally have a considerable *reserve capacity*: it is possible, for instance, to live quite normally with only half a kidney functioning instead of two. However, the loss of organ reserve with age means that an older person cannot react adequately to some extreme physiological stresses, for example, low temperature. We shall return to this point in a moment.

Cells that divide throughout life also show some changes with age — they tend to divide less frequently. The lining cells of the gut, for instance, replace themselves in 30 days in young adults, but only every 40 days in the elderly. This slowing-up of cell-division is reflected in how they function — the gut mucosal cells secrete less mucus and enzymes in old age, which means that the body may digest food less efficiently.

Changes outside cells

The main change outside cells is in the amount and quality of *collagen* — collagen is a long chain protein that forms an important part of all connective tissues in the body. In tissues which do not normally contain much collagen it tends to increase in amount: this occurs, for instance, in the lungs and in muscle (which is why mutton is tougher than lamb). In tissues which are normally rich in collagen, such as tendons, the lens of the eye and the skin, the amount of collagen does not change very much but the collagen fibres become thicker and less elastic. It is this that is responsible for wrinkling of the skin, and for the changes in the lens of the eye.

There are also other extra-cellular changes, for instance, in the bones, which become thinner and less heavily impregnated with calcium salts. This is why old people's bones are more 'fragile' than those of younger people, and why fractures may occur as a result of minor falls.

Degenerative changes and diseases associated with age

□ Do you know what are the major *degenerative changes* and diseases that are associated with age?*

*Summarised in Book IV, *The Biology of Health and Disease*, Chapter 16.

■ You may have thought of the following:

(i) Changes in the arteries: there is a gradual build up of fatty deposits on the walls of the arteries — *atheroma*. This can lead to coronary heart disease and strokes. In industrial societies this process starts in childhood, and its gradual progression is seen as part of the 'normal' process of ageing, even though it is believed to be affected by several other biological and social factors. It affects men at a younger age than women, which may help to explain why there are so many more old women than old men.

(ii) Changes in the joints — *osteo-arthrosis* — occurs particularly in the weight-bearing joints such as the knee and hip, but also in the fingers.

(iii) Changes in the brain — these are due to two main causes: degeneration of nerve cells (which if excessive is known as *Alzheimer's disease*) and to atherosclerosis of the arteries supplying the brain. Both these changes can lead to a gradual loss of intellectual power, known, in its extreme form, as *senile dementia* (a condition which causes severe disablement in 3–6 per cent of people over 65 and 10 per cent of people over 75).

(iv) *Cancers* — the incidence of most (but not all) cancers increases with age.

(v) *Auto-immune diseases* — more old people than young people have circulating antibodies against the tissues of their own bodies.

The causes of ageing

As the incidence of some illnesses in children and adults decreases, so ill-health tends to become concentrated in the older age-groups of the population, particularly among the over-70s. Research into *ageing* and the diseases of ageing is extremely fashionable, and there is considerable talk about the possibility of preventing, or at least slowing down, the ageing of the body. However, although the changes in cells and collagen during ageing are well documented, their causes are still inadequately understood.

Some researchers think ageing is a basic cellular function. Perhaps the ageing of cells is genetically programmed, or is caused by the gradual accumulation of gene defects within the cells, as the enzymes that repair DNA become less efficient, or because of the effects of radiation. Others suspect that it is due to an increased production, or fragility, of lysosomes which break down and release their destructive enzymes within the cell. Some research has suggested that ageing in cells and collagen is due to the accumulation of highly reactive molecules (known as free radicals) within the body, which react with many proteins and disrupt their normal function.

A further suggestion is that all changes in the body are due to the changes in collagen (directly or indirectly), and that the changes in collagen occur simply because chain proteins tend to form cross-linkages in time. This theory has a serious flaw: mouse collagen ages in 2 years to the same extent that human collagen does in 70 years, though the two are almost identical in biochemical structure.

Ageing has also been attributed to an 'ageing' centre in the brain, producing an 'ageing' hormone (but this has not been found); to the disruption of blood supply to tissues caused by atherosclerosis (but ageing seems to occur in tissues with a good blood supply); to viruses, and to the gradual increase in circulating auto-immune antibodies (though one then needs to find the reason for this increase).

All in all, though many clues have been discovered, the picture remains unclear, and partly as a consequence there are as yet no treatments that are known to delay ageing in humans. Some substances have been tested on rats with interesting results, but it is not at all certain that these results are applicable to humans. It is actually rather difficult to test their effects on human ageing since the experiments would take 100 years or so to show results. Thus ageing research badly needs a good way of measuring biological age in humans that does not involve waiting for death.

One very rare disease of children, *progeria*, might be expected to throw light on the causes of ageing. In this condition, the young child ages rapidly from about one year onwards, becoming grey-haired and wrinkled and suffering from osteoarthrosis and severe atheroma. Such children normally die young (e.g. 5 years old) of coronary heart disease. As yet no one has found the cause of their illness.

Although there is as yet no anti-ageing substance known to be effective, this has not prevented many being marketed, usually with grand initial hopes and large profit margins. A few, such as hormones, may make some people feel younger and more vigorous, but so may a glass of sherry. Neither have yet been shown to extend the life-span, nor has any substance been found which effectively prevents wrinkles.

Functional changes with age

So far in this chapter we have described many localised changes that occur with age: all these add up to a gradual loss of function in many organs or mechanisms involved in maintaining homeostasis. Figure 15.1 shows the changes in some basic bodily functions.

□ Which function shows the greatest percentage decrease with age?

■ The maximum amount of air that can be breathed in and out in one minute.

□ Why do you think this shows the greatest fall?

■ It represents the *extremes* of inspiration and expiration that are possible, rather than the resting rates. Remember that the changes of ageing tend to mean that *reserves* of function are lost, but the base level of most functions remains sufficient for a normal range of activities.

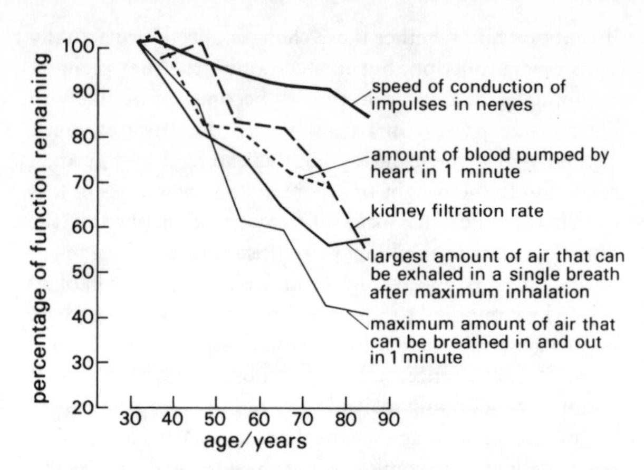

Figure 15.1 Changes in bodily functions with age, taking the average value at age 30 as 100 per cent. (Shock *et al.*, 1957, p.40)

It is important to remember that these are *average* figures.

□ What information is missing from these average trends?

■ The degree of *variation* between individuals.

There is enormous variation in appearance and in changes in physiological functions between different individuals, and training can have a large effect. Figure 15.2 illustrates this fact. Not only are there some 75 year olds running marathons, but they can do this at speeds that would be respectable at the age of 30. A person of 75 who has trained to keep fit (in the absence of any one particular disease) will probably have better lung and heart function than an unfit 30 year old.

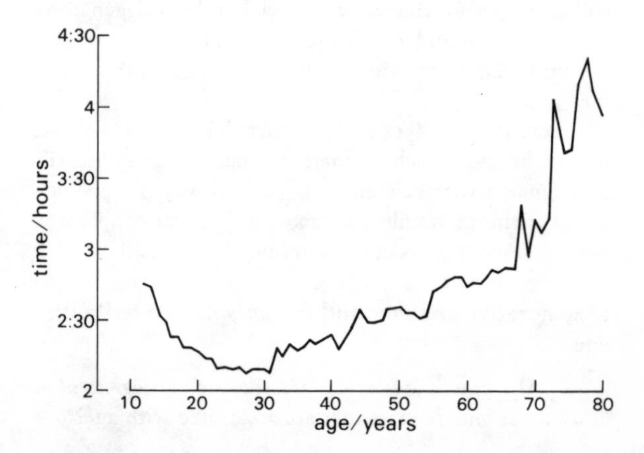

Figure 15.2 World marathon records for men. Note the slow but linear decline in maximum performance between 30 and 70 years. (Fries, 1980, p.134)

Variations occur in other functions that decline with age. Most older people have some difficulties in focusing on near objects, because the lens in the eye becomes stiffer and will no longer change shape to focus the image of the object on the retina. In some people the lens becomes cloudy so that light cannot pass through it and the sight gradually deteriorates — the condition known as *cataracts*. There is also a gradual loss of hearing acuity during life, with a slowly decreasing sensitivity to high pitched noises, and a few people become very deaf. Some lose the ability to *discriminate* between different sounds — older people frequently find it difficult to separate out noise such as conversation from background music.

There are some changes in the immune system with increasing age, as mentioned above. One is the increase in auto-antibodies; the second is a diminished response to infectious disease, which means that old people may not show the same signs of infection that a younger person would show. For instance, pneumonia in an old man may not cause a high fever and cough, but just a feeling of lethargy and confusion. Likewise, because the kidneys and liver do not function so efficiently, older people may respond to drugs differently from young adults. Drugs are often first changed chemically in the liver, then excreted in the urine by the kidneys. Any loss of function in these organs may mean that the drug is excreted only slowly. If normal doses are taken repeatedly the drug will 'build up' in the body.

In addition to all this, popular wisdom has it that memory and intellect decline with age. How far is this true? This is not an easy subject for research since both memory and intellect are complicated functions, and are affected by experience and training. There have been various contradictory results about the effect of age on intellectual capacity in the absence of those conditions which have a recognised debilitating effect such as Alzheimer's disease or atherosclerosis. These confusions probably arise because different experiments test slightly different skills. For instance, as people get older (particularly over 75), their ability to solve problems involving matching shapes or completing word sequences (problems whose answer springs solely from the information given) declines, whereas their ability to solve problems which need other experience or creative thinking *increases*.

There are some changes in memory with age. People seem to find rote learning more difficult as they get older, though there is no change in their ability to remember interesting or connected facts, such as current affairs, or the plot of a novel. Studies have shown people are less able to *recall* facts as they get older, though they can still remember them if prompted (so they must still be stored somewhere, even if difficult to retrieve). Again, these changes in memory become more marked over the age of 75.

Having said this, there are great individual variations in the effect of age on memory and intellect. Some people seem to show no change, especially those who continue to use both capacities in everyday life. There are also difficulties in interpreting some of the results of research in this field, since attention and motivation are both important in memory and problem-solving — and these may also change with age. However, research is proceeding fast on these subjects and more definite results should emerge in the next few years.

We have now looked at the various changes in bodily function that occur in the elderly. We shall move on to consider the effect these may have on the health of an individual.

Health and illness in old people

Many of the diseases that increase in incidence with age are chronic conditions, like coronary heart disease or rheumatoid arthritis. This means that as people get older they tend to 'collect diseases'. Old people often have several obvious disorders, that is they suffer from *multiple pathology*. For instance, patients admitted to a geriatric hospital are found to have an average of 6 distinct diseases; in the general population of over 65s this figure drops to 3. This means that doctors are often not trying to treat one illness, but to help with a complaint that may be due to several disease processes. Consider the following (imaginary) case history:

Mrs Robins, a rather plump lady of 72 who lives on her own in a small terraced house, went to her GP complaining she could no longer manage her stairs.

> It's mainly my hip — it hurts all the time but it really catches me on the stairs. Sometimes I have to wait to get enough courage to try to get up them. When I do I have to go up one at a time, and even then I have to stop twice to catch my breath: I just hang on to the bannister and wait till I can go on. It takes me ten minutes just to get up a dozen stairs, and the lavatory's upstairs.

□ Point out the factors in this case history contributing to Mrs Robin's problem.

■ Pain in the hip; breathlessness; obesity; a house with stairs.

When Mrs Robin's GP examined her he found her hip pain was due to oesteoarthrosis, and the breathlessness to mild heart failure. (The heart is too weak to pump harder on exertion. This leads to a back pressure of blood in the lungs so that fluid tends to pass out of the blood vessels into the surrounding lung tissue which causes breathlessness.) Both these conditions were aggravated by her excess weight since it put more strain on the hip, and there was more of her for

Table 15.1 Capacity for daily activities among people aged 65 and over, England, 1976 (percentages)

Ability	Feed oneself	Bath oneself	Get around home	Go out doors on own	Go upstairs	Garden-ing	Cut own toe nails
can manage without difficulty	96.9	73.1	88.7	75.6	66.9	43.2	61.2
can manage with difficulty	2.1	11.1	9.6	11.5	27.0	21.7	14.1
only with help	0.7	6.6	0.6	6.5	2.4		4.1
cannot manage	—	8.3	1.0	5.9	3.5	12.9	20.5
not stated	0.3	1.0	0.1	0.5	0.2	22.2*	0.1

* Includes 21.1% with no garden

(Data from Hunt, 1978, Tables 10.8.1 and 10.14.1)

the heart to pump blood around. He also noticed that her feet were deformed with bunions and her toe nails very long. She said she could not reach to cut them any more and that they did trouble her, but a lot less than her other problems.

All these conditions are common causes of immobility in the old. Mrs Robin's many diseases may seem daunting, but the encouraging aspect is that there are five separate things to treat (if you include the house) and an improvement in any one will help her become more mobile.

Similarly, confusion in elderly people may be due to many different causes, as well as the degenerative changes in the brain mentioned earlier. It may be caused, or made worse, by depression, loneliness and isolation, vitamin deficiencies, infections, strange surroundings, hormone deficiencies, and drugs. If any of these factors are present, and can be treated, a person's mental state may improve considerably.

So far we have considered illness in relation to the multiplicity of diseases in individual elderly people, but we need also to have some idea of the general level of health of people over 65 as a group. Health is usually assessed by the presence or not of different diseases, but this may not be so applicable to an older population, since it may be difficult to decide where the normal changes of ageing become 'disease'. For instance would you class mild atheroma as a disease, if it was not causing any signs of coronary heart disease or cerebrovascular disease? Would you know if it was there or not? Similar problems arise with degenerative processes such as osteoarthrosis. One solution to this problem is to estimate health in terms of *functional abilities* — whether or not everyday tasks can be performed. This not only gives a measure of the effects of both ageing and disease, but is useful for planning services to help those in need.

Table 15.1 shows the results of such a health survey based on the ability of elderly people to do particular tasks. You should note that it excludes old people in institutions (about 5 per cent of all old people), so it gives a slightly favourable view of the population as a whole.

□ What task causes the most problems?

■ Cutting toe nails causes difficulty to most people, and is also the task that the highest number of people cannot manage at all.

Disability tends to increase with age. The same survey showed that almost one third of the 80–84 group and one half of those people over the age of 85 could not bath without help and more than a third of the 75–79s could not cut their toe nails. The differing amounts of disability in different age-groups are shown in Table 15.2.

The implications of these data vary depending on your point of view. If you are old and stuck in bed it is probably depressing to find you are less healthy than your average contemporary; if you are middle-aged and scared of getting old it could be encouraging to see that people are healthier than popular opinion has it. If you are a health planner then you realise that a small proportion of the elderly who can not cut their nails means an awful lot of people (nearly two million) who need help with this task. In the next chapter we shall look at this group who do need help, and see who it is that helps them.

Table 15.2 Percentage in each age-group who are unable to perform personal tasks

Unable to do without help or totally unable to:	Age-group				
	65–69	70–74	75–79	80–84	85 & over
bath oneself	4.4	11.7	20.2	32.6	51.2
wash oneself	0.8	1.0	2.3	4.6	7.2
get to lavatory	0.4	1.3	2.8	5.1	6.2
get in and out of bed	0.6	1.1	2.7	4.4	4.8
feed oneself	0.1	0.3	1.3	1.8	2.4
shave (men); do hair (women)	0.5	0.6	2.5	3.8	4.3
cut own toenails	12.5	21.3	34.6	42.4	56.9
get up and down steps, stairs	1.6	3.8	10.1	12.8	18.6
get around house or flat	0.2	0.8	2.2	4.6	6.2
go out of doors on own	4.4	9.5	16.5	23.5	48.9
use public transport	5.3	9.3	15.1	23.8	37.9

(Data from Hunt, 1978, Tables 10.8.1 and 10.8.2, p. 73)

Objectives for Chapter 15

When you have studied this chapter, you should be able to:

15.1 Describe the physical and functional changes that occur in the body with age, and the diseases that increase in frequency with age.

15.2 Discuss the importance of defining the health of old people in terms of functional abilities and describe the incidence of disability in people over 65 years of age.

Questions for Chapter 15

1 (*Objective 15.1*) The commonest conditions contributing to problems of mobility in elderly people are disorders of the heart and lungs. From what you know from this chapter and from Book IV, *The Biology of Health and Disease*, why should these disorders affect mobility?

2 (*Objective 15.2*) Several surveys have shown that, on average, people over 65 have three separate recognisable diseases, but more than half of these are unknown to their doctor. Do you think this means there should be a system of regular inspection of old people, like school clinics for children?

16

Growing old and needing help

This is the last of the chapters on old age, and is the one most directly associated with TV programme 6 'Growing Older' that you will watch around this time. During this chapter you will be asked to refer to the short extract from a book by Ellen Newton in the Course Reader, titled 'This bed, my centre' (Part 6, Section 6.4).

In Chapters 14 and 15 we tried to dispel the idea that growing older necessarily means becoming ill and disabled. Nevertheless, although the *majority* of old people are fit and healthy, the incidence of disability does increase with age, and most people have a period of increasing restriction and illness in the last year before they die. In this chapter we shall be looking at the different ways in which old people get help when they need it, and how satisfactory this is for them and for those who do the helping.

Before looking at official estimates you might like to write down who you think gives the most support to elderly people in the sort of situations in which they need help. Then look at Table 16.1 which gives some of the answers.

□ What is the greatest source of help for disabled older people in everyday tasks?

Table 16.1 Sources of help for elderly people, England, 1976, percentages

	Proportion of those unable to perform various tasks without assistance						
Source of help	bathing	cutting toenails	climbing stairs	going outdoors	using public transport	shopping: house-bound	able to go out
person(s) in household	61.0	15.8	53.2	57.0	57.0	63.8	51.0
relative(s) outside	18.5	5.0	21.2	27.7	18.7	21.2	8.8
friend(s) outside	4.7	1.1	8.5	10.7	13.3	10.9	3.9
district nurse/health visitor	8.7	2.6	—	—	—	—	—
home help	1.6	0.1	—	2.0	1.2	13.2	2.0
chiropodist	—	72.6	—	—	—	—	—
other person outside	3.5	0.8	14.9	5.2	16.4	4.0	1.2
no help received	2.0	4.4	7.4	8.1	1.8	—	—
not stated	2.4	—	5.3	6.5	3.6	2.8	1.1
Whether help is enough							
yes	89.0	85.8	79.8	73.0	85.5		
no	2.8	5.2	2.1	6.8	6.1		
not stated	3.9	4.7	5.3	5.5	3.0		
none received/not stated whether any received	4.4	4.4	12.8	14.7	5.5		

(Rossiter and Wicks, 1982, p. 42; data from Hunt, 1978.)

■ Other people living in the same house — this is usually their spouse, but is sometimes a daughter, or, less often, a son.

□ Who gives most of the help that comes from outside the home?

■ Relatives, again.

It is clear that in the UK relatives provide the main support system for elderly people who need help, and that families do in general 'care for their own', despite the popular view that family ties are breaking down.*

The most common source of help is in fact the person's husband or wife. Similarly, elderly brothers and sisters may live together, one supporting the other who is less fit. (There is an example of two neighbours supporting each other in TV 6, 'Growing Older'.)

□ What problems do you think might arise in such a situation, where one elderly person is giving a lot of help to another?

■ There are two main problems in an otherwise mutually satisfactory situation: first, the burden of care may put a considerable strain on the healthier partner, who is also elderly; second, the couple are very vulnerable to any crisis (such as a minor illness for either partner) which may mean that neither can cope.

This means that there is a need for a community service that can provide rapid, temporary support in a crisis. At present this is often not available.

Younger relatives also provide extensive support. When their elderly relatives are in good health this help is usually mutual, with the older people retaining a clear contributory role in the family. When they become more disabled relatives usually continue to give support, both on a regular basis and in emergencies. Sometimes the help and support given is enormous, as in the following two families, described in a study of the care old people received in the year before their death:

> One, a woman in her seventies, had had a stroke. Her son explained: 'When she was first confined to bed we'd each take her for a weekend. There's six of us — two brothers and four sisters — but by the time she'd been round us all once, she'd had enough — didn't want to move around.' They'd worked out a rota system — all the sons and daughters and one daughter-in-law, so it was once a week. Whoever was to stay at night bathed her and gave her breakfast. One son, the respondent, worked fairly near his mother's house and went round four times during the day, missing his tea and coffee breaks. Also, if she was in need, a neighbour would ring him at work and he would go round — often to put her on the commode as she wouldn't let anyone outside the family help her with this.
>
> The other was a woman in her eighties who'd had cancer for eleven years. Her daughter told us how her own daughter, the woman's granddaughter, used to call in on her way home and then go back for the night. The granddaughter had slept on the settee for two years. (Cartwright, 1973, p.9)

Surveys have shown that older people generally prefer to live separately from their families if possible (though seeing them regularly) but, as people become more frail and they (or their relatives) worry about the risk of falls and other accidents, they may go to live with one of their children, usually a daughter. Most care of the very frail occurs in this way — for every confused elderly person in a long-term institution there are five who are cared for at home (Donaldson, 1983, p.424). This may put an enormous burden on those involved. Consider this account of the day by a middle-aged woman who has looked after her mother during the last seven years, during which time her mother has become increasingly frail and confused, rather deaf and unable to move independently.

> Get up about twenty to seven and get myself up and call my daughter and my son, and come down, make sandwiches for my son, and get the breakfast ... My son goes off about twenty to eight to work, and the others at about ten past eight. I usually wash up then, and about half past eight I take in a cup of tea to Mother, depending on really how she is, how she feels, I either dress her first, and then give her breakfast, or give her breakfast first and then dress her. Give her her tablets.
>
> She needs no persuasion with regard to eating, she has a good appetite and she eats well. Sometimes we have had difficulties with the taking of the tablets. We're going through a good phase just now, but I do have to put each tablet in her mouth, and then give her a drink, and ask her if its gone down, and if it hasn't I give her another drink until it does go down, and then she has the next tablet and we do the same thing. Make the beds ... Do any washing or cleaning that needs doing.
>
> I make my Mother a cup of coffee about eleven o'clock and I try to get it round about eleven because she does get a bit upset if she has to wait a long time for it. I always make it in two cups, because, if I give her one full cup, she's inclined to spill it. So two cups

*The subject of lay health care and the high proportion of this falling on women is discussed in *Caring for Health: History and Diversity*, The Open University (1985) U205 *Health and Disease*, Book VII.

half full makes a cup of coffee. Now she has her own coffee, and her own sugar, she likes to have her own things. And when I've taken her's in, and given her a couple of biscuits to go with it, fixed her up, come and make a cup of coffee for myself and then I relax for five minutes while I drink my coffee.

I get Mother a cooked meal. Then of course I have to attend to her after the meal, she usually uses the commode after the meal, sometimes of course in the morning as well.

When I've washed up I'm free to do a bit of shopping. I do my main shopping on a Wednesday, being a quieter day, and I can get round the shops quickly. I go to the local shops on a Friday. Have the baker calling, so that I haven't to keep on trotting out for a loaf of bread. And when I'm out I'm conscious all the time, I mustn't be out too long, must get back, my Mother may be requiring attention. Her condition does vary, she's been quite ill at various times, and sometimes I leave her more happily than others. Sometimes she's having a bout of falling and I think that if I go away for too long, what am I going to find when I come back?

Then the family come in about five o'clock and I give them tea and prepare their main meal which is at about six o'clock, and afterwards there's the washing up. By the time we've washed up the meal it's time to attend to Mother for the night. And get her settled down, it just varies, she's not as fresh in the evenings, so it takes me longer to attend to her, but I usually get her to bed sometime between eight and nine, and then I'm free to do the ironing or whatever else needs doing, and make my husband a drink, and that's about the day.

(From 'Working for Love', TV programme 5, U221 *The Changing Experience of Women*, The Open University, 1983)

□ What do you think would be the greatest problems for this woman in providing this care for her mother?

■ The major problems would seem to be the continuous nature of the commitment (note that she defined 'free time' as time for doing ironing or shopping) and the worry about leaving her mother even for a short time. This woman also commented how hard it is for someone outside to realise how exhausting it is to live like this, day after day, and pointed out the difficulty of convincing the social services that she really did need help.

Caring for a dependent relative thus means a great deal of work and loss of freedom, and frequently a loss of income. It is perhaps not surprising that there are reports of 'granny-battering' under such circumstances. In theory, local authorities and the health service run relief services, with perhaps night sitters, or temporary hospital care while the family go on holiday. In practice these services are totally inadequate. However, the policy is for an increased provision of '*shared care*', where there is more professional help for families willing to look after their older members. At present it is usually impossible to obtain such help unless the relative concerned breaks down under the strain.

What happens to an elderly person living alone with no relatives nearby, when he or she starts to have difficulty with the daily tasks of living? There are various sources of help for them, from both paid and voluntary services. Table 16.2 summarises the sorts of help available. You should study this table before reading on. As you do so you might like to consider which sorts and combinations of help you would prefer if you found yourself in such circumstances.

Table 16.2(a) Places to live, ranked in order of increasingly intensive/specialist care

at home
in sheltered housing (these are specially built groups of flats with a warden nearby on call for emergencies)
private Old People's Homes
Local Authority Old People's Homes
geriatric wards in hospitals
psychogeriatric wards in hospitals

The services listed, if they are all available, *can* provide a combination of arrangements to support any old person who needs help, whether they wish to stay in their own home or live with other people. In practice, however, the situation is far from perfect. Why is this so?

The first set of problems is familiar and pragmatic, concerning the cost and provision of services. Table 16.2(b) gives a rough guide to the cost to the recipient of the various home services, and although these costs are low in commercial terms, they represent a large sum to people on low pensions who are receiving supplementary benefit — and half of old age pensioners are so entitled.

Although the services described are comprehensive, in practice their provision is nearly always inadequate for the numbers of old people requiring them. Most of the staff involved complain that they are overstretched, and the limited amount of each service available means that an old person may not be able to have the type of help they want, or even that the professionals think is most appropriate for them. Thus someone may have to move to *sheltered housing* because there is a shortage of home helps, and medical wards in hospitals are full of old people who need care and support rather than hospital treatment but are

Table 16.2(b) Services available for the elderly in their own homes (including sheltered housing), 1984

Local Authority services	
Home-help	Comes in to clean house; may also do shopping and some nursing tasks. Service varies from maximum of two visits a week in some rural areas to two visits a day in a few towns. Cost varies in different regions (typical cost is £3 a week, reduced to £1.20 for those on supplementary benefit).
Meals-on-wheels	Hot meal brought to the house: varying quality, varying frequency and cost depending on the Local Authority (typical cost, 70p per meal).
Laundry services	For ordinary laundry, and special services for incontinent people. Cost and provision varies in different regions (if available at all).
Mobile Library service	Sometimes available.
Day Centres	'Clubs' for the elderly, providing recreational activities; transport provided and usually a hot mid-day meal (cost perhaps 70p).
NHS services	
Family doctor	For illnesses, etc.
Health visitor	May regularly visit those living alone; also assesses people's needs.
District Nurse	Nursing care — including bathing.
Home Dental Service	Provision varies.
Chiropodist	Provision varies
Home adaptations	Hand-rails, bath-seats, commodes, ramps, telephones, wheelchairs.
Voluntary services	Gardening, decorating, transport, good-neighbour schemes, outings.

waiting for places in sheltered housing to become available.

In some regions, the shortage of hospital beds and enthusiasm for *community care* mean that confused old people who need considerable care live at home with only a daily visit from a home help. In recent Government public expenditure cuts, incontinence laundry services in some areas have been stopped, geriatric wards have been closed, and holiday relief services have been reduced. Why should there be these inadequacies? The Department of Health and Social Security has stated the position quite clearly: 'In practice the extent of public service intervention has been tightly constrained by public willingness to pay through taxation for expansion of service' (DHSS, 1978, p.6). In other words old people get the services that the rest of society decide they should have.

□ Geriatric care has been called one of the 'Cinderellas' of the health and social services. Why do you think our society accepts this level of care?

■ Old people are not generally venerated for their wisdom and experience, they are not producers of wealth, and they do not have a clearly defined role in our society. Their status is lower than other groups in the population, and hence the services and money they receive are also inferior.

Services may fail to satisfy because of lack of resources, but there are other problems not related to money. One of these concerns the relationship between professionals and the people they help.

Look at the two quotations that follow: the first is from a passage you read earlier in this chapter in which a man described how his family had organised a rota system to care for their incapacitated mother in her own home. In the second quotation, the organiser of a day centre for old people is describing the activities provided.

> By the time she'd been round us all once she'd had enough, didn't want to move around. (Cartwright, 1973, p.39)

> Idle hands make idle minds, don't they? If they're doing something they're not thinking about themselves. And they love it, they love to feel they're making something, however small, that might bring some joy to somebody. (quoted in Carver and Liddiard, 1978, p.125)

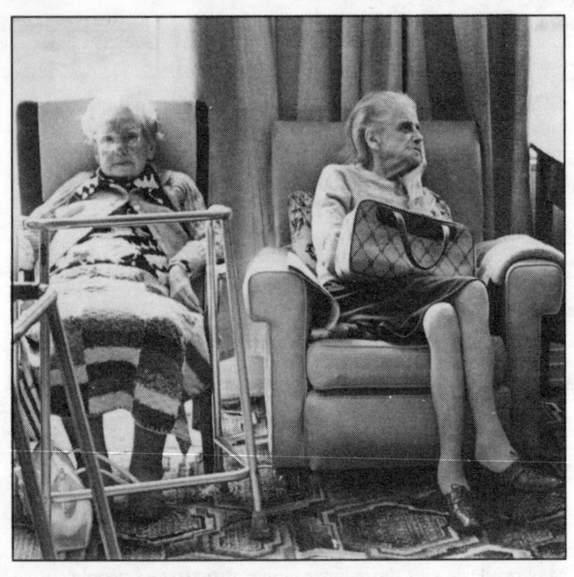

Figure 16.2 (Photo: Maria Bartha)

□ Describe the difference in attitude to the old people in these two quotations.

■ In the first, the man's mother actively put forward her feelings and initiated a change in her care. She was regarded as an equal in making decisions about her future. In the second, the old people do not seem to be regarded as equal, but as a separate group, needing to be kept busy (rather like children).

To some extent professional training is designed to turn helpers into 'experts' who not only give specialised aid, but choose what aid is most appropriate for someone. In consequence, professionals may patronise old people and make decisions about their needs, without allowing them an active role in the decisions. Old people may become the passive recipients of care, unable to control or change their environment or lifestyle. For an extreme example of such a passive role you should now read the extract in the Course Reader from Ellen Newton's book *This Bed My Centre* in which the author, a retired journalist, describes going into a home for old people (Part 6, Section 6.4).*

□ When you have read this extract, look back and list the various ways in which Ellen Newton was not in control of her daily life.

■ You might have noted that:

(i) she had no part in the decision to send her to a home;

(ii) she had no control over her daily routine — meal times and going to bed were decided by the staff;

(iii) she had no choice in the company she kept ('they have put me next to Miss Alice') or where she sat in the afternoon;

(iv) she had no control over her physical environment — dirty laundry was left outside her door, despite its smell;

(v) she had no contact with the 'real world'.

It is obviously unpleasant not to be in control of one's daily life but there is also an increasing awareness that it may affect the health of the old. Ellen Newton describes the withdrawn and unresponsive state of her fellow inmates, and this is now seen as a major side effect of institutional (and other professional) care.

It would be wrong, however, to paint too black a picture. Many professionals do not see old people as needing their lives organised for them, and even crowded and understaffed old people's homes may be arranged to avoid the feeling of a regimented institution. The Matron of the County Council home quoted in Ronald Blythe's book *The View in Winter*, describes her view of the home she runs:

> Out of the fifty-one people here, I should think that ninety-nine percent are contented. And I don't mean that they have all given in or given up. I mean that in the course of their long, long lives they have all had to accept a whole mass of things which made the slow acceptance of being old, and then coming here, rather normal. They have nearly all been very ill, or bereaved, or in two wars, or broke, or disfigured, or forsaken, or disappointed. I mean that big, bad things have happened to them, as they happen to us all, and yet one survives, as they say. Coming here is for most of them a bit more of the surviving which by now they have got used to . . . It isn't ideal here but we all live with each other as well as we can. We are in

Figure 16.3 (Photo: Maria Bartha)

*Nick Black, *et al.* (eds) (1984) *Health and Disease: A Reader*, The Open University Press.

community, I tell them. It's a bit late in the day to be in community, isn't it? But there you are ...

The value of a place like this is that you can get plenty of the talk which you used to have before you got very old. There is none of that 'concern', none of that hovering over them which sends old folk up the wall ... You can hardly expect anyone who isn't a resident to admit that our home has its own genuine life, its own genuine vitality. Of course we have our wars and rows and depressions but mostly we have plenty of plain ordinary give and take. After a time we forget that everybody is 'old'. They are just people. Visitors are always saying, 'Oh you do wonderful work', as if we were in contact with lepers ... It is high time that everybody remembered that however old you get, you stay human. (Blythe, 1979, p.134–41)

The last sentence of this passage once again raises the idea that the inadequacies in society's attitudes and care for the elderly stem from an inability to see them fully as 'people'. In fact as people become old and less able to do all they need for themselves they may require more, not less, recognition of themselves as human beings, if they are to retain their own feelings of self-respect. This point is made dramatically in the poem that follows. It was written by a woman in a geriatric ward, who was unable to speak, but was sometimes seen to write. After her death this poem was found in her locker.

'KATE'

What do you see nurses
What do you see?
Are you thinking
when you are looking at me
A crabbit old woman
not very wise,
Uncertain of habit
with far-away eyes.
Who dribbles her food
and makes no reply,
When you say in a loud voice
'I do wish you'd try'
Who seems not to notice
the things that you do,
And forever is losing
a stocking or shoe,
Who unresisting or not
lets you do as you will
With bathing and feeding
the long day to fill,
Is that what you're thinking,
is that what you see?
Then open your eyes nurse,
You're not looking at me.
I'll tell you who I am
as I sit here so still,
As I use at your bidding
as I eat at your will.
I'm a small child of ten
with a father and mother,
Brothers and sisters who
love one another,
A young girl of sixteen
with wings on her feet,
Dreaming that soon now
a lover she'll meet:
A bride soon at twenty,
my heart gives a leap,
Remembering the vows
that I promised to keep:
At twenty-five now
I have young of my own
Who need me to build
a secure happy home.
A young woman of thirty
my young now grow fast,
Bound to each other
with ties that should last:
At forty my young ones
now grown will soon be gone,
But my man stays beside me
to see I don't mourn:
At fifty once more
babies play around my knee,
Again we know children
my loved one and me,
Dark days are upon me,
my husband is dead,
I look at the future
I shudder with dread,
For my young are all busy
rearing young of their own,
And I think of the years
and the love I have known.
I'm an old woman now
and nature is cruel,
'Tis her jest to make
old age look like a fool.
The body it crumbles,
grace and vigour depart,
There now is a stone
Where once I had a heart:
But inside this old carcase
a young woman still dwells,
And now and again
my battered heart swells,
I remember the joys,
I remember the pain,
And I'm loving and living
life over again.
I think of the years
all too few — gone too fast,
And accept the stark fact
that nothing can last
So open your eyes nurses,
Open and see,
Not a crabbit old women,
look closer — see ME.
(quoted in Carver and Liddiard, 1978, p.ix)

Old age — a growing 'problem'?

So far in this chapter you have read about care for the elderly in relation to the needs of each individual. However, there has also been considerable attention paid to the total cost of all this care.

□ Why do you think the cost of services to the elderly commands such attention?

■ Because it is growing. The proportion of old people in the population has doubled since the beginning of this century and the proportion of very old people (over 75) is still increasing.

□ In what ways do old people cost the community more than young people?

■ It costs more (a) in health care, because old people accumulate diseases; (b) in services — old people need support more often than young people, and (c) in retirement pensions.

In the UK (as in most European countries) such services are paid for by taxation, national insurance and pension schemes from those in paid work, so people in the labour force meet the cost of services to old people (this system is sometimes called Pay-as-you-go). The ease with which this system works depends on how many people there are in the labour force for each old person — the so-called *support ratio*.

□ What factors do you think might affect this support ratio?

■ (i) Further changes in life expectancy.

(ii) Changes in fertility, which in time alter the numbers of people of working age and eventually the numbers of old people needing pensions and health services.

(iii) Changes in employment rates, which change the size of the labour force.

(iv) Changes in other groups of 'dependants' — for instance, the young, the handicapped and the unemployed.

Figure 16.1 shows how the support ratio has changed in Great Britain between 1951 and 1981, and how it might change (under various circumstances) up to the year 2031. From 1951–81, the number of people in the labour force for each pensioner fell from 3.4 to less than 2.8.

This change in the support ratio goes some way to explain why the changes in demographic structure in this century have come to be considered a 'problem'. 'The problems of an *ageing population*', 'the crisis of old age',

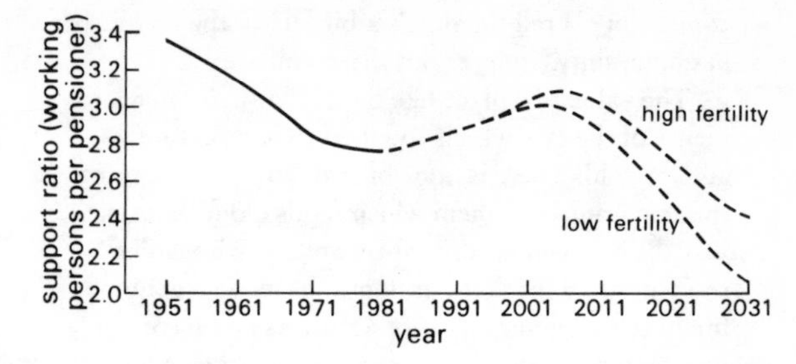

Figure 16.1 The support of pensioners in Great Britain, 1951–2033. (Data from Ermisch, 1981, Table 1, p.214) Data from 1981 onwards are projected on the basis of assumptions made about future fertility rates.

and 'the impending demographic crisis', are common labels attached to this issue.

□ Does anything strike you as odd about the labels listed above?

■ The demographic changes which have brought about an increased elderly population reflect improvements in nutrition, housing, sanitation and the general standard of living, and advances in medicine. These are often seen as symbols of progress, especially in comparison with poorer parts of the world. Yet their consequences for the demographic structure are seen as a problem rather than an achievement. You may have wondered whether this 'problem status' stems from the real difficulties in paying for services, or from some aspect of the ageist attitudes prevalent in our society.

It is probable that both these attitudes *and* the real increase in numbers of old people have contributed to the concern about our ageing population. But what changes can be expected in the future? Figure 16.1 shows that the support ratio is expected to *rise* a little until the year 2000 (as the post-war baby bulge enters the work force) and will then drop again. During the first three decades of the twenty-first century it is estimated that people in work will have to increase their financial support for the pension scheme by as much as 40 to 60 per cent.

This is a worrying prospect. Even with the present support ratio pensions are low and services stretched, but it does seem that our society has twenty years to prepare for the future, to predict future costs and to plan insurance rates and pension contributions accordingly. And perhaps those twenty years may also see some changes in the negative attitudes towards age and growing older.

Objectives for Chapter 16

After you have studied this chapter, you should be able to:

16.1 Discuss the different ways in which old people with physical or mental impairments receive help in the UK.

16.2 Discuss the advantages and disadvantages of the sorts of care for the elderly offered by families and by professionals.

16.3 Describe the way in which the demographic changes in the UK in this century may affect the support services available to elderly people.

Questions for Chapter 16

1 (*Objective 16.1*) 'People no longer look after their own.' Discuss the accuracy of this statement with regard to the care of old people.

2 (*Objective 16.2*) Read the following explanation from the woman you read about earlier in Chapter 16, who looks after her ailing and dependent mother at home, as to why her mother did not go to a day centre.

> ... She did go there for a little while but it meant that I had to take ... I didn't *have* to take her but she doesn't travel awfully well in ambulances and they go all round the world to pick everyone up and it makes her very bad tempered. So I used to take her, and get her there about eleven o'clock ... and then I had to collect her between three and four so it wasn't a tremendous help ... But she became poorly after that and was away for a long time because she was too ill to go and she refused to go afterwards. (From 'Working for Love')

This quotation demonstrates some of the advantages and disadvantages of care for the elderly by their relatives. Can you summarise what these are?

3 (*Objective 17.3*) Future standards of living and of services for the elderly will be influenced strongly by the 'support ratio'. What is this, and how might it change in the next few decades?

17 Death and dying

This is the first of three chapters dealing with death and dying. Although they come after the chapters on ageing, they consider the possibility and impact of death at all ages. In this chapter you will be asked to listen to the audiotape sequence 'Facing Death' on audiocassette AC805, Band 4. The biological material in this chapter draws on material from Book IV, *The Biology of Health and Disease*, about the circulation, respiration, and kidneys (Chapters 7 and 8). You may need to revise these subjects if you have forgotten them.

When compared with the stretch of time unknown to us, O King, the present life of men on earth is like the flight of a single sparrow through the hall where, in winter, you sit with your captains and ministers. Entering at one door and leaving by another, while it is inside it is untouched by the wintry storm; but this brief interval of calm is over in a moment and it returns to the winter whence it came, vanishing from your sight. Man's life is similar; and of what follows it, or what went before, we are utterly ignorant. (The Venerable Bede, *c.* AD 673–735, quoted in Enright, 1983, p.2)

At this point in this book we have come to the last and universal loss — that of life itself. Death is the loss of everything we know, and each person's death is a loss to their family and friends and a reminder, despite all our medical advances, of the fragility of our existence.

Death comes to everyone, though it may occur at different ages and in different ways, and it is not surprising that it has been a favourite subject in literature and the arts through the ages, its appeal assured by its relevance to all people (Figure 17.1).

Despite the universality of the subject, little was written about dying in the scientific world during this century until

Figure 17.1 Images of death: (a) death, in the fifteenth century, depicted as a dancing partner throughout life.

Figure 17.1 (b) death comes to the rich man (sixteenth century); (c) death on the barricades in the Revolutions of 1848. (E. and J. Lehner, *Devils, Demons, Death and Damnation*, Dover Publications, New York, 1971)

the 1950s when a trickle of papers appeared on the feelings of those who had fatal illnesses or had been bereaved, and on the medical care of the dying. This trickle became a flood and the study of death and dying (called *thanatology* from the Greek word *thanatos* meaning death) is now well established; papers have even been written on the anxiety produced in sociologists who study how nurses react to caring for the terminally ill.

In the next three chapters you will be reading about death and dying from several points of view — why death happens, how people feel about it, and how, as a society, we deal with death. In our culture, death is a matter for medical supervision, so we shall be considering how health professionals 'manage' patients who are dying, and the ethical problems that new medical treatments have brought. We start this chapter with very basic questions: What is death? Is it inevitable? When and why does it occur?

What is death?

> I know when one is dead, and when one lives; she's dead as earth. Lend me a looking glass; if that her breath will mist or stain the stone, why then she lives . . . (King Lear, in Shakespeare's play of that name, talking about his daughter, Cordelia).

The difference between life and death has been discussed at length by philosophers and religious thinkers, but in practical terms the difference has usually been decided by the presence or absence of the so-called *vital signs* of breathing and heart-beat.

□ What controls (i) respiration, and (ii) heart-beat?*

■ (i) The respiratory centre in the brain stem sends nervous impulses to the muscles of respiration. It responds to chemical changes in the blood by increasing or decreasing the rate of respiration.

(ii) The heart muscle has an inherent rhythmic contractability, but the speed and strength of contraction depends on control by the autonomic nervous system, via the vagus nerve and circulating adrenalin.

□ What will happen if either breathing or the circulation of blood stops?

■ Oxygen will no longer reach the cells of the body, which will therefore gradually stop those functions which require energy, including those that maintain the integrity of the cell.

It is clear that once the heart or respiration stops, the cells of the body will die. But why should this happen? In some cases the reasons are easy to see.

For example, if someone falls off a roof and breaks their neck, then the nerves between the brain stem and the chest muscles are interrupted and breathing stops. The heart will normally continue to pump blood around the body until all

*Refer to Book IV, *The Biology of Health and Disease*, Chapters 7 and 8.

its oxygen is used and the heart muscle itself stops functioning through lack of oxygen and build-up of carbon dioxide. Conversely if someone has an extensive heart attack and the heart stops, they will continue to breathe until the brain stem cells become damaged by the local lack of oxygen and build-up of carbon dioxide — breathing will then stop.

In more slowly progressive illnesses, or extreme old age, the moment of death may not be so well-defined. In the last hours of life, breathing becomes gradually shallower and the pulse weaker, until there comes a point when it is clear that both have stopped. Why exactly this happens is not always obvious. Sometimes particular organs, such as the kidneys, fail.

□ What are the main functions of the kidneys?*

■ They filter the blood, removing excesses of various ions and waste products, and in this way control the concentrations of chemicals in the blood.

Where there is kidney failure, the concentration of various substances may be much higher or lower than is normal, and other cells in the body then may also fail in this unfavourable environment. But in old age there is often no evidence of failure in one particular organ, but rather of small changes in all of them. It is postulated that the accumulative effect of all these changes means that the body cannot maintain *homeostasis*† over even mild environmental changes, and that the multiple changes in the body's internal environment mean that cells begin to die, until eventually the heart and brain cease to function. This would be a true 'death from old age', a diagnosis no longer recognised as a cause of death on death certificates, and thus never found in official mortality figures.

Having established what happens when someone dies, the next question is whether death has to happen.

Is death inevitable?

> Certain, 'tis certain; very sure, very sure: death as the psalmist saith is certain to all; all shall die. (William Shakespeare, 2 *Henry IV*)

> The days of our years are three scores and ten; and if by reason of strength they be four score years, yet is their strength labour and sorrow; for it is soon cut off, and we are gone. (Psalm 90 : 10)

*See Book IV, *The Biology of Health and Disease*, Chapter 8.

†Homeostasis is a state of dynamic equilibrium within the body, whereby vital parameters, such as temperature and sugar levels are kept at the optimum value for health. (See Book IV, *The Biology of Health and Disease*, Chapter 5.)

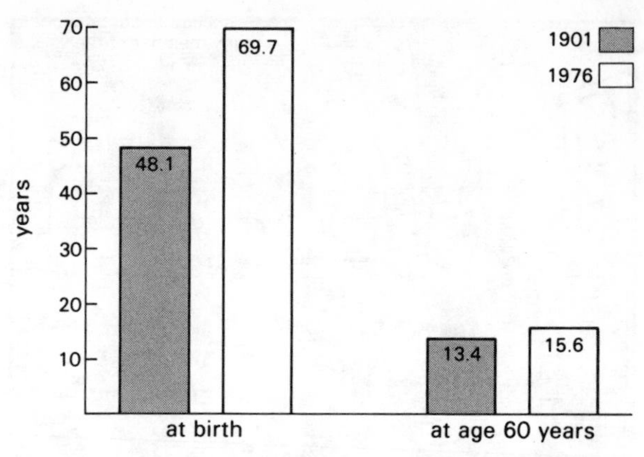

Figure 17.2 Expectation of life for males in Great Britain, 1901 and 1976. (Donaldson and Donaldson, 1983, p.427)

> Some people want to achieve immortality through their works or descendants. I prefer to achieve immortality through not dying. (Woody Allen, American humorist, 1970s).

Despite much research into ageing and huge amounts of money spent on medical treatment the psalmist's estimate of life span is still essentially true. Figure 17.2 shows the life expectancy for men at birth and at the age of 60 in 1901 and 1976.

□ What do you notice about the relative differences in life expectancy in 1901 and 1976?

■ In 1901 the life expectancy of a man at birth was considerably less than in 1976. However, the life expectancies at the age of 60 were very similar.

□ Can you explain this?

■ The increase in life expectancy at birth is largely due to the decreased mortality in childhood, and not because we are better at curing, or preventing illnesses in middle and old age.

In fact, immortality is no nearer than it was eighty years ago. Medical science has had little effect on death rates over the age of 60. Only about 1750 people a year in Britain reach their hundredth birthday and there is only one authenticated case of someone living to 114 years in the world. Tales of much greater longevity occur only where accurate records of birth are not kept, or where they are known to have been altered to escape being drafted into the Army (as is thought to be the case with the celebrated old men of Georgia in the USSR).

This limit to the life span is not very surprising since it is true of other species as well, though obviously the life span varies from species to species. *Homo sapiens* is probably the longest living mammal, but is beaten by some birds, such as parrots and swans, and by some reptiles. For

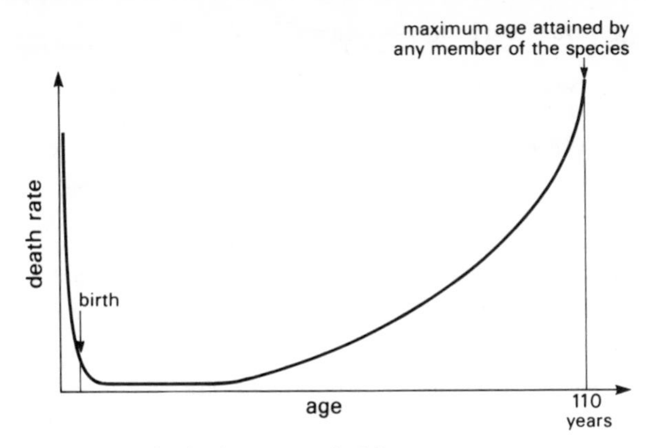

Figure 17.3 The death rate over the lifespan.

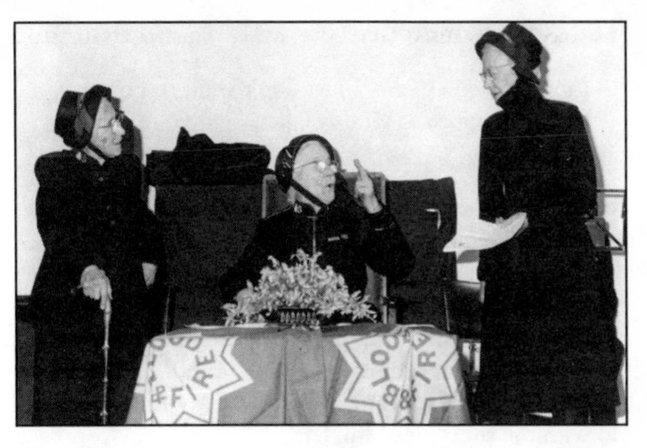

Figure 17.4 Catherine Branwell-Booth, aged 100, and her two sisters, both in their nineties – all officers in the Salvation Army. Perhaps an advertisement for the influence of female biology, heredity, companionship, and an abstemious life, on longevity? (Courtesy of the Salvation Army)

each species, including humans, the death rate shows a similar pattern throughout life (see Figure 17.3).

□ At what points during the life span is the risk of dying highest?

■ From conception to birth, and just after, the mortality rate is high. It is then low for about half the average life span when it starts to rise again. After this time, the mortality rate rises rapidly.

For humans the line becomes almost vertical by the age of 110 — after this age the chance of dying becomes almost infinitely great.

Everyone agrees that humans do not live for ever, but why this is so is not clear. It is not clear why individual cells die throughout the life of an individual, though it does seem possible that it may follow from the changes of ageing, and it is possible that if we can slow down the *rate* of cellular ageing, this might extend the life span by ten to twenty years. As you read in Chapter 15 this is not yet a practical proposition.

Although humans do have a defined average life span, within the population there are of course individual variations. When someone lives to a great age they are generally asked how they managed it. No universal secret of longevity has been found, though a study of longevity reveals some interesting (but inconclusive) associations with the following factors:

1 *Sex* Women live on average six years longer than men.

2 *Heredity* Nonagenarians (people in their nineties) are said to run in families. There is not much scientific evidence supporting this, but there are a few spectacular cases of identical twins in dissimilar environments dying within a few days of one another.

3 *Nutrition* This is a contentious point. It is possible in rats to delay puberty by underfeeding. These rats then live longer than their well-fed counterparts. This does not seem very relevant to humans trying to live longer, but there is a correlation between obesity and early deaths in humans.

4 *Exercise* This may reduce the likelihood of heart attacks.

5 *Companionship* Marriage is associated with lower mortality rates in men, but has little or no effect on women's rates.

When do people die?

□ Look back at Table 10.1 (p.103). At what age do most people in England and Wales die?

■ The majority of people survive into old age. Only a few people die in childhood or middle-age. At any stage during life, mortality rates are lower for women than for men.

It is clear that in the UK most people die when they are old, but there are still deaths among children and young and middle-aged adults, and in considering death and its impact on our lives in these chapters we will have to consider deaths among the young as well as the old.

We have set the scene in these last pages with some facts and figures about death. There is a danger, however, in being too 'objective' about a subject which is important because it is frightening. Unless we understand the fear and uncertainty that death arouses we will not understand the impetus for medical research, the rituals surrounding death, or the inadequacies of terminal care. As André Malraux (a French writer of this century) said, 'There is no death . . . There is only . . . me . . . me . . . who is going to die . . .' With that in mind, we shall continue this chapter by considering the individual experience of death.

The shadow of death

> I'm not afraid to die. I just don't want to be there when it happens. (Woody Allen, quoted in Enright, 1983, p.39)

Woody Allen's remark encapsulates the ambivalence we feel about dying — our theories don't quite match our feelings on the matter. Before you consider other people's reactions you might like to write down how you think you would react if told you had only six months to live. Consider both your emotions and practical considerations — who would you tell and how? What would you actually do with the short bit of life left?

This is obviously difficult to do in the abstract. To show how people may feel when really faced with this situation we have recorded some extracts from conversations with people who are dying, or who have faced death, and with their relatives. You may find some parts of this recording upsetting — this is a proper reaction. As we suggested before, death is an important subject *because* of its emotional force; accepting our own feelings about death is a necessary start to understanding its effect on our lives.

You should now listen to the audiotape sequence 'Facing Death' (Cassette AC805, Band 4). These recordings demonstrate some of the very different reactions and attitudes that people have towards death. Some of these differences reflect different circumstances.

□ What factors do you think might govern what a person feels about dying?

■ There are of course many. You might have suggested some of the following:

1 Age — death in old age is perhaps more acceptable than for a younger person who may find it very unfair to be singled out by fate in this way.

2 What you lose — for different people death means the loss of different things. For an adolescent it may be never to have their own independent life; for a younger mother it may be leaving her children and feeling that she is failing them.

3 The type of illness — a gradually progressive illness may promote different reactions from one that is punctuated by rare but severe periods of incapacity with the constant fear of sudden death.

4 Beliefs about an afterlife — some people are sustained by strong beliefs in a happy existence after death, some fear a miserable one. Those with less certain beliefs may be fearful of the uncertainty of what dying means.

Different people have different reactions. Nevertheless, it is possible to pick out some feelings that many people experience. The first is perhaps shock, or disbelief:

> Now and then the whole thing becomes unreal. Out of the middle of the night's darkness, or bringing me to a sudden, chilling halt during the day, the thought comes: This can't be happening to me. Not to me. *Me* with a malignant tumor? *Me* with only a few months to live? Nonsense. And I stare up at the darkness, or out at the sunlit street, and try to encompass it, to feel it. But it stays unreal. (Thomas Bell, 1961, quoted in Imara, 1975, p.149)

When this unreality wears off, feelings are often turbulent and confused, a mixture of anger, grief and fear. Some people try to bargain with God, Fate or the medical profession to see if they could possibly avoid death this way. For instance, a woman who had learnt the previous day that she had widespread cancer originating in an ovary, was typical in asking her doctor if it would help if she gave up smoking, and also typical in bursting into tears when she was told it would not.

At the same time as the dying person is trying to come to terms with the drastic change in their life and future plans, their family will be experiencing many of the same feelings. They too have to adjust to the changes in their relative, and to his or her impending disappearance from life. For some people the experience may bring them closer together, but even in good relationships the anger and grief may make it difficult to communicate. Where there are difficulties already, in an unhappy marriage for instance, illness and the emotional needs of both partners may worsen an already difficult situation.

Death is hard to face — for yourself or for someone you love. Nevertheless, some people do manage to accept their anger and grief, and get over their fear of death, and find that they can play an active (though different) role as their death approaches. This acceptance may be eased by increasing disability which may mean that life itself becomes too tiring and more than they can cope with. This may also occur in extreme old age:

> Dear death, how I look forward to it. I look forward to it because I am so tired. So weary, you know. This tiredness just falls on top of me like a dead weight. Such utter, utter weariness — you have no idea. It's worth talking about because it is quite something. I mean I've known what it it is to be really tired, like everybody else, but never a tiredness like this. If I tell you that it is too important a tiredness simply to sleep through, you'll know what I mean. It keeps me awake so that I can feel every bit of it. I lie on the sofa — or even get the tea — in this huge, huge tiredness. It's not exactly unpleasant but it is becoming rather a nuisance. I wouldn't mind if I could just doze off and

> wake up and find it gone, but I can't. That's not its little game. Being so old is a very funny business ... Let's be serious. This weariness is death. (quoted in Blythe, 1979, pp.278–79)

So far we have dealt almost entirely with adults and their view of dying. But what of children and their feelings? About 20 per cent of all childhood deaths between the ages of one and fourteen are from cancers or congenital abnormalities and these children tend to have a long period of illness, with recurrent medical treatment and periods of hospitalisation. Research has shown that in such cases children from the age of three onwards can have a clear idea of their condition and of death as the end of themselves. Often, their realisation comes from seeing another child die with the same condition.

Most studies show that they do not talk directly about death but ask indirect questions like 'Will I be getting a large coat, or one that fits?' One study by Myra Bluebond-Langner in 1978 described how children often indicated their awareness of death by statements such as 'I'm not going to school anymore'; by asking for Christmas presents in October; or by their drawings of storms, fires and scenes of destruction such as a crucifixion with the child as the crucified subject. One eight year-old with leukaemia made numerous cut-out paper dolls, which she then buried in a Kleenex box which she called their grave.

Other children mentioned in this study were more direct, such as a five-year-old boy who was lying uncomfortably on his back, but refused to be turned over, saying, 'No, I'm practising for my coffin'. Some children would use the medical staff's discomfiture over the subject of death, by asking questions about it to make them go away, thus avoiding some painful medical procedure.

It seems likely that the behaviour and attitudes of dying children are, to a great extent, governed by the attitudes of their parents and the medical staff. Adults do not like to talk about death with children, and so the children, though aware of their prospects, may refer only obliquely to death, unless they wish to embarrass or discomfort the staff. Children are certainly aware of adults' fears — some dying children in the terminal ward of one London hospital were reported as asking new staff, 'Am I going to die?' If the answer was a truthful 'Yes', the person was accepted by the child. If he or she lied or equivocated they were ignored from then on.

For adolescents the situation is different. They have known a more normal life (they have not been ill for all of it), and have had clearer expectations from the future. For them the anger that most dying people experience is often profound and continuing. One doctor described a teenager who died from a bone cancer at the age of seventeen, after three years of treatment (including amputation of a leg and several courses of anti-cancer drugs which made him very sick):

> He was furious towards the end, just continuously angry. Angry that it had happened to *him* out of all the people in the world; angry that when there was a chance he could have been cured by his treatment, yet he didn't get the benefit of that chance — out of all those with the disease for *him* the treatment didn't work. He was angry that we kept him in hospital, and that he couldn't finally die at home. Once (when he was apparently doing well) I suggested he was smoking rather too much, and he shouted back, 'You've taken everything else I've got, including my leg — you won't take this from me.' (Bristol doctor, 1984, interviewed by a Course Team member)

Suicide

A discussion of attitudes to death would be incomplete without some reference to death that is chosen, rather than imposed. Four thousand people in the UK are known to commit *suicide* every year (1984). What are their feelings and why do they do it?

Research into suicide is not easy. The most obvious reason for this is that the successful suicide is no longer available for questioning about his or her motives. The second main difficulty is in distinguishing between genuine suicide attempts (whether or not they are successful), and so-called *para-suicides* when suicide is apparently attempted (and may accidentally result in death) but the main aim is not to die, but rather to communicate the person's emotional state to people around.

Any general theory about why people commit suicide would need to explain several epidemiological facts, such as that women attempt suicide at least twice as often as men but twice as many men as women actually die in suicide attempts; different cultures have different suicide rates; economic depression is followed by an increase in the suicide rate, while war results in a decrease.

One of the first people to try and explain these sorts of facts was Emile Durkheim, a French sociologist, who did research into suicides at the turn of the last century (*Suicide. A Study in Sociology*, 1897). He suggested that suicides could be categorised into three main groups: those who committed suicide for egotistical reasons — where excessive individualism outweighed social ties; those who committed suicide for socially altruistic reasons — as in Japanese kamikaze pilots; and finally, what he called *anomic suicide* (anomic literally means without laws or rules), when a society changes rapidly, or a person's place within it, so that the old rules no longer hold, and their previous ways of coping with problems no longer work.

Durkheim's theories and later variations explain some

of the variation in suicide rates between societies, between social subgroups (because the degree of social integration and individualism varies) and the changing suicide rates in depressions and wars. However, in these chapters we are more concerned with what it is in the nature of an individual's experience that brings him or her to commit suicide. One way to study this is to look at suicide notes, which are left by about 35 per cent of people who successfully commit suicide (though this figure may be an underestimate since some notes are probably destroyed by relatives).

Here are three examples of suicide notes. You should read them and then answer the questions beneath.

> 1 Dearest, I feel certain I am going mad again: I feel we cant go through another of those terrible times. And I shant recover this time. I begin to hear voices, and cant concentrate. So I am doing what seems the best thing to do. You have given me the greatest possible happiness. You have been in every way all that anyone could be. I dont think two people could have been happier till this terrible disease came. I cant fight it any longer, I know that I am spoiling your life, that without me you could work. And you will I know. You see I cant even write this properly. I cant read. What I want to say is that I owe all the happiness of my life to you. You have been entirely patient with me and incredibly good. I want to say that — everybody knows it. If anybody could have saved me it would have been you. Everything has gone from me but the certainty of your goodness. I cant go on spoiling your life any longer.
>
> I dont think two people could have been happier than we have been.
>
> V. (Virginia Woolf to her husband, Leonard, 18 March 1941, quoted in Enright, 1983, p.93)
>
> 2 Mary, I hope you're satisfied. Bill. (quoted in Jacobs, 1967, p.69)
>
> 3 Dear Jane: You are ruining your health and your life for me, and I cannot let you do it. The pains in my face seem worse every day and there is a limit to what a man can take. I love you dear. Bill. (quoted in Jacobs, 1967, p.69)

□ What appear to be the main differences in attitude in the people who wrote these three different notes?

■ 1 In Virginia Woolf's note she mentions her inability to face the future with another exacerbation of a long-standing problem; she describes a feeling of worthlessness, and wishes to avoid being a burden to her husband once again. (The length of the letter and her efforts to explain and justify her suicide are typical of many suicide notes.)

2 In the second letter the main aim, of the note at least, is to put the blame of the suicide on Mary, Bill's wife. This suggests that the suicide was to some extent an act of revenge.

3 The third note, like the first, explains the reason for the suicide but it is much shorter and less emotional — the desire to avoid the pain of an already fatal illness is normally considered to be a reasonable one and needs little defence.

The majority of suicide notes resemble one of these three types giving clear reasons for the suicide (or contain simple instructions about money and arrangements), but this still does not explain why some people, when faced with such problematic situations, feel that death is the only answer. Psychologists have identified several attributes which may predispose people to suicide (Lester, 1971). They suggest that people who kill themselves are often impulsive people; they tend to be rigid in their thinking and to think in extremes; they generally have disturbed social relationships, and may be very isolated, with few possibilities for communication of their feelings; they generally have little self-esteem, and they are likely to have suffered a major loss, such as a bereavement or the loss of a job within the last few years. There is, however, no general description of a 'suicidal personality' and studies of the personalities of people who kill themselves reveal more differences between them than similarities.

Bereavement

For a dying person, the story of their feelings and experiences (at least as far as we know) ends with their death, but for their friends and relatives this is the real beginning of their loss.

Just as experiences of impending death vary between different people, so does the experience of losing a friend or relative. Much depends on the relationship between the mourner and the mourned, and on the way in which death occurred. A sudden and unexpected death is usually harder to get over than one where there was time to grieve before the death actually happened (this is sometimes called *anticipatory* or *prebereavement mourning*). There is not enough space here to cover all aspects of *bereavement*: instead we shall focus on the experience of losing a husband, a profound loss that many women suffer (there are far more widows than widowers). The quotations used come from a book by Liz McNeill Taylor, who wrote about her feelings and gradual recovery after her husband died suddenly at the age of forty-three (*Living With Loss. A Book for the Widowed*, 1983). She begins by describing her feelings when she was first told the news:

> Everything can be brought back in painful immediacy — the weather ... the taste of my tears and the

> racking pain in my chest that comes when sobs rise from deep down inside you. Most vivid of all is the memory of my utter disbelief in what was being said ... disbelief and a terrible, numbing coldness ...
>
> When the word 'dead' was first pronounced on my husband, only half of my mind believed it. Even in shock it was always hard for me to show emotion before strangers but now I clung to this friend in an ecstasy of grief, weeping, 'He can't be dead, he can't be dead. I loved him so much, you see.'
>
> I became a sort of schizophrenic. Half of me knew it to be true, but the other half was seized with a strange ability immediately to fantasise the situation ... it took weeks for me to accept the fact [that my husband had died] with the conscious part of my brain and years for me to come to terms with it in my subconscious. (Taylor, 1983, pp.9–11)

After the numbness wore off, she describes the 'prolonged and complicated emotional chaos that follows widowing'. She talks of:

> ... the terrible desolation that comes when the full realisation of what has happened begins to sink in ... and life is a bleak vista of unending misery ... It was the nadir of my life. Never have I been so desperate and I hope never to feel that way again. (Taylor, 1983, p.42)

She notes her surprise on discovering that 'sorrow is a physical pain and can bring on symptoms as definite as any illness ... During the first weeks on my own, my body seemed numb, almost anaesthetised', and later, 'an ugly rash appeared on my face and neck' (Taylor, 1983, p.49, p.57). She also suffered from frightening fluttering sensations from her heart.

She dreamt about her husband:

> I frequently had the most vivid dreams about him ... I would awake tranquil and content with the memory of them — until a slow dawning of the truth came with my returning consciousness. I would slide my hand over to his side of the bed and find it empty ... (ibid, p.129)

It was some time before she realised she had to make a new life for herself, and became aware of how much of herself seemed to have gone with her husband's death.

> The feeling of surgical cutting off is at times overwhelming and it affects the mind as well as the body. For my own part I really felt as if I had been split down the middle like a piece of wood. Through the years of marriage, almost without realising it, Adam and I had grown together like a knotted vine and the cutting away of one part almost killed the other. I was left with all my broken parts exposed, told to go on functioning with what was left. (ibid, p.63)

It was not only grief that she felt:

> [I had] the feeling that I was carrying a repressed scream inside me. It was difficult for me to work out exactly what I was *angry* about — until I realised it was against Adam himself ... The first articulation of this was the day when I heard my mind asking myself — 'Why did he have to die and leave me on my own?' In a way, when trouble struck, it seemed as if he had chosen the easy way out by dying. I was also resentful that he had failed to leave a will or to make any provision for what could happen to us if he died ... [this] led me on to recall other past derelictions on his part. I remembered things he had said or done which had rankled at the time ... And all this time I still missed him bitterly ... (ibid, pp.127–28)

She also felt guilt for his death:

> Could I have in some way prevented what had happened? I also felt a terrible guilt for the fact that he had to die alone. If only I had been with him I could at least have helped him to die ...
>
> [These and other guilts] gradually extended to a feeling of more seriously having let him down — had I in some way abandoned him to death? Had I given him up to it, allowed it to happen almost by some sort of witchcraft? (ibid. pp.134–45)

In all she found that the whole cacophany of different emotions continued, though getting less, for several years, disappearing for a while then recurring, at the same time as she was learning to cope with the practical problems of her widowhood — coping with her four children (also grieving), the loss of her social and sexual partner, and the difficulties of providing for herself and her family. It was months and years before she felt she had come to terms with her loss and could truly say she was happy again.

□ Do you notice any similarities between the emotions described here and the emotions felt by those who face the prospect of dying?

■ In both conditions the bad news is followed by a period of shock or numbness. After this there was a time of turbulent emotions, such as grief, anger, guilt and fear, which gradually gave away (for some) to a feeling of acceptance or resignation.

These similarities were noticed by doctors such as Elizabeth Kübler-Ross (an American psychiatrist) and Colin Murray Parkes (a British psychiatrist) who worked with dying patients and their relatives. Elizabeth Kübler-Ross described the various emotions such as grief, anger, and bargaining, as stages or phases that had to be worked through before resignation was achieved. By contrast, Colin Murray Parkes has stressed the variability and recurrence of different emotions, while agreeing that the griever moves from a state of incomprehension or numbness, to a period of intense emotion when the sufferer battles between wanting the lost person (or lost health) back, and accepting the reality of the new situation. This, he has argued, is often followed by a time of hopelessnesss or dejection, as the reality is accepted, but the sufferer has no place in it. Little by little the person comes to find a new role to play in life — whether it is a role as a dying patient instead of a healthy business man, or a single person instead of a wife.

These patterns of responses are also seen in reaction to other types of loss. Here we shall end on a note of caution. Though most people are able to work through their grief at losing something or someone they love, this is not true of everyone. Some people *never* recover from the death of their wife or husband, but continue to mourn miserably for the rest of their life. Some people cannot bear the pain of their grief — it is important that our analysis of such pain does not mean we underestimate the anguish involved. The following quotation is from the diary of Dora Carrington, written a month after the death of Lytton Strachey (her companion for many years) and one month before she committed suicide, in March 1932.

> They say one must keep your standards and your values of life alive. But how can I, when I only kept them for you? Everything was for you. I loved life just because you made it so perfect, and now there is no one left to make jokes with, or to talk about Racine and Molière and talk about plans and work and people.
>
> I dreamt of you again last night. And when I woke up it was as if you had died afresh. Every day I find it *harder* to bear. For what point is there in life now? . . . I look at our favourites, I try and read them, but without you they give me no pleasure. I only remember the evenings when you read them to me aloud and then I cry. I feel as if we had collected all our wheat into a barn to make bread and beer for the rest of our lives and now our barn has been burnt down and we stand on a cold winter morning looking at the charred ruins. For this little room was the gleanings of our life together. All our happiness was over this fire and with these books. With Voltaire blessing us with upraised hand on the wall . . . It is impossible to think that I shall never sit with you again and hear your laugh. *That every day for the rest of my life you will be away.* (quoted in Enright, 1983, pp.105–6)

Objectives for Chapter 17

When you have studied this chapter, you should be able to:

17.1 Describe the biological changes that occur when someone dies, and the patterns of mortality at different ages in the UK.

17.2 Describe the range of feelings that are experienced by the dying and the bereaved and the similarities in patterns of grief, and how these feelings may differ particularly in children, adolescents, and in people who commit suicide.

Questions for Chapter 17

1 (*Objective 17.1*) 'People now live longer than they did a hundred years ago.' Is this a true statement?

2 (*Objective 17.2*) Look back at Dora Carrington's diary entry. What major losses does she feel after Lytton Strachey's death?

18
Society and death

Figure 18.1 (a) A fifteenth-century depiction of a death-bed scene. (Source as for Figure 17.1)

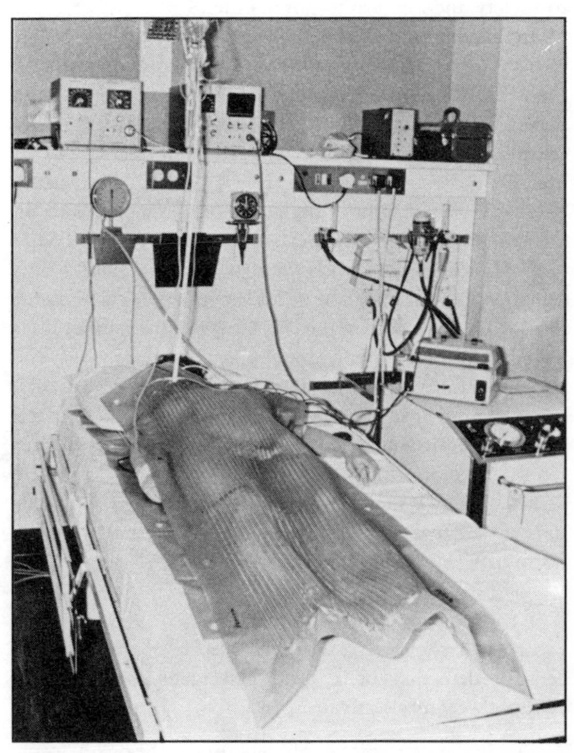

Figure 18.1 (b) A twentieth-century death-bed scene. (Photo: Blackwell Biovisual)

Human beings have always attempted to control chaotic or disruptive processes, to produce order and security in their existence. *Death* is one natural process that has never been controlled: it remains inevitable and causes fear for the individual, grief in the bereaved and leaves a 'hole' in the community where there was previously a person.

You have already seen in this book how one such

disruptive and potentially dangerous transition — birth — is surrounded by rituals which attempt to render it less frightening. Similarly, in the vast majority of cultures, death and mourning are contained and made more bearable by ceremonies and beliefs. Since the beginning of this century, anthropologists have studied the impact of death in different cultures and have identified common patterns. Typically, a definite role is assigned to the dying person with a 'proper' way to behave. Between death and the disposal of the body there are communal ceremonies. After this, the mourners go through a withdrawal from society during which time they change their appearance — by wearing different clothes or shaving their head for example — so that all who meet them can treat them in a prescribed manner. This period of seclusion is followed by a re-entry to society and a return to normal life.

In this chapter we shall try to see how customs in the UK fit into such a pattern. To do this we will draw heavily on the work of Geoffrey Gorer, a British anthropologist, who was struck by the gradual change in funeral and mourning customs when he lost close relatives at various stages of his life. He did a survey in the early 1960s of 359 recently bereaved people from differing social classes and in different regions of England and Scotland (*Death, Grief and Mourning in Contemporary Britain*, 1965). This remains the major source of information on customs for dealing with the dead in the UK. However, the survey does have limitations: Gorer's sample consisted mainly of white people, and was principally composed of Protestants, though he did have some Roman Catholic respondents, and rather fewer orthodox Jews. The discussion in this chapter tends, therefore, to concentrate on the habits of white Protestants. We shall contrast these at times with rituals that are current in other ethnic groups, or that were the norm in Western Europe before this century.

The moment of death

Figure 18.1 shows two deathbed scenes: one a fifteenth-century depiction of a death-bed scene, and one its twentieth-century equivalent.

□ In these two pictures (i) where does the death occur, and (ii) who is with the dying person?

■ (i) Both die in bed; one at home and the other in hospital; (ii) The dying person in Figure 18.1a has family, friends, and priest with him. In Figure 18.1b the dying person is alone, although there are presumably other patients and medical staff in the vicinity.

These contrasts highlight a change in customs in Europe that has occurred over the last century. One hundred years ago, less than ten per cent of people died in hospitals, asylums or workhouses in the UK. In 1965, half of all deaths occurred in hospitals and that number had risen to 56 per cent in 1974, with only 31 per cent of people dying at home in bed — the traditional place of death for over one thousand years (the rest died neither at home nor in hospital).

Perhaps this shift of location explains why the moment of death is no longer a social event. Gorer found that less than half of spouses were present at their partner's death. Of other close relatives, fewer than a quarter were present, though this was class-related, being less than seven per cent in professional classes. This is in marked contrast to customs in Europe before this century. In France, for instance, in the early nineteenth century, when the last sacrament was being given to a sick person, anyone, even strangers, could come in off the street to the bedroom to watch and pray as the person died. Such relatively public deaths do still occur in the UK, though they are rare. Lily Pincus, author of a book on death and mourning, describes the death of her Victorian mother-in-law in the 1950s.

> On the day before her seventieth birthday she had a stroke and was unconscious for a few hours. When she awoke, she asked to be sat up in bed and then ... demanded to see all the different people in the house. She said good-bye to each individually as if she were going on a long journey, with thank-you messages for friends and relatives and all who had cared for her ... When after nearly an hour of this 'reception' her strength left her, Fritz and I stayed on with her alone until she bade us farewell most lovingly and said 'Now let me sleep'. (Pincus, 1975, pp.4–8)

This woman was at home, well aware of her impending death, and made her own preparations for it openly. This again is not typical of our times. The patient in Figure 18.1b is the passive recipient of medical care, and often has not been told he is dying (though research has shown that 50 per cent of terminally ill patients know they are dying without being told). The matter is often not admitted or discussed. 'A good death' nowadays is one which happens quietly and unobtrusively: phrases such as 'he never knew anything about it' or 'she went quite peacefully in her sleep' are modern phrases of consolation and comfort, whereas in the past such ignorance was considered tragic or even criminal since it left no time to make one's peace with God.

From death to the funeral

In his book on death and funeral customs in Europe through the ages, Philippe Aries (a French historian) has described the involvement of the community between a death and the funeral at the beginning of this century:

> In the early twentieth century, before World War I, throughout the Western world of Latin culture, be it Catholic or Protestant, the death of a man still

> solemnly altered the space and time of a social group that could be extended to include the entire community . . .
>
> After death, a notice of bereavement was posted on the door (in lieu of the old abandoned custom of exhibiting the body or the coffin by the door of the house). All the doors and windows of the house were closed except the front door, which was left ajar to admit everyone who was obliged by friendship or good manners to make a final visit. The service at the church brought the whole community together, including late comers who waited for the end of the funeral to come forward; and after the long line of people had expressed their sympathy to the family, a slow procession, saluted by passers-by, accompanied the coffin to the cemetery. And that was not all. The period of mourning was filled with visits: visits of the family to the cemetery and visits of relatives and friends to the family. (Aries, 1983, p.559)

Gorer found that many of these traditional activities had disappeared. Although 80 per cent of his respondents had some sort of family gathering at home before the funeral and 80 per cent made some change in the house to indicate mourning (like drawing the curtains or displaying cards of condolence in the windows), these habits were related to class and religion, being less common in the South and among the professional classes.

Two-thirds of Gorer's sample went to view the body. This custom was almost universal in the North West of England, where there are a considerable number of Roman Catholics of Irish origin. Many of these (and some Church of Scotland members) continue the custom of having the body laid out in the front room, so that friends and relatives can visit to pay their respects. In interviews with a Course Team member (1984), one Catholic commented on this custom, after the death of his father: 'It was really very good — it kept all of us busy for the three days. My mother had to keep making cups of tea and talking to people — it kept her going.' Another commented on the effect of having his mother's body in the house for this time: 'To start with she looked quite normal — just as if she were asleep, but over the three days her face gradually changed. By the time the funeral came round, she wasn't my mother any more, just a dead body.' Such visits of condolence before the funeral are also normal among Hindu and Sikh groups in the UK, but Gorer noted that such activities were no longer universal, and had almost completely disappeared among professional classes and in the South of England. This was not true of the funeral itself.

Gorer found that nearly all his sample had a funeral and, for all but five per cent, it was a religious one. Unlike marriage, there is no popular non-religious alternative; those without faith tend to default to Church of England (or Scotland) ceremonies. The disposal of the dead was by cremation or burial. Most people chose between them for definite reasons: cremation was considered more final by some and chosen or rejected for that reason. Some people thought it more hygienic, or more suitable after a disfiguring illness. Cremation may be chosen to avoid the expense and upkeep of a gravestone, or if there is danger that a grave would be neglected. Cremation only became accepted in the UK in the late nineteenth century. By 1963, 41 per cent of bodies were cremated, and by 1983, this had risen to 65 per cent and seems to be becoming the preferred practice.

Funerals, such as Gorer described, are organised by undertakers, who offer a variety of services. A very basic funeral cost (in 1984) about £350 and for this the undertaker provides a coffin, picks up the body, and prepares it for the funeral (washing, shaving, and dressing the body as required), and provides a hearse and bearers, together with a car to carry the deceased's relatives. Additional services, such as organising flowers, a reception, and service music can bring the cost up to £1 000 or so.

The funeral, which Gorer described as the commonest rite after death, does not extend to one group — stillbirths. Especially if the baby born is very premature, or disfigured by having spent some time dead in its mother's uterus, it is often disposed of rapidly and without any ceremony (see discussion in Chapter 11). In recent years there has been increasing publicity about the feelings of mothers who have a stillborn child (though not much has been said about the father's feelings) and some maternity units now encourage the mother to hold the dead baby. Sometimes the hospital chaplain is called in to baptise the baby and say funeral prayers. It is possible that this will become more widespread to fill the ceremonial vacuum which ignores the fact of stillbirths.

After the funeral it is the custom in most ethnic groups in the UK for the mourners to gather in the house for a family meeting, normally with food and drink. Gorer found that nearly everyone in his sample followed this practice, and, apart from the funeral itself, it seemed to be the most widespread ritual of mourning in Britain in the 1960s. It would seem that other rites (such as condolence visits, the funeral procession, and drawing the curtains of the house) that were the norm fifty years ago have gradually disappeared particularly in the South of England and in the professional and upper middle classes, and funerals have become more and more discrete and private. The funeral feast has remained; it has a long tradition, as is shown by this Mauritanian inscription from the third century AD.

> We all set out the furnishings suited to a worthy grave,
> And on the altar that marks the tomb of our mother,

> Secundula,
> It pleased us to place a stone table-top,
> Where we could sit around, bringing to memory her many good deeds,
> As the food and the drinking cups were set out, and cushions piled around,
> So that the bitter wound that gnawed our hearts might be healed.
> And in this way we passed the evening hours in pleasant talk,
> And in the praise of our good mother.
> The old lady sleeps: she who fed us all
> Lies silent now, and sober as ever.
> (quoted in Enright, 1983, p.130)

In passing, you should note that this picture of diminishing publicity of funerals is not true for the USA. There, funeral parlours have become big business, embalming is common, and it is customary for the corpse to be made as life-like as possible for the 'viewing' by the family and friends. Coffins are ornate and burial is preferred to cremation. So much is this so that there has been an outburst of satirical writing on the subject, and there is considerable opposition among intellectuals to what they consider to be the 'exploitation' of grief and death.

After the funeral

It was after the funeral that Gorer noticed the greatest changes in mourning rituals. When his father died in 1915 he was given black ties and had bands of crepe sewn onto the sleeves of his suit. His mother wore the full panoply of widow's weeds in unrelieved black with a crepe veil shrouding her face. As time passed,

> . . . she followed scrupulously the modification of her outdoor costume, the shortening and abandoning of the veil, the addition of a touch of white at proper calendrical moments. It would have been unthinkable at that date for a respectable woman to do otherwise. In early 1917, when she could otherwise have worn some colour, her father died at a ripe old age and she had to return to black for a further six months. (Gorer, 1965, p.5)

During the time of mourning she was treated as 'different', and needing support and compassion. She would also have refused all invitations and avoided public places for the first year, before gradually resuming her place in society.

This custom of mourning clothes began to disappear at the end of the First World War and is now rare. In fact Gorer found there were virtually no outward demonstrations of grief after the funeral or ritualisation of mourning in his sample, except among Orthodox Jews, where relatives follow a set pattern of mourning for eleven months after the death. The most intensive period is just after the funeral when the closest relatives sit at the dead person's home each day from sunrise to sunset for a week. During that time they wear an old garment that has been torn, they move as little as possible and do no work at all. During this seven days of intensive mourning, prayers are said frequently. Visitors come bringing ritual food for the mourners to eat. They greet the mourners briefly, then talk to each mourner about the person they have lost.

Orthodox Jews in Gorer's study made these comments about this week of grieving:

> It is amazing how these visits comfort you. They talk to you and start discussing the person you have lost; picture albums are brought out and everyone reminds you of little episodes in their lives. Suddenly one laughs and enjoys those memories. One's grief is lightened; it is a most healing and comforting week. Brothers and sisters who have drifted apart come together again and recall good memories. It is a comfort . . .
>
> Well, you do these things, you don't worry about them . . . It's actually a good thing; the week of grief gives you time to get over all the worry and what not . . . Even though it seems outlandish at the time — it really is a help — you're away for a week and get over all your grief. You get it all concentrated in one week . . . I always thought before [his first wife died] it was a waste of time; but you realize when you go through it that it isn't really; it's there for a purpose. (Gorer, 1965, p.75)

For most people in Britain there is no such prescribed ritual: people choose their own method and time-scale for their grief. Some people in Gorer's study kept up old traditions such as mourning clothes, and giving up socialising, but the majority kept their grief private. Some tried to keep busy and pursue life as normal in order to overcome their grief; others expressed their grief but kept it private and in the home. Nearly always, public grief was considered unacceptable, and many people worried about the possibility of breaking down in public.

> Meeting people was terrible, that's why I had to go to the doctor's; I couldn't face them at all. As long as they stop and say, 'how are you?' — that's enough . . . But my husband was a very popular man, and lots of people stopped me whom I didn't know. It made me cry. Anyway, I stopped taking a handkerchief with me, thinking I wouldn't cry if I hadn't got one. (Gorer, 1965, p.60)

Gorer, himself, had experienced society's dislike of expressing grief after his brother died:

> A couple of times I refused invitations to cocktail

parties, explaining that I was in mourning; the people who invited me responded to this statement with shocked embarrassment, as if I had voiced some appalling obscenity. Indeed, I got the impression that, had I stated that the invitation clashed with some esoteric debauchery I had arranged, I would have had understanding and jocular encouragement; as it was the people whose invitations I had refused, educated and sophisticated as they were, mumbled and hurried away. They clearly no longer had any guidance from ritual as to the way to treat a self-confessed mourner; and, I suspect, they were frightened lest I give way to my grief, and involve them in a dreadful upsurge of emotion. (Gorer, 1965, p.14)

One custom after a burial does remain — the visit to the cemetery. It is common for those who bury their dead to erect a gravestone and visit it at regular intervals, sometimes weekly, to lay flowers on the grave. In general, cremation obviates such a custom, though some relatives visit annually when the Book of Remembrance is open at the page with the name of their relative inscribed. Some families also send memorial notices to the local newspaper on the anniversary of a relative's death.

It is interesting to see how people behave, but it is also important to look at the reasons for their behaviour. A lot has been written on this subject: we shall pick out just two important factors that underly changing attitudes to death in the UK — the relative decline in death rates, and the decline in a common belief in an afterlife.

How common is death?

Intuitively one would imagine that, since we all die, the frequency of death should be fairly constant. In fact this is not so: the *crude death rate* in 1869 was 22.6 per thousand whereas in 1969 it was 11.6. (If you find this confusing remember that the death rate is the number of deaths per thousand people in the population. If people live longer, on average, then the death rate is lower.)

Death is now half as common in the UK as it was a century ago, and moreover usually occurs in old age. This sort of death is considered 'natural' and far more acceptable than the death of a young person. It has not always been like this. The idea of the natural death of old age only appeared in Europe in the sixteenth century. Montaigne, the French humanist and essayist (1533–92), ridiculed the idea:

> What an idle conceit it is to expect to die of a decay of strength, which is the effect of the extremist age, and to propose to ourselves no shorter lease on life ... as if it were contrary to nature to see a man break his neck with a fall, be drowned by shipwreck, to be snatched away with pleurisy or the plague ... we ought rather to call natural death that which is general, common, and universal.

Death by accident or illness was common and was received with resignation rather than outrage: 'I have lost two or three children in their infancy, not without regret, but without great sorrow.' (Montaigne, quoted by Parkes, 1975, p.148). Similar acceptance is expressed by this description of a nineteenth-century Irish mother mourning the death of the sixth and last of her sons:

> They've all gone now, and there isn't anything more the sea can do to me ... They're altogether this time, and the end is come. May the Almighty God have mercy on Bartley's soul and on Michael's soul, and on the souls of Sheamus and Patch, and Stephen and Shawn, and may he have mercy on my soul, and on the soul of everyone left living in the world ... Michael has a clean burial in the far north, by the grace of the Almighty God. Bartley will have a fine coffin out of the white boards and a deep grave surely. What more can we want than that. No man can be living for ever, and we must be satisfied. (J.M. Synge (1871–1909), *Riders to the Sea*, quoted in Enright, 1983, pp.109–10)

By comparison, in the UK nowadays, the death of a child or young adult is a profoundly shocking event. This, and the small size of families, means that many people in the UK have not experienced the death of a close relative, even an old one. They have had little practice in grieving, and may be bewildered by their own emotions when they do finally lose someone they love.

What happens after death?

'Death is not lived through', said the philospher Ludwig Wittgenstein (1889–1951), but lack of empirical evidence has not prevented numerous types of belief in an afterlife.

□ Look back to Figure 18.1a. What do you think were the dying man's beliefs about life after death, and how would it affect his attitude to death?

■ When he dies he believes he will go either to heaven or to hell, depending on the manner of his life and death. It is his responsibility to make a good confession, renounce the things of this world and make a 'good death'. The priest, family and friends will help with their prayers.

The population in the UK is very unusual in having no such dominant belief in an afterlife, but instead a wide range of individual variations. In his study, Gorer found that one quarter of people thought there was no life after death: one quarter were uncertain; only seven per cent believed in a Christian afterlife; nine per cent believed in reincarnation; the rest thought there was life after death but were not sure

Fury in village over churchyard party plan

They will be dancing on my father's grave

By STEVE BRENNAN

A VILLAGE has been split in a row over a church barbecue and dance.

For the revellers are planning to dance on the graves of people buried there.

And relatives of the dead are outraged.

The barbecue, at St Laurence Parish Church, Winslow, is advertised in the parish magazine.

But the son of a war hero buried in the churchyard wants the event cancelled.

Jock Isham, of Lowndes Way, Winslow, whose father died in World War I said: "I can hardly believe it. They are planning to dance on my father's grave."

Many of the gravestones have been removed from the churchyard and the graves grassed over to form a lawn.

No harm

The plan is for a barbecue, country dancing, food and drink inclusive on September 3.

Mr Isham's wife, Anne, said: "It has broken his heart. He says there is no way they are going to dance on his father's grave."

Neighbour, Mrs Lena Hall, said: "Everybody you speak to is against it. Even regular churchgoers who are friendly with the vicar don't like it."

But the Reverend Arthur Barnes can see no harm in the dancing.

He said: "I don't think Mr Isham's father would object.

"There are only bones there now, the spirit has long gone."

Mr Isham, however, does object. He said: "Nobody with any commonsense would have dances on consecrated ground."

Tickets, priced at £2.00 for adults and £1.00 for OAPs and children, are being sold in local shops and at the church. There are no plans to cancel the barbecue.

CHURCH: St Laurence, Winslow.

Figure 18.2 Some people in the UK feel that the body of a dead friend or relative should be respected because the identity of the dead person persists in the body long after death. (Photo: *Milton Keynes Mirror*.)

of what sort. Other studies have found varying beliefs, depending on the questions asked, but usually suggest that a belief in the afterlife is declining faster than a belief in God, and that the belief in Judgement or Hell has virtually disappeared (though the absence of such studies in the past makes comparisons difficult). It is worth noting that an individual's beliefs are not necessarily static: a study of 360 terminally ill patients showed that 84 per cent accepted the possibility of an afterlife compared with only 33 per cent of a control group that were *not* facing death (Witzel, 1975).

A similar ambivalence is shown by people's attitudes to the graves of their dead. Though most people will say that a dead body is no longer a 'person', remarks such as 'I worry about him out there in the rain', or 'I wanted him buried where he would be remembered and respected' do not suggest that death is final. Figure 18.2 shows the headlines of a local newspaper announcing opposition to a barbecue planned in a (deconsecrated) church yard, as 'disrespectful' to the dead bodies buried there.

Such attitudes recall the early medieval ideas of 'the sleep of the dead' when bodies were considered to keep some residual lower order of consciousness. Pope Urban VIII, after he had died and been buried, was exhumed, tried for simony*, and punished by having his right hand cut off.

□ What consequences do you think the modern uncertainty about the nature of death might have for a dying person?

■ It is likely to make them more afraid. In fact one study (Witzel, 1975) has shown that people with a weak belief in an afterlife are more anxious about dying than either those with a strong belief in life after death or a strong belief that death is the end of existence. Uncertainty about life after death makes it difficult to prepare for: twentieth-century people do not, for instance, have the set task of a final confession and renunciation of the world, laid down in fifteenth-century society as the proper preparation for death.

Conclusions and consequences

□ Having read the previous pages on 'Society and Death', what would you pick out as the major characteristics that Gorer's study showed about customs surrounding death in the UK?

■ Death is less public and less familiar than in the past. Mourning is kept private, and follows no set pattern (except in some religious groups). Beliefs about the nature of death vary widely.

Gorer suggested that death had become not only *unfamiliar* but *hidden*, and that death and mourning are now treated with the same prudery as were sexual impulses a century ago. Other writers have since agreed that death is 'denied' in Western Europe and North America: despite medical and technical advances death remains 'undefeated'. As such, it is kept hidden as much as possible. Since Gorer's study in the 1960s there has been considerable academic and media coverage of death and dying, but it is still true to say that it remains a taboo subject in everyday life.

□ We have already mentioned some effects of this taboo on the bereaved and their acquaintances. What were these?

■ Bereaved people have no set pattern of mourning but must create their own. Some are embarrassed about crying, both in public and in private, and try to drive their grief away by 'keeping busy'. Friends and acquaintances do not know how to treat people who are bereaved, and may avoid them.

Psychologists who work with bereaved people generally deplore these effects, saying that the expression of grief helps the mourner to accept the death that has occurred, and that more, not less, contact with friends is needed in the time of mourning. Most do not, however, favour a return to a rigid system of public mourning (which did not allow for different people's needs) but aim to give bereavement enough publicity so that people are more conversant with its effects, and less embarrassed by its emotional demands.

*Buying or selling of ecclesiastical preferment.

Other writers have looked at slightly different aspects of the 'hidden' nature of death in Western Europe and North America. Philippe Aries, for instance, suggests that death has become an embarrassment — 'the scandal we are unable to prevent' — one of the forces or experiences that have proved resistant to control by powerful technology. He notes also that the practical details of death have become distasteful — the smells and sounds of a dying person are considered offensive — and suggests that these two sources of embarrassment about death may explain why death is becoming more and more confined to hospitals and 'distanced' from the community. Ivan Illich has gone further in describing this 'medicalisation' of death as part of the process by which doctors have 'expropriated' people's health — he notes that now 'the doctor, rather than the patient, struggles with death.'

You may think that this medicalisation of dying is a good or a bad thing but it is certainly true that the experience of dying is now intimately related to the medical care that is received. In the next chapter, we shall be considering this aspect of medicine, the care of the dying by health professionals.

Objectives for Chapter 18

After you have studied this chapter, you should be able to:

18.1 Describe the way in which people in the UK bury and mourn their dead, and in what way death can be said to be 'denied' in the UK.

18.2 Describe the effects that the 'hidden' nature of death may have on the experience of bereavement.

Questions for Chapter 18

1 (*Objectives 18.1 and 18.2*)

> They probably felt a little bit embarrassed; I'd have felt a little bit embarrassed. When I've met people before, I've thought: 'Oh dear, what shall I say? Shall I look the other way?' and I think my neighbours have felt the same ... I think people tend to be embarrassed if you speak to them; they feel they must say something, and they don't quite know how to say it. (A woman who had lost her husband, quoted in Gorer, 1965, p.59)

Explain why some people in the UK, like this woman, feel embarrassed about a bereavement.

19

The medical management of dying

This chapter is the last on death and dying. As you study it, you will be asked to read the article 'Caring for the spouse who died' in the Course Reader taken from *Life After A Death* by Ann Bowling and Ann Cartwright (Part 6, Section 6.5). You will also be asked to listen to the audiotape sequence 'Ethical dilemmas' starting on audiocassette AC805, Band 5. (This audiotape sequence can be omitted if you are short of time.)

The majority of people now die in hospitals. Over the last twenty years health professionals have begun to realise that the dying are not always well treated there, or at home; that their emotional needs are not always met, and their medical management is not always appropriate to the fact that they have an incurable illness. In 1963 John Hinton, a London psychiatrist, studied a group of dying patients and compared their feelings and sufferings with a control group, also in hospital, with severe non-fatal illnesses. He found the dying group were more likely to experience distressing symptoms which were not well-controlled medically; more than half the dying suffered from a distressing degree of depression, and the degree of depression was clearly related to the severity of their physical symptoms. He also found that three-quarters of this group knew that death was possible or probable, although they had not been told this was so (Hinton, 1963).

Studies such as these highlighted the inadequacies of the care and knowledge of dying patients in the 1960s and inspired some doctors and nurses to regard the care of dying patients as a branch of medical care requiring special skills. One result of this interest has been the establishment of *hospices* for the dying. These are usually separate from NHS general hospitals and are largely supported by charity. In addition to providing specialised nursing care, they are centres for research into the best control of symptoms in incurable illnesses. Hospices may act as advisory services for GPs and hospital doctors, and some run domiciliary nursing services. All this has had a profound though patchy effect on the care of dying patients in general hospitals, but many of the inadequacies described by Hinton still remain. There are reasons for this as we shall see.

The emotional support of the dying and their relatives

□ From what you've read in the previous chapter, what reasons can you suggest for dying people not getting much emotional support?

■ Health workers may share in the dislike of discussing death that Gorer found to be prevalent in his study. They may also be reluctant to face up to the *possibility* of death in their patients.

This fact was illustrated when the psychiatrist Elizabeth Kübler-Ross first started her research in America in the 1960s. Her request to hospital authorities for permission to interview the dying was refused with the reply, 'There are no dying patients here' (quoted in Ariès, 1983, p.589). This statement reflected the attitudes of the medical profession, whose practice and training concentrated on the *diagnosis* and *cure* of illness, ignoring the fact that though many patients cannot be cured, they still need medical and nursing *care*.

This concentration on *cures* may make doctors (and nurses) very uncomfortable with dying patients; they may feel they have 'failed' them and hence find it embarrassing to talk to them. This problem is compounded if patients do not know that they are dying, since all conversations then involve deception. One young doctor spoke of her difficulties in these situations (when she had been instructed not to reveal the truth):

> I just find it very difficult to get close to someone if I feel I'm not being truthful. How can I put my arm round a dying woman and tell her lies about how she's progressing? I find myself avoiding her bed, walking down the other side of the ward, or, if I have to go near, I make bright and meaningless conversation to keep any real questions at bay. (Milton Keynes doctor, 1984)

This lack of honesty used to be the rule, though, as Hinton found, many dying patients had a good idea of their prognosis. Usually a relative was told instead and this custom is still continued by some doctors, who feel the truth is too cruel and may cause anxiety and grief. Others now feel that such deceit is very hard on the relatives who have to lie to the ill person. In Gorer's study several widows remarked how hard it was to maintain this deception: 'I knew he was dying but he didn't ... It was terrible having to lie to him; I had to be cruel really. I was abrupt with him sort of, or I would have broke down.' (quoted in Gorer, 1965, p.18), and again:

> He was ill for 22 months with cancer. I knew, but he didn't ... It was a great strain; I'd break down when he was upstairs. Now I think: 'Did I do right not to tell him? ... It was very hard ... He used to ask me if he was going to get well ... My doctor said *he* wasn't going to tell him, and the hospital wouldn't either, so if I tell him, he's not going to have much faith in the hospital is he? It's just one of those things. I told him awful lies. (quoted in Gorer, 1965, p.18)

This conspiracy of silence is often not effective: people who are gradually getting weaker are unlikely to believe they are being cured.* Colin Murray Parkes, a British psychiatrist who has researched into bereavement and dying, suggests that, even when these benevolent conspiracies work, they are unnecessary.

> Experience has repeatedly shown that if a person is given the opportunity to learn the facts of his case, little by little, at his own pace, and provided he is encouraged to share with others the feelings which these facts evoke, and provided that others are not constantly feeding back to him their own fears, he will move progressively closer to a full realisation of the situation without suffering overwhelming panic and despair. (Parkes, quoted in Saunders, 1978, p.50)

Such attitudes and practices are becoming much more common but it is still true that nurses and doctors may find it difficult to be honest about incurable illness and supportive to patients and their relatives. Murray Parkes suggests that they cannot do so until they have come to terms to some extent with the idea of their own death. But this is perhaps easier said than done. To test your attitudes to the idea of death try to decide how you would set about telling a twenty-three year old woman with two children under the age of three that her twenty-six year old husband has been knocked off his bike and has died a few minutes after arriving at the local hospital. You may find it helpful to write down how you would start and what you would say and do.

You would be unusual if this exercise did not make you feel very uncomfortable — doctors tend to feel just as bad. A doctor describes how the job of telling such a wife of her husband's sudden death fell to her in the first fortnight of her first job after qualifying:

> My SHO [her immediate senior] said to me, 'His wife and parents are in the Casualty department. Come down with me.' I was still shaking from the events of the last hour [when they had been working, unsuccessfully to save the injured man's life] and we walked in silence down to Casualty. When we arrived there my SHO (a man) said 'I'll tell the father, you talk to the women,' and he went up to them and detached off the man, leaving me standing looking at these two women who were sat on two chairs in a cubicle looking up at me expectantly — they'd just been told to come to the hospital and had no idea it

*Dilemmas about truthfulness in relationships with cancer patients are discussed in Book VI *Experiencing and Explaining Disease*, Chapter 5.

> was serious. I'm not sure exactly what I said, but I do remember standing rigidly and forcing out the words — something like, 'You know your husband had an accident. Well, I'm afraid it's more serious than that. He had a very bad injury to his head and ... he died ... he's dead.' I may not remember my words but I'll never forget hers — she just sat for a second frozen and then screamed out, 'He can't die, he can't die. Who'll look after the children?' Then they both sat there stricken and silent, and I stood there also silent. Finally, the wife stood up, completely calm and quiet she shook my hand and said, 'Thank you for your kindness' and walked off with her mother. (Milton Keynes doctor, 1984)

Telling this sort of bad news is not easy, nor is telling a person of their own fatal illness. It is perhaps not surprising that many doctors are unable to give emotional support to relatives, or to patients of theirs who are dying. Dying in hospital may be a lonely business, as this poem describes:

> It begins with an easy voice saying,
> Just a routine examination;
> as October sunlight
> pierces the heavy velvet curtains.
>
> Later it is the friends who write but do not visit,
> it is (after all these years)
> getting thinner,
> it is boiled fish,
> it is a folded screen in the corner,
> it is doctors who no longer stop by your bed
> but only say 'Good-night' or 'Good morning';
> it is terror every minute of conscious night and day to
> a background of pop music.
> It is trying not to think of it.
>
> At the end you are left with the thought
> that from Mozart to Siegfried Sassoon
> all the people you respect
> are dead anyway.
>
> (Lyall Wilkes, 'Nightmare' quoted in Enright, 1983, p,76)

Attitudes in the medical profession *are* changing. Recently, some medical schools have started formal training on how to deal with death and dying, and many health professionals who have learnt to be honest about death, have found such truthfulness preferable to false encouragement. It is, however, possible that a new danger is emerging as these attitudes become more widespread. Such new, trained doctors and nurses can now 'cope' with people's fear or grief or anger, and are eager to see them through to a peaceful acceptance of death. As with any established view, there is a danger that it will be applied to people who do not want it. Some people (approximately half, according to several studies) prefer not to know they are dying; some wish to stay angry and not to become resigned. Whereas those experienced in the care of the dying accept these variations and try, as far as their insight and experience allow them, to treat people as they wish, there are as yet no hospices designed to help people deny the fact of death with frivolity and indulgence — none with a cabaret each night at the end of the ward and with nurses dressed as bunny-girls, or Italian waiters. And the fact that the idea of such an institution is shocking, demonstrates that our new idea of an aware and peaceful death, may be as oppressive to some people as was the old system of a conspiracy of silence.

The medical treatment of the dying

The need to cure may make doctors ignore the dying patient, but it may have another effect — that of over-treatment, a phenomenon made possible by relatively simple technology and drugs by which life can be extended even in a patient with a fatal illness. To give a simple example, patients may stop drinking much as they get weaker from their main incurable illness. Dehydration will be one factor in finally causing their death but can be prevented by giving fluid directly into a vein — a standard hospital procedure in many short-term illnesses. Similarly, the immediate cause of death in a person dying from cancer or old age may be bronchopneumonia (infection in the bronchi of the lungs) caused because they are too weak to cough properly. This illness used to be called 'the old man's friend' because it is a quick and painless end to life, but it can be treated, and sometimes cured, by antibiotics and physiotherapy. Where such treatments are routine hospital practice for anybody with a chest infection, it takes a positive decision *not* to use them even for patients where the extension of life will be short and uncomfortable. It is the junior doctors, qualified for a year, who are called to see patients when they first develop a cough; it may be easier for them to start treatment than to ring up their boss, perhaps at night, to ask if they are allowed *not* to give antibiotics in this case. A decision such as this, which involves withholding simple treatments that would probably prolong life, may be seen as immoral by some staff members. You will hear more about such ethical problems in the last section of this chapter.

Sometimes it is hard for doctors and nurses to stop treatments even when they are clearly not working. Anti-cancer drugs, for instance, which frequently cause nausea and vomiting, may be continued after it is clear that the cancer is not responding to them, in the hope that some miracle may occur, or because it is easier to do *something* than to admit that there is no longer hope of a cure. There has been much debate in recent years about the point at which treatment of terminal cancer should switch from *'cure' techniques* to *care of symptoms* only, but there has been less discussion in other serious illnesses, especially if there is some hope of recovery. In such cases, intensive treatment is often started. If the patient lives it all seems worthwhile, but he or she may eventually die amidst a host of tubes, support machines and monitors. There is little dignity or peace in such a death, and it may be extremely distressing for the patient and relatives. On the other hand, they may find it comforting that 'they did everything they could'. There are no easy answers to such problems, but it is worth noting that in one hospital in Boston, USA, 30 per cent of people who had undergone successful emergency resuscitation when their hearts stopped, said they had not wished for such treatment and would not welcome it again (Bedell and del Banco, 1984, p.1089–23).

Dying patients may be over-treated to keep them alive; in some aspects, such as pain-relief, they may be *under*-treated to keep them alive. Inadequate pain-killing drugs may be given for two reasons. First, nearly all the opiates (pain-killers like heroin and morphine) depress respiration (that is they cause shallow breathing), which makes getting bronchopneumonia slightly more likely. They could, therefore, be said to hasten death. Some people have moral objections to giving a drug which, though necessary to control pain, may shorten life. The second reason for inadequate pain relief is the fear of addiction to opiates. Forty per cent of cancer patients suffer pain at some stage of the disease, and if this is severe, large doses of opiates may be needed at regular intervals to control it adequately. This may be disturbing to nurses and doctors who are used to dispensing such drugs for temporary pain, under strict control for only short periods of time. Research at St. Christopher's Hospice in London has now shown that addiction (the need to increase the dose to get the same effect) does not occur when morphine and heroin are used for pain control (Saunders, 1978, pp.82–85). In fact, once pain has been controlled and the fear of pain removed, the dose can often be reduced to a lower maintenance level. This information is gradually becoming more widely known and *pain control* in terminal care *is* improving.

Pain is not the only distressing symptom that may afflict the dying person. Nausea and breathlessness can occur and there are other less common discomforts. Treatment of these has also improved and in nearly all cases a person *should* be able to die without much discomfort, but access to this quality of care is limited — there are now (1984) about eighty hospices for the dying in the UK but their size and the extent of their domiciliary or advisory service varies. Hospital doctors and general practitioners vary in their knowledge of these new developments in the medical care of the dying, and not all dying patients in hospital or at home receive the benefits of the new expertise.

Dying at home

So far you have read primarily of the reasons for inadequacies in the care of the dying in hospitals, but one third of people still die at home, some after a long illness. Once again the professional care that is given varies in different places. Some hospices work with local GPs to give extensive help in medical and nursing care at home. Some general practitioners and district nurses are skilled in the care of the dying and good at mobilising local authority services to help in the care of a sick person at home. But this is by no means always the case, and there is often little support either for the person who is dying or for their relatives who shoulder the responsibility of care. Some of the problems they may have are described in the article in the Course Reader by Ann Bowling and Ann Cartwright, who undertook a survey of people who had cared for a relative who subsequently died. Although many had received help from doctors and nurses, for many the illness had proved a considerable burden. You should now read this article (Course Reader, Part 6, Section 6.5)*, which has been edited to show particularly the strains on the relatives at home.

□ What, in the article, were the main difficulties experienced by relatives in caring for someone at home?

■ The main difficulties were: (i) inadequate help in heavy duties such as lifting; (ii) not enough help with laundry; (iii) no free time; (iv) loneliness and isolation; (v) extra expense; (vi) the stress of having the major responsibility for someone's comfort when they were themselves rather frail or in poor health.

Community care for the dying is improving. The problems are better recognised by professionals, and specific services for the dying are increasing (though from Chapter 16 you will remember that many NHS and local authority community services have recently been reduced). As the Reader article shows, however, there is a considerable way to go before death with dignity at home is a possibility for all those who wish for it.

Death and medical ethics

Several of the situations discussed in this chapter may lead to a moral or ethical problem for doctors or nurses: for instance, whether or when to stop life-extending treatment in a dying patient, and whether to give drugs which relieve symptoms but may hasten death. These problems are just a few of many that have arisen with the introduction of more effective drugs and therapies in medicine. The problems lie in two main areas: in the definition of life and

*Nick Black *et.al.* (eds) (1984) *Health and Disease: A Reader*, The Open University Press.

death, and in the treatment to be given to those with severe, incapacitating or fatal illness.

Defining life and death causes problems at both ends of the lifespan. Different groups hold that life begins at the moment of conception (when the sperm enters the female ovum), or when the rudimentary nervous system is laid down (and the fetus might be considered to have an 'awareness' of its surroundings), or when the fetus can survive outside the womb (at between 23–28 weeks of pregnancy). Such diversity of opinion has led to controversy, for instance about the rights and wrongs of *elective abortion* (and the time of pregnancy at which it is acceptable). The 1967 Abortion Act States that abortion is permissible when the continuation of the pregnancy would involve risk to the physical or mental health of the pregnant woman greater than if the pregnancy were terminated. The decision as to the pregnancy's effect on the woman's physical or mental health is left up to the doctors involved (and statistically, a pregnancy completed to delivery carries a higher risk than abortion).

□ What consequences do you think the vagueness of this wording might have on the way in which different doctors treat women's requests for abortion?

■ Doctors with different attitudes to the ethics of abortion will interpret the Abortion Act differently. Such differences of practice always occurs when there are widespread differences in attitudes and the legal guidelines are imprecise.

In fact, as you read in Chapter 11, there are marked regional variations in Britain in the extent to which abortion is available on the NHS. These differences are thought to partly reflect the differences in attitude of gynaecologists (and GPs) to the acceptability of abortion.

At the other end of life the definition of death is not always easy — there is no legal definition.

□ In Chapter 17 you read of the usual criteria used to establish that death had occurred. What were they?

■ Cessation of breathing and heart beat.

Such a definition was adequate for many years until the introduction of machines (ventilators) which could pump air into a person's lungs. Consider a person with a severe head injury who stops breathing because of damage to the respiratory centre in the brain. This injury would normally lead to death, but, if a ventilator is used to keep their lungs full of oxygen, then the oxygen level in the blood is kept at the normal level and the heart will continue to beat. Although the person is deeply unconscious, because of brain damage, the rest of their body is 'alive': at least, it is performing the many biochemical reactions that maintain life, and needs to be given food and water to fuel these reactions. So, is this person alive or dead? And, following from this question, how long should they be kept on the ventilator? How much does their nursing care cost? Is it a 'good' use of money? And, finally, could their organs be used for transplants?

In finding answers to these questions, a new way of defining death has emerged, using the idea of *brain death*, which really refers to a state when the brain stem is not functioning. (The brain stem is that part of the brain which is responsible for the control of breathing, blood-pressure and other very basic functions, without which an independent existence is impossible.) Various tests on the unconscious patient can test the function of the brain stem. If it is not functioning because of brain damage then recovery is deemed to be impossible, the person is technically dead and the ventilator can be switched off, and any organs used for transplant surgery (provided the person expressed a wish for this, and/or their relatives agree).

Because of public concern that the demand for organs for transplant operations might mean that people are certified as 'brain-dead' with undue haste and insufficient care, a Working Party for the Health Departments of Great Britain and Northern Ireland have laid down a code of practice for the procedure, suggesting among other things that the tests of brain-stem function must be made by two independent, experienced doctors (who are not members of a transplant team) on two successive occasions (often 24 hours apart).

However, no such clear code of practice exists where someone is deeply unconscious and on a ventilator following a head injury, but whose brain stem retains some function. How long should one continue to keep such people alive, bearing in mind that occasional, unexpected recoveries do occur? This type of problem leads onto the second type of ethical dilemma to do with death and dying — the amount of treatment to give to people with a fatal illness, brain damage, or severe disability.

Traditionally, doctors were enjoined to save lives first and foremost, but many people now agree that this is no longer a sufficient guide-line, since the life prolonged may be painful, or so restricted that it seems not worth living to the person concerned. Pope Pius XII in 1957 stated the Roman Catholic point of view when he said that doctors were not obliged to give, nor patients to accept, 'extraordinary medical measures', but this phrase can be interpreted in different ways. English law allows a doctor, if he or she can no longer hold back the approach of death, to take measures that may hasten death, provided the doctor's aim is only the relief of pain; it is not however permissible to take measures specifically *aimed* at hastening death.

In practice, decisions are made on an ad-hoc basis, with underlying principles varying from team to team, from those with the attitude that life should be preserved at all cost, to those who consider that the quality of future life is of decisive importance. The range of attitudes evokes a range of public concern. Some groups such as 'Life' feel that there are many instances of immoral lack of treatment (or treatment designed to kill) and have instituted legal proceedings against doctors whom they feel have acted criminally in allowing and encouraging, for instance, a severely disabled baby to die. Other groups, such as the Euthanasia Society feel that medical treatment often condemns people to a life of unbearable suffering. The Voluntary Euthanasia Society of Scotland has issued cards which its members can sign while in good health, asking:

> If there is no reasonable prospect of my recovery from physical illness or impairment expected to cause me severe distress or to render me incapable of rational existence, I request that I be allowed to die and not be kept alive by artificial means and that I receive whatever quantity of drugs may be required to keep me free from pain or distress even if the moment of death is hastened.

□ What problem might there be in interpreting this request?

■ 'Rational existence' and 'reasonable hope of recovery' are not clearly definable. Their interpretation will depend again on the personalities, moral views and special skills of the people actually treating the patient.

Like abortion, this is an area where there is a wide range of opinion of the rights and wrongs of this subject. To illustrate this point there is an audiotape sequence with parts of a discussion between doctors, nurses, social workers, and lawyers over the correct treatment of severely damaged babies. You should now listen to this audiotape sequence, 'Ethical dilemmas' on Audiocassettes AC805, Band 5 and AC806 Band 1 and then answer the following question.

□ On what points did the various people disagree?

■ There were disagreements on the following points:

1 *Whether* to give normal life-saving treatment (the newborn baby with broken bones, and the handicapped baby with obstruction of the bowel) when there was doubt about the eventual outcome.

2 *How much* treatment to give the baby, as in the case of the child with spina bifida. Here there was agreement about not attempting surgical repair (since the condition has been well studied and the outcomes are well known) but no agreement about whether to treat infections, whether to feed with milk or water, and how much sedation or pain control to give.

3 The *legal* aspects of the case, as to who had the right to make these difficult decisions; though the Lord of Appeal was clear that the law says that life must be preserved and the parents do not have the right to refuse an operation for their child.

This brief discussion can give you only a glimpse into the many complex problems created by new techniques in medicine. For some problems a consensus has evolved (within the health professions, at least), for example, on use of opiates in terminal illness, the immediate treatment of various degrees of spina bifida, and the certification of brain-death. However, for many less common situations, no such consensus exists, and doctors must make up their own minds according to their own experience, ethics, and concerns about possible litigation.

Objectives for Chapter 19

After you have studied this chapter, you should be able to:

19.1 Discuss the ways in which our culture's fear of death and the emphasis in medical training on diagnosis and cure may lead to poor emotional support and medical management for dying patients, and in what ways this type of care has changed in the last twenty years.

19.2 Discuss the problems that arise from the difficulties in defining life and death, and from the lack of consensus over the criteria to be used in decisions in the treatment of severely handicapped or terminally ill babies and adults.

Question for Chapter 19

1 (*Objectives 19.1 and 19.2*) Mrs H. is a widow of 84, reasonably fit physically but with severe senile dementia so that she requires constant supervision and bathing (because she is incontinent). She develops a chest infection and a doctor is called. He finds her lying in bed, drowsy, and apparently comfortable. He knows that she may die from her chest infection, and that giving antibiotics might cure it.

What factors do you think might influence his decision as to whether to give her antibiotics? (Try to think of all the factors you have met in the last three chapters that might affect this decision.)

20

Crises of identity: a lifelong challenge

This chapter draws together the major themes of Book V and reviews the lifespan in terms of the incidence of inevitable and unexpected changes. You may find it helpful to look back at Book IV, *The Biology of Health and Disease*, Chapter 15, where the effects of stress on health were discussed. Parallels are drawn between the effect of bereavement (Chapter 17), and the response to other forms of loss. An audiotape sequence, 'Reactions to loss', on cassette AC806, Band 2, accompanies this chapter.

Some discouragement, some faintness of heart at the new real future which replaces the imaginary, is not unusual, and we do not expect people to be deeply moved by what is not unusual. That element of tragedy which lies in the very fact of frequency, has not yet wrought itself into the coarse emotion of mankind; and perhaps our frames could hardly bear much of it. If we had a keen vision and feeling of all ordinary human life, it would be like hearing the grass grow and the squirrel's heart beat, and we should die of that roar which lies on the other side of silence. As it is, the quickest of us walk about well wadded with stupidity. (George Eliot, *Middlemarch*, 1872)

In this final chapter, we shall look back over the lifespan and focus both on the inevitability of change and the unpredictability of events. If health is not simply the absence of disease, but encompasses emotional wellbeing, then an ability to cope with change is an essential requirement for health — not as important perhaps as a nourishing diet, a safe water supply and adequate housing, but a significant contributor nonetheless, and one we call upon frequently in a lifetime.

□ What view of change is expressed in the extract from *Middlemarch*?

■ Eliot notes that it is usual to feel fainthearted at the prospect of change, but since it occurs so frequently, we treat it as commonplace; this very familiarity dulls us to the tragedy of life moving inexorably forward (by implication, to the grave). The smartest people close their eyes and ears to the painfulness of reality.

Everyone does this to some extent almost daily, as Eliot suggests — indeed life would be insupportably painful if we felt the full shock of tragedy at each act of cruelty, each accidental death, each famine or war reported in the news. But most people are not so 'well wadded about with stupidity' that they are immune to feeling when change touches them personally.

In this book we have drawn attention to the major turning points in a lifetime — the *life-course transitions* — which are experienced by all or many people in the UK. As you have seen throughout this book, the lifespan is divided up into a series of phases, delineated by chronological age and by biological or social watersheds such as puberty or voting age. Passing through one of these transitions can be an unsettling experience, especially if there is a significant loss of status, rights and responsibilities. As a consequence of this, some writers have argued that all such transitions are inherently problematic:

> There are immanent sources of conflict and tension in the very process of life-course transitions. Because ageing is inevitable and continuous, the society must accommodate the perpetual flow of one cohort into the array of social roles that is available. One possible solution is to allow natural forces to operate. Younger people assume adult roles when they are ready to do so; older people give up roles when they are ready or when they become ill and die. Another solution is to regulate this continuous flow of people by establishing firm norms for entering roles and leaving them: that is, by establishing clearly defined points of life-course transition. Both solutions are problematic and can have adverse consequences for the society: the first because there is no guarantee that the readiness of those who must give up roles fits in with the readiness of those who are waiting in the wings; the second, because the age-norms may not be in accord with individual needs or societal requirements ... In changing times, age-norms may not mesh with changes in supply and demand for role-players of given ages ... (Foner and Kertzer, 1978, p.1095)

Such a view seeks to explain, for example, delinquency in adolescence, or depression after childbirth, or insomnia in the first months of retirement as an expression of inner conflict as the person undergoes a profound change in status. The child becomes a young adult, the woman becomes a mother, the employee becomes a pensioner, and, in addition to the biological changes of puberty, pregnancy or ageing, they must cope with the cultural values and expectations associated with this 'new real future which replaces the imaginary'. Another Eliot has also written of this:

> See, now they vanish,
> The faces and places, with the self which, as it could, loved them,
> To become renewed, transfigured in another pattern.
> (T.S. Eliot, 'Little Gidding', III, lines 14–16)

Transitions, therefore, involve the loss of an old familiar *identity*, and the reconstruction of a new one. This is a disruptive experience in itself, but can be extremely distressing when society places a low value on the phase a person is entering. Thus distress during the menopause or the so-called mid-life crisis may in part flow from the low status accorded to those who are completing the transition to retirement and old age. Each of these transitions is forced upon us by the practice of stratifying our society on the basis of age — age-grading.

Much of this book has been about the complex interactions between biological and social factors that shape the ways in which each new phase of life is viewed by those outside it, and is experienced by those within. Personal history also plays a part in this — each of us has a particular view of childhood or being grown up which has been influenced by the people we have known and events that happened in our lives. But in addition to the more-or-less fixed points of transition determined by biological developments or social customs and laws, each of us also experiences a less predictable series of significant changes, some of them chosen, others totally unforeseen.

□ Suggest some examples.

■ Becoming a parent or grandparent for the first time; getting married or divorced; a major bereavement; a promotion or redundancy; a long illness or accidental injury.

Changes such as these are termed *life events* by sociologists, and are extremely common — each of us will experience at least one of them, and probably more, in a lifetime. How are these changes coped with? Do they present the same sort of conflicts about changing status as the more predictable transitions which all members of the society share at approximately the same age? Do they also involve a loss of identity and the need to construct a new one? Consider the following extracts from a series of interviews recorded by Ruth Jacobs, a sociologist at Stoke Mandeville Hospital in Buckinghamshire. Jacobs has been researching the ways in which people come to terms with sudden paralysis. The transcript below is from interviews conducted with a 25 year old man, paralysed from the waist down after a road traffic accident. The dates refer to the number of weeks that have elapsed since the injury.

2 weeks I feel beaten at the moment ... It's such a tragedy — all these blokes around here, all with broken backs. I feel so useless ... I don't feel I can face it ... It's the first time my body has let me down ... I'm a bit of a cynic, but one of the things about this has been that since the accident, everyone's been absolutely wonderful. One of the redeeming features of this has been that it's restored my faith in human nature a bit ... I used to shoot a lot, box, play rugby union — do all sorts of things like that. What sort of life am I going to have now?

3 weeks It's all very well to say 'any kind of life is a life' but it won't be *my* life. I could never be the same kind of man I was ... It's a matter of re-programming your life ... You're reborn. For 25 years I've worked at building up my character and image ... and now I'm going to have to start again. It's like being born again. But having done it once, no doubt one can do it again ... If I don't get any better, I'm going to have to tailor-make a character to suit my situation.

3½ weeks I'd do without my legs if I could get everything else back — control of bladder, bowels and sexual function. I wish I'd bloody died. Everything, everything I enjoyed doing I can no longer do. If there were any justice I'd have died in the accident. Instead of that I'm going to live a half-life for the rest of my life ... I believe in God and in a life hereafter ... and it's very difficult not to believe this is a punishment.

4 weeks I think I'm beginning to come round a bit. I was feeling a bit sorry for myself ... I must be coming round because I'm starting to think about the future ... I'm trying to come to terms with things a bit ... There are certain things I'll never accept — or should I say never like ... I've had quite a life when I think about it. I've no regrets.

6 weeks I admit the fact that I'm now crippled and will spend the greater part of my life in a wheelchair ... I've got to make a new life — though I don't yet know how I'm going to do it. I've got to start my life all over again.

7 weeks I must be getting better because I feel like getting out of bed and doing some mischief ... my mind is getting better. The human body can stand anything — it's the mind that gives way.

9 weeks I feel terrible this morning ... I feel as if I'm being imprisoned and yet I've done nothing. This morning I feel jailed. There are bars and I can't get out — I can't do what I want to do ... it must be so nice to walk out in the rain, and not be reliant on people to bring food, or do a loo, or ... I'm not depressed — I refuse to be depressed — I'm just bitter.

10 weeks I feel I've got this incredible power. I'm bloody indestructible. After going through this accident, my ego will be invincible ... It's no wonder people in wheelchairs are arrogant. If they survive, they *do* survive.

19 weeks I don't see any huge metamorphosis in myself, but I've gained patience ... For me, the whole thing is to become as near normal as you possibly can ... For me, the real work will begin when I leave [the hospital].

26 weeks (after being offered a job) You're back in living ... the wheels are turning ... I must admit it lifts your morale ... My confidence is coming back, and I'm going to live the same way I've always lived. I'm just going to bulldoze my way through.

The idea that he must build a new identity comes out very strongly in this man's account — he sees himself as having to give up certain rights and expectations associated with being active and athletic, and as 're-programming' his life instead to incorporate the paralysis and the wheelchair into his sense of self.

□ In what ways does his view of the able-bodied people around him change?

■ He begins by expressing gratitude — their kindness restores his faith in human nature. Later he feels bitter — they can take a walk in the rain, whereas he is reliant on them for the most basic functions. At one point he feels invincible, by implication stronger than people who have not had to survive such a devastating shock.

So the change in personal identity also means that the world looks different too. You were probably struck by the peaks of elation and troughs of despair which alternate as the weeks passed. This is reminiscent of the fluctuating emotions of Liz McNeill Taylor, whose account of coming to terms with her husband's unexpected death figured in Chapter 17.

□ Did you notice any other similarities between the response to paralysis (above) and the earlier discussion of bereavement in Chapter 17?

■ There are clear moments of pining for the lost life, 'I used to shoot a lot, box, play rugby union ... What sort of life am I going to have now?' He feels bitter at several points and, despite his denials, sounds depressed when he says 'I'm going to live a half-life for the rest of my life'. He feels like bargaining with his fate, 'I'd do without my legs if I could get everything else back', and feels that his accident could be a punishment. Finally, he begins to come to terms with the loss.

The similarity between grieving after a death and the response to physcial injury was investigated by Colin Murray Parkes, a British psychiatrist whose work on bereavement you met in Chapter 17. Parkes was one of the first to publish research in this field, in 1975, comparing the reactions of 21 widows with those of 46 amputees. Half of both groups reported initial numbness and a tendency to deny that the loss had happened. Later came similar phases of pining for the lost husband or for the way of life that seemed to have been lost along with the limb. Both groups expressed bitterness and phases of depression and had a tendency to evoke strong sensations of the dead husband or the amputated limb as being physically present. More than a year later, they showed similar rates of emotional disturbance.

Parkes has argued that a significant loss — whether it be of a person, a physical faculty, a way of life, or even a particular identity — precipitates rather similar states of grief, but that this fact has been neglected by doctors, with serious consequences for patients.

> I know of only one functional psychiatric disorder whose cause is known, whose features are distinctive, and whose course is usually predictable, and that is grief, the reaction to loss. Yet this condition has been so neglected by psychiatrists that it is not even mentioned in the indexes of most of the best-known general text books of psychiatry. (Parkes, 1978, p.20)

In his view, too little attention is paid to the crisis of identity which people experience when they pass through a significant turning point in life. Help tends to be restricted to the immediate practical details — finances, aids such as wheelchairs or artificial limbs, and so forth — often without recognising that the person is also suffering acute grief.

You should now listen to a short audiotape sequence, 'Reactions to loss,' on cassette AC806, Band 2, in which a number of people suffering very different states of loss talk about the period between learning the truth of what has happened and coming to terms with it, at least to some extent. Listen out for similarities in their accounts.

□ What was the most common reaction to the realisation of what happened?

■ Several speakers described shock, numbness and disbelief, followed by a rush of extremely powerful feelings, very like the reaction of someone hearing of a bereavement — for example:

> That was the darkest hour because the shock it was great, when he said 'you will never see again'. Well, you know, it was the end of the world ... weeks after I was shot, possibly I could have killed the man who shot me in cold blood, but time is a good healer. (Policeman blinded by gunshot while on duty)

> [The doctor] said 'You'll never walk again and the chances are you'll never move again' and I just didn't believe him — I would not believe him. I had no feeling at all, I didn't cry, I didn't weep, I wasn't brave — I was just numb ... One Friday evening my husband and son came straight from school ... my son walked down the ward and I looked at him and his tie was at half-mast, his top button open, and his collar was sort of sticking up — and I thought to myself, 'My God, here's a motherless boy. I'll never be able to wash a shirt, iron a shirt or put that child tidy again', and after they went I cried, and I cried literally for a month. (School teacher paralysed after a car crash)

> I thought 'I've been burgled'. So I started trembling and I couldn't sort of move, there was shock ... I wanted to tidy up but I couldn't, so I felt totally, a word that came to mind was naked, totally vulnerable ... [now] the main feeling is anger that I can't turn their heads through a hundred and eighty degrees. (Technician, 3 weeks after being burgled)

The man who had been burgled spoke of similarities between that experience and the break-up of his marriage several years before.

□ What were they?

■ His sense of identity had had to undergo a radical change following both these losses — not only was *he* a different person before and after, but the world looked different too. Of his divorce he says: 'I was a daddy you know, and I had a routine and a life — then all of a sudden you're a bachelor again and you're living in somebody's back bedroom and you've gotta compete, you know? You don't realise till you leave what you've lost.' Of the burglary he says: 'Walking in there and seeing all that — it was like suddenly seeing a gaping wound in your leg ... you don't realise how much your home is your little cave, your little security, until somebody comes in there, and it's not like that anymore.'

Overcoming the feeling of loss, anger and grief may be a lengthy process, as a young doctor suffering from multiple sclerosis records in a personal paper to the *British Medical Journal*:

> I have now accepted the disease to a greater extent and no longer feel either depressed or angry about it. It has been like a long drawn-out bereavement, and I have had to come to terms with loss of health and ability and also to establish a new identity. (Burnfield 1977, p.436).

In recent years the medical profession has begun to recognise that grief is a *normal* reaction to any loss which the person feels as significant:

> Depressive symptoms may occur in grief without necessarily indicating clinical depression requiring psychiatric treatment. Insomnia, anorexia, weight loss, inability to concentrate, restlessness, hyper-sensitivity, sadness, weeping and self-reproach are ... common in normal grief. (Peretz, quoted in Haney, 1977, p.227)

According to this view, the loss of health which inevitably

accompanies grief usually resolves as the person comes to terms with their loss, but can become chronic and deep-seated for some people unless appropriate help is offered. This need not necessarily involve medical intervention; skilled counselling can alleviate the prolongation of symptoms where the person is not getting adequate support from among their own circle of friends and relatives.*

Note that grief is not only experienced following a *tragic* loss — it may occur after *any* event which causes a significant disruption to a person's sense of self, even if the event looks like a *positive* change from the outside.

□ Can you think of examples?

■ Depression following the birth of a baby might fit this theory. You may also have experienced disorientation, anxiety or depression after moving house: even though the change may have been to better accommodation, it still means the loss of the old house and its memories, neighbours, the familiar shops and so forth. Promotion at work can have a similar effect — new responsibilities, new workmates.

The idea that 'positive' changes may be just as disorienting as 'negative' ones was first proposed by the French sociologist Emile Durkheim in the nineteenth century. As you read in Chapter 17, his classic study of suicide revealed that some people kill themselves when their social world alters out of all recognition, not only as a result of disasters, but also when the 'rules' of their life change after extraordinary good fortune. (In modern terms, the pools winner or overnight star might fit this description.)

There has been a very considerable research interest since the 1950s into the health consequences of life events, including births, deaths and marriages, house moves, changes of job, redundancy, retirement, children leaving home, etc. Most of this research has been in *case-control studies***; people suffering from a particular state of ill-health (the 'cases') have been interviewed to discover whether they experienced a higher incidence of significant life events prior to the illness, than people of the same age, sex and class who were not ill (the 'controls'). Such studies are usually *retrospective*, and rely on the subject's memory of events in the past.

□ How would you design a *prospective cohort study*?**

■ An initially healthy group of people of the same age, sex and class (that is a 'cohort') would be monitored for several years and each life-event and illness recorded to see if there was an association between the two.

*One of the 'risk-factors' for depression is the absence of a trusted confidant; Book VI, *Experiencing and Explaining Disease*, Chapter 8.

To date, results from such research have been conflicting, possibly because the methodological problems involved in designing studies which produce unambiguous answers are so great. Nonetheless, there are intriguing clues in the research literature, most of which relate to the onset of *psychiatric* illness following a significant loss, a life-course transition or an unusually high incidence of disorienting life events.

For example, psychiatrist Eugene Paykel and his colleagues at an American hospital published a study in 1975 of 274 people who had attempted suicide. They found that the incidence of significant life events in the previous six months was four times higher in the suicidal patients than in matched non-suicidal controls. The research of Peter Maguire, a British psychiatrist, reveals that one in five cancer patients require psychiatric treatment within a year of diagnosis; the morbidity is even higher among individuals who undergo disfiguring or disabling surgery, for example, amputation, mastectomy (removal of the breast), or colostomy (the re-routing of the bowel so that waste emerges from an opening made in the abdomen).

Some forms of loss are associated with increased incidence of marital problems: for example, research at the Welsh National School of Medicine by B.J. Tew and co-workers showed that marital breakdown was nine times higher following the birth of a child with spina bifida than that for the local population. Ann Gath, a consultant child psychiatrist, has found similar increases in marital breakdown following the birth of a baby with Down's syndrome.

□ What might be the effects of marital breakdown on health?†

■ Divorced people suffer more ill health and, on average, have higher mortality rates than their married counterparts. Divorced men seem to be at greater risk than divorced women.

Research which investigates the association of life events with *physical* illness has produced more ambiguous answers than the investigation of mental distress or disorder. For example, a study by Stefan Stein and Edward Charles in 1971 claimed to reveal a significantly higher incidence of loss in the family backgrounds of adolescent diabetics (mainly bereavement or parental separation or divorce) than in a matched group of adolescents suffering from other types of chronic illness.

**Case-control, cohort, prospective and retrospective studies are discussed in Book I, *Studying Health and Disease*, Chapter 6.

†The association of mortality and morbidity with marital status is discussed in Book III, *The Health of Nations*, Chapter 9.

Table 20.1 Observed (O) and expected (E) deaths, 1971–76, following widow(er)hood earlier in the period 1971–76

Number bereaved	Females (8 563)			Males (4 016)		
Observed/expected deaths	O	E†	SMR†	O	E	SMR
All causes	691	665.9	104	662	587.1	113**
All cancers	135	134	101	137	120.1	114
All non-cancers*	555	530.4	105	524	463.5	113**

* Predominantly diseases of the heart and circulatory system.
** Statistically significant increases.
† The expected numbers of deaths (E) are calculated using age- and sex-specific death rates for all people (widowed and not widowed) and represent the numbers that would have died if bereavement had *no* effect on mortality. The SMR (standardised mortality ratio) is calculated by dividing O by E, expressed as a percentage. (See Book I, *Studying Health and Disease*, Chapter 5)
(Data from Fox and Goldblatt, 1982.)

□ Can you conclude from this that a disturbed family is a precipitating factor in diabetes mellitus?

■ No. Retrospective studies are open to the criticism that a gradual deterioration of health *before* illness was diagnosed clinically, may have precipitated the life events, rather than the other way round. Other research shows that chronic illness in the child is associated with raised incidences of family disturbance (for example, marital breakdown).

Recent reviews of research into diabetes assert that there is no evidence that loss is a precipitating factor.* However, the notion persists in lay folklore that diabetes may be brought on in middle or old age by a sudden shock, especially a bereavement. The death of a spouse has also been linked to the onset of cancer in popular mythology. However, although some research studies have reached the same conclusion, weaknesses in design — particularly in the composition of control groups — have rendered the results suspect. Carefully designed studies show no such association, for example, the OPCS Longitudinal Study of 1 per cent of the population of England and Wales, referred to previously in this book. Table 20.1 shows some of its results.

□ How do you interpret these data?

■ Women do not suffer a significantly increased risk of death following widowhood, whereas there is a higher mortality rate for widowers from causes *other* than cancers. Note that there is no statistically significant increase in mortality from cancers, but since the number of cases is relatively small the possibility that widowers *may* be more susceptible to cancers cannot be ruled out.

Colin Murray Parkes was among the first to document the vulnerability of widowers to premature death. For nine years he and his colleagues monitored the health of 4486 widowers aged 55 years or older when their wives died in 1957. The number of widowers who died within 6 months of the wives was 40 per cent greater than that expected for non-bereaved married men, matched for age and social class. Figure 20.1 shows their causes of death.

Taken together, diseases of the heart and circulatory system accounted for two thirds of the increase in mortality. As Parkes observed: 'To most of us death from a "broken heart" is a figure of speech, yet the term reflects a bygone belief that grief could kill, and kill through the heart.' (Parkes, Benjamin and Fitzgerald, 1969, p.740).

Can other forms of loss kill us 'before our time', or even precipitate serious illness? This is a question worth answering since everyone will inevitably suffer a random assortment of significant changes during a lifetime, some of them predictable and shared with all members of the species or at least society (the so-called life-course transitions); others entirely unpredictable, such as a

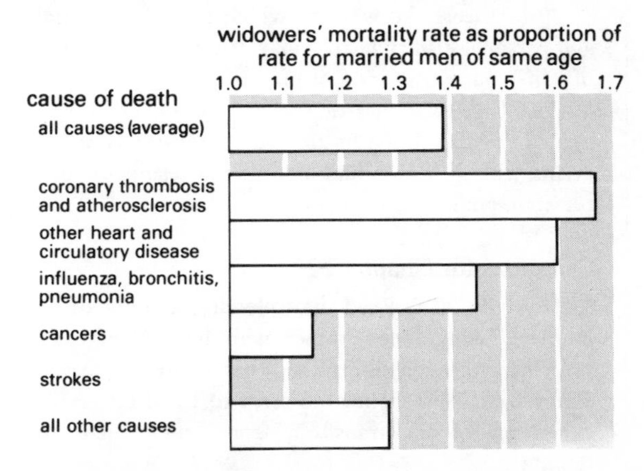

Figure 20.1 Mortality rate of widowers during first six months of bereavement as a proportion of the rate for married men of the same age, by cause of death. (Number of widowers = 4486). (Data from Parkes *et al.*, 1969, p. 741.)

*The biological, social and personal-history aspects of diabetes mellitus are discussed in Book I, *Studying Health and Disease*, Chapters 2, 7 and 11.

burglary or accidental injury. As yet, no unequivocal answer can be given. Some studies appear to reveal such an association, while others do not.

For example, a three-year prospective study of 87 medical students by Arthur Schless and colleagues at an American medical school failed to find any statistically significant association between life events and illness. A massive prospective study of all 270 000 men employed by the Bell Telephone Company in America by Lawrence Hinkle and colleagues throughout the 1960s reached a similar conclusion about life events and the incidence of coronary heart disease. However, such events could precipitate a heart attack in people already diagnosed as having symptoms of coronary disease. Hinkle's research shows that the incidence of ill-health is not evenly distributed through groups of people matched for all the obvious biological and social variables such as age, sex, occupation and social class — some people experience far more episodes of illness than others. These 'vulnerable' individuals are more likely to become ill following a life event than are more 'robust' individuals faced with the same transition (see Hinkle, 1974, for a review).

In summary, we can say that within the span of any lifetime, each of us is faced with certain inevitable losses as we grow older, plus a less predictable assortment of turning points, crises and temporary or permanent change. The transition need not be sudden, but may be a gradual biological change such as puberty or the menopause, which is given a particular meaning by cultural values. No matter how attached we may feel to one phase of life, continued existence inevitably prises us away from childhood or fertile adulthood, and propels us forward towards the final earthly loss — that of life itself. Similarly, events such as marriage or divorce, becoming a parent or grandparent, finding or losing a job, a house, a role in life, separate us from our old identity and face us with the task of constructing a new one.

This process goes on throughout life. Despite weaknesses in the research literature, there is enough evidence to conclude that most transitions render the person undergoing change vulnerable to grief, which, if not resolved, can lead to psychiatric illness. Far less clear cut is the association with physical disease. But whatever the underlying causes, health is in transition in every moment of life, from birth to old age, and an ability to let go of old attachments and make new ones may have an influence on health and disease.

> There are three conditions which often look alike
> Yet differ completely, flourish in the same hedgerow:
> Attachment to self and to things and to persons, detachment
> From self and from things and from persons; and growing between them, indifference
> Which resembles the others as death resembles life.
>
> (T.S. Eliot, 'Little Gidding', III, lines 1–5)

Objectives for Chapter 20

When you have studied this chapter, you should be able to:

20.1 Discuss the ways in which biological, social and personal history factors may affect the experience of a life-course transition or life event.

20.2 Give examples of research which has investigated the association of life-course transitions or life events with ill-health, and analyse the results of such research, pointing out its possible pitfalls.

Questions for Chapter 20

1 (*Objective 20.1*) Read the following account of an interview with a coal miner who had taken early retirement through ill-health. What biological, social and personal history factors seem to be affecting his experience of the transition from employment to retirement?

> Albert had gone straight to the pit on leaving school and was working on the coal face at the age of 18 ... The coal was won with pick and shovel and the pay was poor. Poor though it was, it was better than the dole.
>
> When machine mining and better wages began to come in the early 1950s, Albert was already experiencing difficulties with his breathing due to bronchitis. He began to have periods off sick every winter ... eventually he was off work for two or three months at a time ... and now after 15 months continuous absence he would have to accept early retirement ...
>
> He told me how sitting still he felt fine, but the least effort was too much for him. He, who had earned his living and supported his family by shovelling coal, couldn't even make the fire up ...

He had a special contempt for young miners who thought their work was hard — he'd had to get the coal by hand — they'd got machines to do it for them. He had gloried in the sense of belonging to a special breed of men ... Now he belonged no more. His sickness benefit and social security payment did not enable him to call at the institute for a pint more than once a week, and pride forbade that he should go there hoping one of his mates would treat him. (quoted in Speck, 1978, pp.88–9)

2 (*Objective 20.2*) Table 20.2 shows the results of two studies on the association between life events and the onset of illness. In the retrospective study, 88 American hospital doctors (86 were men) filled in a questionnaire giving the dates of all the major health changes they had experienced in the previous 10 years, and the dates of life events. The stressfulness of these events was then analysed using the Social Readjustment Rating Scale, a list of 43 such events ranged in order of the distress and upheaval they tend to cause in many people's lives, on the basis of extensive research. Each item is assigned an average stress score, ranging from 100 for the death of a spouse down to 11 for minor violations of the law. A health change was arbitrarily considered to be associated with a life event if it occurred within 2 years following the event.

In the prospective study, 84 of the same doctors agreed to report any instances of ill-health for the next 9 months; these were then related to the extent of life events in the previous 18 months.

Examine the data in Table 20.2, and then answer the following questions.

(a) Which aspects of the *design* of these studies must be taken into account when interpreting the results? (For example, consider the group being investigated; the method of rating stressful events, and the definition of an 'association' between an event and an illness.)

(b) Accepting these reservations, what do these studies suggest?

Table 20.2 Relationship of critical life events to significant changes in health among the same group of American doctors (retrospective data relates to 88 doctors, prospective to 84 doctors)

	Percentage of subjects experiencing a significant health change associated with the life event	
extent of life events	retrospective data	prospective data
mild life crisis	37	9
moderate life crisis	51	25
major life crisis	79	49

(Data from Rahe and Holmes, unpublished; quoted in Dohrenwend and Dohrenwend, 1974, pp. 61 and 64.)

References and further reading

References

ADLER, M.W. (1980) The terrible peril: an historical perspective on the venereal diseases, *British Medical Journal*, **2**, pp.206–11.

AGE CONCERN (1974) *The Attitudes of the Retired and the Elderly*, Manifesto Series, No. 32, Research Report, Mitcham Age Concern, England.

AITKEN-SWAN, JEAN (1977) *Fertility Control and the Medical Profession,* Croom Helm.

ALLMAN, L.R. and JAFFE, D.T. (1977) *Readings in Adult Psychology: Contemporary Perspectives*, Harper and Row.

ANTI-SLAVERY SOCIETY (1980) *Child Labour: Published and Unpublished Material*, Anti-Slavery Society for the Protection of Human Rights.

ARENSBURG, CONRAD and KIMBALL, SOLON (1968) *Family and Community in Ireland*, Oxford University Press, 2nd edn.

ARIÈS, PHILIPPE (1973) *Centuries of Childhood,* Penguin Books.

ARIÈS, PHILIPPE (1983) *The Hour of our Death,* trans. Helen Weaver, Penguin Books.

ARMSTRONG, DAVID (1983) *Political Anatomy of the Body,* Cambridge University Press.

ASHTON, JOHN (1980) Experiences of women refused National Health Service abortion, *Journal of Biosocial Science,* **12**, pp.201–10.

AUDEN, WYSTAN HUGH (1969) *Collected Shorter Poems 1927–1957*, Faber.

BALLINGER, C. BARBARA (1975) Psychiatric morbidity and the menopause: screening of general population sample, *British Medical Journal*, **iii**, pp.344–46.

BARTRAM, ALAN (ed.) (1965) *World of the Child*, Penguin Books.

BEAUMONT, P.J.V., BEARDWOOD, C.J. and RUSSELL, G.F.M. (1972) The occurrence of the syndrome of anorexia nervosa in male subjects, *Psychological Medicine,* **2**, pp.216–31.

BECKER, G. (1981) *A Treatise on the Family*, Harvard University Press.

BEDELL, S.E. and DEL BANCO, T.L. (1984) Choices about cardiopulmonary resuscitation in the hospital; when do physicians talk with patients?, *New England Journal of Medicine,* **310**, pp.1089–93.

BELL, THOMAS (1961) *In the Midst of Life,* Atheneum, New York.

BELL, COLIN, MCKEE, LORNA and PRIESTLEY, K. (1983) *Fathers, Childbirth and Work,* Equal Opportunities Commission.

BELL, A.P. and WEINBERG, M.S. (1978) *Homosexualities: A Study of Diversity among Men and Women*, Mitchell Beazley.

BLACK, N., BOSWELL, D., GRAY, A., MURPHY, S., POPAY, J. (1984) *Health and Disease: A Reader*, The Open University Press.

BLAXTER, MILDRED (1983) The causes of disease: women talking, *Social Science and Medicine,* **17**, No. 2, pp.59–69, and (edited version) in Black *et al.* (eds) (1984).

BLUEBOND-LANGNER, MYRA (1978) *The Private Worlds of Dying Children,* Princeton University Press, N.J.

BLYTHE, RONALD (1979) *The View in Winter*, Allen Lane.

BOYD, CATHERINE and SELLERS, LEA (1982) *The British Way of Birth,* Spastics International Medical Publications.

BRITISH SOCIETY FOR POPULATION STUDIES (1983) *The Family,* Occasional Paper 31, OPCS.

BUHRICH, NEIL (1981) Frequency of presentation of Anorexia nervosa in Malaysia, *Australian and New Zealand Journal of Psychiatry,* **15**, pp.153–55.

BUNGAY, GEOFF, VESSEY, MARTIN and MCPHERSON, KLIM (1980) Study of symptoms in middle life with special reference to the menopause, *British Medical Journal*, 19 July, pp.181–83.

BURNFIELD, ALEXANDER (1977) Multiple sclerosis: a doctor's personal experience, *British Medical Journal,* **1**, pp.435–6.

CALDEYRO-BARCIA, R. (1979) Physiological and psychological bases for the modern and humanised management of normal labour, in *Recent Progress in Perinatal Medicine and Prevention of Congenital Anomaly,* Tokyo Ministry of Health and Welfare.

CAMPBELL, JOHN D. (1975) Attribution of illness: another

double standard, *Journal of Health and Social Behaviour*, **16**, Part 1, pp.114–26.

CAMPLING, JO (1981) *Images of Ourselves*, Routledge and Kegan Paul.

CARD, FRANCES M. (1969) Senility or garden variety maladjustment, *Journal of Gerontology*, April.

CARTWRIGHT, ANN (1976) *How Many Children?* Routledge and Kegan Paul.

CARTWRIGHT, ANN, HOCKEY, LISBETH and ANDERSON, JOHN (1973) *Life Before Death*, Routledge and Kegan Paul.

CARVER, VIDA and LIDDIARD, PENNY (eds) (1978) *An Ageing Population*, Hodder and Stoughton in association with Open University Press.

CARTWRIGHT, ANN (1979) *The Dignity of Labour?: A Study of Childbearing and Induction*, Tavistock Publications.

CAVENDISH, RUTH (1982) *Women on the Line*, Routledge and Kegan Paul.

CENSUS 1981 (1984) *Household and Family Composition, England and Wales*, HMSO.

CENTRAL POLICY REVIEW STAFF (1980) *People and their Families*, HMSO.

CHALLIS, J. and ELLIMAN, O. (1979) *Child Workers Today*, Quartermaine House, Sunbury, Middx.

CHAMBERLAIN, R., CHAMBERLAIN, G. and HOWLETT, B. (1975) *British Births 1970: Volume 1, The First Week of Life*, Heinemann.

CHAPMAN, EVA MARIA (1983) *Attitudes of Mothers and Doctors to Childbirth Practice*, unpublished thesis, The Open University.

CHARD, T. and RICHARDS, MARTIN (1977) *Benefits and Hazards of the New Obstetrics*, Spastics International Medical Publications, Heinemann.

CHECKLAND, S.G. (1969) *The Rise of the Industrial Society in England, 1815–1885*, Longman.

COMFORT, ALEX (1977) *A Good Age*, Mitchell Beazley Publishers Ltd.

COOLEY, MIKE (1980) *Architect or Bee? The Human/Technology Relationship*, Hand and Brain Publications.

COOPER, W. (1975) *No Change*, Arrow.

COOPER, PETER J., WATERMAN, GEORGE C. and FAIRBURN, CHRISTOPHER G. (1984) Women with eating problems: a community survey, *British Journal of Clinical Psychology*, **23**, pp.45–52.

COVENEY, PETER (1967) *The Image of Childhood*, Penguin Books.

COX, C.A., FOX, J.S., ZINKIN, P.M. and MATTHEWS, A.E.B. (1976) Critical appraisal of domicilary obstetric and neonatal practice, *British Medical Journal*, **1**, pp.84–86.

COX, C.A., ZINKIN, P.M. and GRIMSLEY, M.F.J. (1977) Aspects of the six-month developmental examination in a longitudinal study, *Developmental Medicine and Child Neurology*, **19**, No. 2, pp.149–59.

CUBAN FAMILY CODE (1975) Law No. 1289, February 14th, Official Publication of the Ministry of Justice, Havana, Cuba.

DABROWSKI, IRENE (1983) Developmental job patterns of working-class women, *Qualitative Sociology*, **6**, No. 1, pp.29–50.

DAVIES, M.L. (ed.) (1978) *Maternity: Letters from Working Women*, Virago.

DAVISON, G.C. (1976) Homosexuality – the ethical challenge, *Journal of Consulting and Clinical Psychology*, **44**, pp.157–62.

DE BEAUVOIR, SIMONE (1977) *Old Age*, translated by Patrick O'Brien, Penguin Books.

DHSS (1978) The DHSS perspective, in Barnes, J. and Connelly, N. (eds) *Social Care Research*, Bedford Square Press.

DHSS (1980) *Inequalities in Health: Report of a Research Working Group under the Chairmanship of Sir Douglas Black* (The Black Report).

DOHRENWEND, BARBARA SNELL and DOHRENWEND, BRUCE P. (eds) (1974) *Stressful Life Events: Their Nature and Effects*, John Wiley and Sons, New York.

DONALDSON, R.J. and DONALDSON, L.J. (1983) *Essential Community Medicine*, MTP Press Ltd.

EASTERLIN, R.A. (1980) *Birth and Fortune*, Grant McIntyre.

EBRAHIM, E.J. (1981) *Paediatric Practice in Developing Countries*, Macmillan.

ELDER, GLADYS (1977) *The Alienated – Growing Old Today*, Writers and Readers Publishing Cooperative.

ENKIN, MURRAY and CHALMERS, IAIN (eds) (1982) *Effectiveness and Satisfaction in Antenatal Care*, Spastics International Medical Publications, Heinemann.

ENRIGHT, D.J. (1983) *The Oxford Book of Death*, Oxford University Press.

ERMISCH, J. (1981) Paying the piper: demographic changes and pension contributions, *Policy Studies*, Vol. 1(4).

ETZIONI, AMITAI (1978) Future evolution of the family, pp.19–25 in WOOD, C. (ed.), *Health and the Family*, Academic Press.

EUROPEAN PARLIAMENT (1980) Committee on Social Affairs and Employment, *'Building Europe with and for the Family'*, Working document 70147 (18 December) in preparation for the report on: *Family Policy in the EEC*.

EVELETH, P.B. and TANNER, J.H. (1976) *Worldwide*

Variation in Human Growth, Cambridge University Press.

FAIRHURST, E. and LIGHTUP, R. (1980) Being menopausal: women and medical treatment, paper presented to the *British Sociological Association,* September 1980.

FARRELL, CHRISTINE (1978) *My Mother Said... The Way Young People Learned About Sex and Birth Control,* Routledge and Kegan Paul.

FONER, ANNE and KERTZER, DAVID (1978) Transitions over the life-course: lessons from age-set societies, *American Journal of Sociology,* **83**, pp.1081–104.

FORBES, THOMAS, R. (1979) By what disease or casualty: the changing face of death in London, in Webster (1979), pp. 117–38.

FORD, C.A. (1964) *A Comparative Study of Human Reproduction,* Human Relations Area File Press, Newhaven.

FORD, C.S. and BEACH, F.A. (1952) *Patterns of Sexual Behaviour,* Eyre and Spottiswoode.

FOX, A.J. and GOLDBLATT, P.O. (1982) *OPCS Longitudinal Study, 1971–75: Sociodemographic Mortality Differentials,* HMSO, Series LS No. 1.

FREEDMAN, RICHARD (1978) Sufficiently decayed: gerontophobia in English literature, pp.49–61 in Spicker *et al.* (1978).

FREUD, SIGMUND (1905) *Three Essays on the Theory of Sexuality,* Pelican, 1973.

FRIES, JAMES, F. (1980) Aging, natural death and the compression of morbidity, *The New England Journal of Medicine,* Vol. 303, No. 3, pp.103–35.

GADOW, SALLY and BERG, GERI (1978) Towards more human meanings of aging: ideals and images from philosophy and art, pp.83–92 in Spicker (1978).

GALBRAITH, JOHN K. (1975) *The Affluent Society,* Penguin.

GALLIE, D. (1978) *In Search of the New Working Class,* Cambridge University Press.

GANSCHOW, THOMAS W. (1978) The aged in a revolutionary milieu: China, pp.303–20 in Spicker *et al.* (1978).

GARNER, DAVID M., GARFUNKEL, PAUL E., SCHWARTZ, DONALD and THOMPSON, MICHAEL (1980) Cultural expectations of thinness in women, *Psychological Reports,* **47**, pp.483–91.

GATH, ANN (1977) The impact of an abnormal child upon the parents, *British Journal of Psychiatry,* **130**, pp.405–10.

GELDER, M., GATH, D. and MAYOV, R. (1983) *Oxford Textbook of Psychiatry,* Oxford University Press.

GLENDINNING, C. (1980) *After Working All These Years,* Disability Alliance.

GMWU (1980) *Shiftwork: A General and Municipal Workers Union Discussion Document,* GMWU.

GOLDACRE, M.J. and VESSEY, M.P. (1983) Health and sickness in the community, in WEATHERALL, D.J., LEDINGHAM, J.G.G. AND WARNELL, D.A. (eds) *Oxford Textbook of Medicine,* Oxford University Press.

GOLDSTEIN, H. (1971) Factors influencing the height of 7 year old children: results from the National Child Development Study, *Human Biology,* **43**, pp.92–111.

GOMEZ, JOAN (1967) *Dictionary of Symptoms,* Centaur Press.

GORDON, H. SCOTT (1977) *On Being Demographically Lucky: The Optimum Time To Be Born,* Presidential address to the Western Economic Association, Anaheim, California.

GORER, GEOFFREY (1965) *Death, Grief and Mourning in Contemporary Britain,* Cresset Press.

GORNICK, V. and MORAN, B.K. (1971) *Woman in Sexist Society,* Basic Books, New York.

GRAHAM, HILARY (1977) Smoking in pregnancy: the attitudes of expectant mothers, *Social Science and Medicine,* **10**, pp.300–405.

GRAHAM, HILARY (1982) Perceptions of parenthood, *Health Education Journal,* **41**, No. 4, pp.119–21.

GRAHAM, HILARY (1984) *Women, Health and the Family,* Wheatsheaf Books.

GRAHAM, HILARY and MCKEE, LORNA (1980) *The First Months of Motherhood: Summary Report of a Survey of Women's Experiences of Pregnancy, Childbirth and the First Six Months after Birth,* Health Education Council Monograph No. 3, HEC, London.

GROSSMAN, M. and BART, PAULINE (1982) Taking the men out of menopause, in HUBBARD, R., HENIFIN, M.S. and FRIED, B. (eds), *Biological Woman: The Convenient Myth,* Schenkman, Cambridge, Massachusetts.

GRUELICH, W.W. (1958) Growth of children of the same race under different environmental conditions, *Science,* **127**, pp.515–6.

GUILLEBAUD, JOHN (1980) *The Pill,* Oxford University Press.

HALEY, BRUCE (1978) *The Healthy Body and the Victorian Culture,* Harvard University Press.

HALL, MARION and CHNG, PANG, K. (1982) Antenatal care in practice, in Enkin and Chalmers (1982) pp.60–8.

HALMI, KATHERINE A. (1980) Anorexia nervosa, in KAPLAN, M.I., FREEDMAN, A.M. and SADOCK, B.J. (eds) *Comprehensive Textbook of Psychiatry,* Williams and Williams, Baltimore, Vol. 2 pp.1882–92.

HAMILTON, H. (1965) *History of the Homeland,* Allen and Unwin.

HANEY, C. ALLEN (1977) Illness behaviour and psychosocial correlates of cancer, *Social Science and Medicine,* **11**, pp.223–28.

HARRINGTON, J.M. (1978) *Shiftwork and Health: A Critical Review of the Literature,* Health and Safety Executive document, HMSO.

HARRISON, PAUL (1978) Living with old age, in Carver and Liddiard (1978) pp.121–27.

HAVILAND, JEANNETTE M. and SCARBOROUGH, HOLLIS S. (1981) *Adolescent Development in Contemporary Society,* D. Van Nostrand Company, New York.

HAYNES, S. and FEINLAB, M. (1980) Women, work and coronary heart disease: prospective findings from the Framingham Heart Study, *American Journal of Public Health,* **70**, pp.133–41.

HENDRICKS, JOHN and HENDRICKS, C. DAVIS (1978) Sexuality in later life, in Carver and Liddiard (1978), pp.64–71.

HENNIGAN, ALISON (1984) Raid on the articulate, *New Statesman,* 27 April, p.28.

HEWITT, M. (1958) *Wives and Mothers in Victorian Industry,* Rockcliff.

HILL, G. (1896) *Women in English Life from Medieval to Modern Times,* Richard Bentley and Sons.

HIMES, NORMAN E. (1970) *Medical History of Contraception,* Schocken, New York.

HINKLE, JR. LAWRENCE E. (1974) The effect of exposure to culture change, social change, and changes in interpersonal relationships on health, in Dohrenwend and Dohrenwend (1974) pp.9–44.

HINTON, JOHN (1963) Mental and physical distress in the dying, *Quarterly Journal of Medicine,* **32**, p.1.

HITE, SHERE (1977) *The Hite Report,* Talmy Franklin.

HOBSON, DOROTHY (1978) Housewives: isolation as oppression, in *Women Take Issue,* Women's Studies Group, Centre for Contemporary Cultural Studies, Hutchinson.

HOLT, K.F. (1980) Early motor development: posturally induced variations, *Journal of Paediatrics,* **57**, pp.571–75.

HOMANS, H. (1982) Pregnancy and birth as rites of passage for two groups of women in Britain, in MACCORMACK, C.P. (ed.) *Ethnography of Fertility and Birth,* Academic Press, Chapter 9.

HSU, L.K.G. (1980) Outcome of anorexia nervosa, *Archives of General Psychiatry,* **37**, pp.1041–46.

HULL, DAVID and JOHNSTON, DEREK I. (1981) *Essential Paediatrics,* Churchill Livingstone.

HUMPHREYS, CHARLOTTE (1979) Disability in Britain today, *Medicine in Society,* **6**, No. 1, pp.11–12.

HUNTINGFORD, PETER (1979) Obstetric practice: past, present and future, in Kitzinger and Davies (1978).

ILLICH, IVAN (1976) *Limits to Medicine,* Marion Boyar.

IMARA, MWALIMU (1975) Dying as the last stage of growth, in Kübler-Ross (1975), pp.147–63.

INCH, SALLY (1982) *Birthrights,* Hutchinson.

INTERNATIONAL LABOUR OFFICE (1971) *Minimum Age for Admission to Employment,* Report to the 57th session of the International Labour Conference, ILO, Geneva.

JACOBS, JERRY (1967) A phenomenological study of suicide notes, *Social Problems,* **15**, pp.60–72.

JOLLY, HUGH (1982) The Odent way of birth – can it happen in Britain?, *The Listener,* 18th March, pp.7–9.

JOSEPH, JENNY (1982) Warning . . ., *New Internationalist,* June 1982.

KEMP, ROBERT (1962) Diagnosis of old age, *The Lancet,* 15 September, p.515.

KENYON, F.E. (1980) Homosexuality in gynaecological practice, *Clinics in Obstetrics and Gynaecology,* **7**, Part 2, pp.363–86.

KIERNAN, KATHLEEN E. (1983) The structure of families today: continuity or change? in *The Family*, British Society for Population Studies, OPCS.

KITZINGER, SHEILA and DAVIS, J. (eds) (1978) *The Place of Birth,* Oxford University Press.

KLINE, MICHAEL, LLOYD, IVOR and REDMAN, CHRISTOPHER (1983) A comparison of low risk pregnant women booked for delivery in two systems of care, Parts 1 and 2, *British Journal of Obstetrics and Gynaecology,* **90**, pp.118–22 and pp.123–28.

KÜBLER-ROSS, ELIZABETH (1975) *Death – The Final Stage of Growth,* Prentice Hall, Inc., New Jersey.

KULKA, R and WEINGARTEN, H. (1979) The long term effects of parental divorce in childhood on adult adjustment, *Journal of Social Issues,* **35**, No. 4, pp.50–78.

LACEY, K.A. and PARKIN, J.M. (1974) Causes of short stature: a community study in Newcastle-upon-Tyne, *The Lancet,* **i**, pp.42–45.

LASLETT, PETER (1984) Super Performers, *London Review of Books,* 6 May.

LAWRENCE, MARILYN (1984) *The Anorexic Experience,* The Women's Press.

LEAN, NICKY (1981) Positions in labour, *Association of Radical Midwives,* No. 12, December 1981.

LESTER, GENE and LESTER, DAVID (1971) *Suicide – The Gamble With Death,* Prentice Hall Inc., New Jersey.

LORENCE, BOGNA, W. (1974) Parents and children in eighteenth-century Europe, *History of Childhood Quarterly,* **2**, No. 1, pp.1–30.

LOUDON, IRVINE (1980) Chlorosis, anaemia and anorexia nervosa, *British Medical Journal,* 21, (20–27 December), pp.1669–75 (reprinted in the Course Reader, Black *et al.* (1984), Part 1, Section 1.6).

LOVELL, A. (1983) Some questions of identity: late

miscarriage, stillbirth and perinatal loss, *Social Science and Medicine,* 17, pp.755–61.

MACFARLANE, A. and FOX, J. (1978) Child deaths from accidents and violence, *Population Trends,* **12**, pp.22–27.

MACFARLANE, ALISON and MUGFORD, MIRANDA (1984) *Birth Counts: Statistics of Pregnancy and Childbirth,* HMSO.

McKINLAY, SONJA, M. and JEFFERYS, MARGOT (1974) The menopausal syndrome, *British Journal of Preventative and Social Medicine,* **28**, pp.108–15.

MACLEOD, SHEILA (1981) *The Art of Starvation,* Virago.

MARSHALL, PIERRE (1979) quoted in How to tackle sexual taboos, *Psychology Today* (London edition), February, pp.20–23.

MARSHALL, W.A. and TANNER, J.M. (1969) Variations in the pattern of pubertal changes in girls, *Archives of Disease in Childhood,* **44**, pp.291–303.

MARSHALL, W.A. and TANNER, J.M. (1970) Variations in the pattern of pubertal changes in boys, *Archives of Disease in Childhood,* **45**, pp.13–23.

MEHL, LOUIS, PETERSON, G.H., LEAVITT, L.A. and CREEVY, D.C. (1976) Home vs. hospital delivery: Comparisons of matched populations, *American Public Health Association,* 20th October 1976, cited in Kitzinger and Davis (1978).

MERRITT, GILES (1982) *World Out of Work,* Collins.

MILLER, F.J.W., COURT, S.D.M., KNOX, E.G. and BRANDON, S. (1974) *The School Years in Newcastle-upon-Tyne, 1956–1962,* Oxford University Press.

MITCHELL, R.G. (ed.) (1980) *Child Health in the Community,* Churchill Livingstone.

MODELL, JOHN; FURSTENBURG, JR. FRANK F. and HERSHBERG, THEODORE (1976) Social change and transitions to adulthood in historical perspective, *Journal of Family History,* **1**, No. 1, pp.7–32.

MORGAN, BARBARA, M., BULPITT, C.J., CLIFTON, P. and LEWIS, P.J. (1982) Analgesia and satisfaction in childbirth, *The Lancet,* 9 October, pp.808–10.

MOSS, WALTER G. (1978) Why the anxious fear? Aging and death in the works of Turgenev, in Spicker *et al.* (1978), pp.241–60.

MUSGROVE, FRANK (1964) *Youth and the Social Order,* Routledge and Kegan Paul.

MUSGROVE, FRANK and MIDDLETON, ROGER (1981) Rites of passage and the meaning of age in three contrasted social groups, *British Journal of Sociology,* **32**, pp.39–55.

NATIONAL BOARD FOR PRICES AND INCOMES (1970) *Hours of work, Overtime and Shiftwork,* Report No. 161, Cmnd 4554, HMSO.

NELSON, M.K. (1983) Working class women, middle-class women and models of childbirth, *Social Problems,* **30**, No. 3, pp. 284–97.

NWAEFUNA, ABUA (1981) Anorexia nervosa in a developing country, letter to the *British Journal of Psychiatry,* **138**, pp.270–71.

OAKLEY, ANN (1974) *Housewife,* Penguin Books.

OAKLEY, ANN (1980) *Women Confined,* Martin Robertson.

O'BRIEN, M. and SMITH, C. (1981) Women's views and experiences of antenatal care, *The Practitioner,* **225**, pp.123–5.

OFFICE OF HEALTH ECONOMICS (1979) *Perinatal Mortality in Britain – A Question of Class,* O.H.E. Briefing No. 10, December 1979.

OFFICE OF HEALTH ECONOMICS (1981) *Accidents in Childhood,* Briefing No. 17, September 1981.

OPCS (1984) *Legal Abortions 1983,* OPCS Monitor, 7 August 1984, Ref. AB 84/6, Government Statistical Service.

OPEN UNIVERSITY (1982) D301 *Historical Sources and the Social Scientist,* Units 3–5 *An Introduction to Parish Register Demography,* The Open University Press.

ORR, J.B. (1936) *Food, Health and Income,* Macmillan.

OSBORN, A.F., BUTLER, N.R. and MORRIS, A.C. (1984) *The Social Life of Britain's Five-Year Olds: A Report of the Child Health and Development Study,* Routledge and Kegan Paul.

PARKES, COLIN MURRAY (1975) Psycho-social transitions: comparisons between reactions to loss of a limb and loss of a spouse, *British Journal of Psychiatry,* **127**, pp.204–10.

PARKES, COLIN MURRAY (1978) *Bereavement: Studies of Grief in Adult Life,* Penguin Books.

PARKES, COLIN MURRAY, BENJAMIN, B. and FITZGERALD, R.G. (1969) Broken heart: a statistical study of increased mortality among widowers, *British Medical Journal,* **1**, pp.740–43.

PAYKEL, EUGENE S., PRUSOFF, BRIGITTE A. and MYERS, JEROME K. (1975) Suicide attempts and recent life events, *Archives of General Psychiatry,* **32**, pp.327–33.

PERETZ, DAVID (1970) Reaction to loss, in SCHOENBERG, B., CARR, A.C., PERETZ, D. and KUTSCHER, A. (eds), *Loss and Grief: Psychological Management in Medical Practice,* Columbia University Press, New York, pp.20–35.

PFEFFER, N. and WOOLLETT, A. (1983) *The Experience of Infertility,* Virago.

PHELPS BROWN, H. (1979) *The Inequality of Pay,* Oxford University Press.

PIKE, E. ROYSTON (1974) *Human Documents of the Victorian Golden Age,* Unwin University Books.

PINCHBECK, I. (1977) *Women Workers and the Industrial Revolution, 1750–1850*, Frank Cass.

PINCUS, LILY (1975) *Death and the Family*, Vintage Books, New York.

PLATH, SYLVIA (1971) Three Women, *Winter Trees*, Faber, pp.40–54.

POLLOCK, LINDA A. (1983) *Forgotten Children: Parent-Child Relations from 1500 to 1900*, Cambridge University Press.

PRINGLE, M.K., BUTLER, N.R. and DAVIE, R. (1966) *11 000 Seven Year Olds*, Longman.

PUNER, MORTON (1974) *To the Good Long Life*, Universe Books.

RAHE, R.H. and HOLMES, T.H. (unpublished) in HOLMES, T.H. and MASUDA, MINORU (1974) Life change and illness susceptibility, in Dohrenwend and Dohrenwend (1974), pp.45–72.

REGISTRAR GENERAL (ENGLAND AND WALES) (1982) *Mortality Statistics: Childhood England and Wales*, Series DH3 NO. 8, HMSO.

REID, IVAN (1981) *Social Class Differences in Britain*, Grant McIntyre.

REID, M.E. and McILWAINE, G.M. (1980) Consumer opinion of a hospital antenatal clinic, *Social Science and Medicine*, 14A, pp.363–68.

RHYS, JEAN (1975) Whatever became of old Mrs Pearce, *The Times*, 21 May 1975, p.16.

RICHARDS, I.D. GERALD (1980) The epidemiology of disease in childhood, in Mitchell (1980), pp.126–146.

RICHARDS, MARTIN P.M. and DYSON, M. (1982) *Separation, Divorce and the Development of Children: A Review*, Child Care and Development Group, University of Cambridge.

RIMMER, L. (1981) *Families in Focus: Marriage, Divorce and Family Patterns*, Study Commission on the Family.

ROBERTS, HELEN (1981) *Women, Health and Reproduction*, Routledge and Kegan Paul.

ROMEDER, J.M. and MCWHINNIE, J.R. (1977) Potential years of life lost between ages 1 and 70, *International Journal of Epidemiology*, **6**, pp.143–51.

ROSSER, C. and HARRIS, C. (1965) *The Family and Social Change*, Routledge and Kegan Paul.

ROSSITER, CHRIS and WICKS, MALCOLM (1982) *Crisis or Challenge? Family Care, Elderly People and Social Policy*, Study Commission on the Family.

ROYAL COLLEGE OF OBSTETRICIANS AND GYNAECOLOGISTS (1982) *The Obstetrician's Report: Report of the RCOG Working Party on Antenatal and Intrapartum Care*, RCOG.

ROYAL COMMISSION ON VENEREAL DISEASES (1916) *Final Report of the Commissioners*, HMSO, Command No. 8189.

RUTTER, B.M., GRAHAM, P. and BIRCH, H.G. (1970) *A Neuropsychiatric Study of Childhood*, Clinics in Developmental Medicine No. 35/36, Heinemann.

RUTTER, MICHAEL, GRAHAM, PHILIP, CHADWICK, O.F.D. and YULE, W. (1976) Adolescent turmoil: fact or fiction?, *Journal of Child Psychology and Psychiatry*, **17**, pp.35–56.

SAUNDERS, CICELY (1978) (ed.) *The Management of Terminal Disease*, Edward Arnold.

SAVAGE, WENDY (1982) Taking liberties with women: abortion, sterilization and contraception, *International Journal of Health Services*, **12**, No. 2, pp.293–308.

SCHLESS, ARTHUR P., TEICHMANN, ALICIA, MENDELS, J., WEINSTEIN, NORMAN W. and WELLER, KENNETH (1977) Life events and illness: a three year prospective study, *British Journal of Psychiatry*, **131**, pp.26–34.

SHIMMIN, SYLVIA, MCNALLY, JOYCE and LIFF, SONIA (1981) Pressures on women engaged in factory work, *Employment Gazette*, August, pp.344–49.

SHORT, RENÉE (Chair) (1980) *Second Report from the Social Services Committee on Perinatal and Neonatal Mortality*, House of Commons Paper 663–1 (Session 1979–80), HMSO.

SIBERT, J.R. (1975) Stress in families of children who have ingested poisons, *British Medical Journal*, 12 July, pp.87–9.

SMIRNOV, S. (1977) The employment of old-age pensioners in the USSR, *International Labour Review*, **16**, pp. 87–94.

SOCIETY OF NURSE ADVISORS (Child Health) (1983) *Child Health Record*, B. Edsall and Co. Ltd.

SPECK, PETER (1978) *Loss and Grief in Medicine*, Bailliere Tindall.

SPICKER, STUART F. (1978) Gerontogenetic mentation: memory, dementia and medicine in the penultimate years, pp.153–80, in Spicker *et al.* (1978).

SPICKER, STUART F., WOODWARD, KATHLEEN M., VAN TASSEL, DAVID D. (1978) *Aging and the Elderly – Humanistic Perspectives in Gerontology*, Humanities Press Inc., Atlantic Highlands, New Jersey.

STEARNS, PETER N. (1977) *Old Age in European Society*, Croom Helm.

STEIN, STEFAN, P. and CHARLES, EDWARD (1971) Emotional factors in juvenile diabetes mellitus: a study of early life experience of adolescent diabetics, *American Journal of Psychiatry*, **128**, No. 6, pp.700–04.

STERN, GWEN and KRUCKMAN, LAURENCE (1983) Multidisciplinary perspectives on post-partum depression: an anthropological critique, *Social Science and Medicine*, **17**, No. 15, pp.1027–41.

STOLZ, L. (1960) Effects of maternal employment on children: evidence from research, *Child Development*,

31, pp.749–82.

STOPES, MARIE (1923) *Contraception: Its Theory, History and Practice*, John Bale, Sons and Danielsson.

STRAUSS, A.L. (ed.) (1970) *Where Medicine Fails*, Transaction Books.

STUNKARD, A.J., D'ACQUILI, E. and FOX, S. (1972) The influence of social class on obesity and thinness in children, *Journal of the American Medical Association*, **221**, pp.579–84.

STURDEE, D.W., WILSON, K.A., PIPILI, EVA and CROCKER, ANN D. (1978) Physiological aspects of menopausal hot flush, *British Medical Journal*, **2**, pp.79–80.

SUNDAY TIMES (1982) Childbirth: whose right to decide? 7 March, p.13.

SUNDAY TIMES (1982) Childbirth: a breech of the peace, 4 April, p.36.

SUSSER, M.W. and WATSON, W. (1971) *Sociology in Medicine*, Oxford University Press, (2nd edition).

TALC (1979) (Teaching Aids at Low Cost), *Malnutrition in an Urban Environment*, P.O. Box 49, St. Albans.

TANNER, J.M. (1975) Growth and endocrinology of the adolescent, in GARDNER, L. (ed.) *Endocrine and Genetic Diseases of Childhood*, Saunders, Philadelphia and London.

TANNER, J.M. (1978) *Foetus into Man*, Open Books.

TANNER, J.M. and WHITEHOUSE, R.H. (1976) Height and weight attained charts, *Archives of Disease in Childhood*, **51**, pp.107.

TAYLOR, LIZ MCNEILL (1983) *Living with Loss*, Fontana Paperbacks.

TAYLOR, M. (1981–2) Active management of labour, *Association for Improvement in the Maternity Services* (AIMS), Quarterly Journal, Winter 1981–2, pp.19–20.

TAYLOR, R.B. (1973) *Sweatshops in the Sun*, Beacon Press.

TAYLOR, P.J. and POCOCK, S.J. (1972) Mortality of shift and day workers 1956–68, *British Journal of Industrial Medicine*, **29**, pp.201–7.

TEW, MARJORIE (1979) The safest place of birth: further evidence, *The Lancet*, 30 June, pp.1388–90.

TEW, MARJORIE (1980) Facts, not assertions of belief, *Health and Social Services Journal*, 12 September, pp.1194–7.

TEW, B.J., LAURENCE, K.M., PAYNE, H. and RAWNSLEY, K. (1977) Marital stability following the birth of a child with spina bifida, *British Journal of Psychiatry*, **131**, pp.79–82.

THE LANCET (1934) Antenatal care on trial, Notes and Comments, No. 2, p.104.

THE SIGHTHILL MATERNITY TEAM (1982) Community antenatal care: the way forward, *Scottish Medicine*, April.

TITMUSS, RICHARD M. (1963) *Essays on the Welfare State*, Unwin University Books (Chapter 5; The position of women, pp.88–103, reprinted in the Course Reader, Black *et al.* (1984), Part 2, Section 2.3).

TOWNSEND, PETER (1963) *The Family Life of Old People: an Inquiry in East London*, Penguin Books.

TOWNSEND, PETER (1979) *Poverty in the United Kingdom*, Penguin Books.

TOWNSEND, PETER and DAVIDSON, NICK (1982) *Inequalities in Health: The Black Report*, Penguin Books.

TURNBULL, ALEC (1977) in the introduction to Chard and Richards (1977).

WADSWORTH, JANE, BURNELL, IOANNA, TAYLOR, BRENT and BUTLER, NEVILLE (1983) Family type and accidents in pre-school children, *Journal of Epidemiology and Community Health*, **37**, pp.100–04.

WEBSTER, CHARLES (ed.) (1979) *Health, Medicine and Mortality in the 16th Century*, Cambridge University Press.

WEIDGER, PAULA (1977) *Female Cycles*, The Women's Press.

WELBURN, VIVIENNE (1980) *Postnatal Depression*, Manchester University Press.

WHITTAKER, J. (1980) *Transport and Road Research Laboratory Report, Number 193*, Department of the Environment and Department of Transport.

WIDDOWSON, E.M. (1951) Mental contentment and physical growth, *The Lancet*, 16 June, pp.1316–18.

WITZEL, L. (1975) Behaviour of the dying patient, *British Medical Journal*, **2**, pp.81–2, 12 April.

WOLFE, TOM (1981) *The Right Stuff*, Bantam Books.

YAGER, JOEL (1981) Psychological aspects of anorexia nervosa, in SCHWABE, A.D. (ed.) Anorexia Nervosa, *Annals of Internal Medicine*, **94**, pp.371–81.

YATES, ALAYNE, LEEHEY, KEVIN and SHISSLAK, CATHERINE (1983) Running – an analogue of anorexia, *The New England Journal of Medicine*, **308**, pp.251–55.

ZANDER, LUKE (1982) The challenge of antenatal care: a perspective from General Practice, in Enkin and Chalmers (1982) pp.247–53.

Further reading

Chapter 2

ARMSTRONG, DAVID (1983) *The Political Anatomy of the Body*, Cambridge University Press. A valuable, exploratory review of the growth of medical surveillance in twentieth-century Britain.

Chapter 3

EASTERLIN, RICHARD (1980) *Birth and Fortune: The Impact of Numbers on Personal Welfare,* Grant McIntyre. A stimulating and controversial investigation of the effect of generation size on the life fortunes of individuals. The wealth of material contained in this book relates mainly to post-Second World War America, and includes speculation and predictions about the rest of the twentieth century.

Chapter 4

LASLETT, PETER (1971) *The World We Have Lost,* Methuen. A fascinating social history exploring the nature of family and other social networks in Britain, and the ways in which these have changed since the Industrial Revolution.

RIMMER, LESLEY (1981) *Families in Focus,* Study Commission on the Family. An easy to read introduction to contemporary facts and figures about births, marriage, divorce and other aspects of family life.

Chapters 5 and 6

BELL, COLIN., MCKEE, LORNA and PRIESTLEY, K. (1983) *Fathers, Childbirth and Work,* Equal Opportunities Commission. The report of a specially commissioned study into the pattern of leave-taking by men during their partners' pregnancy, at the time of the birth and shortly thereafter. Throws light on the relationship between work and the family, and concludes with policy recommendations.

ENKIN, MURRAY and CHALMERS, IAIN (eds) (1982) *Effectiveness and Satisfaction in Antenatal Care,* Spastics International Medical Publications, Heinemann. A comprehensive collection of articles by obstetricians, midwives and sociologists who argue that more antenatal care is not necessarily more effective and that a more humane service should be a goal for the future. This book is quite expensive, but can be obtained through a library.

Chapters 7 to 10

ARIÈS, PHILIPPE (1973) *Centuries of Childhood,* Penguin. The classic modern study of childhood by a leading historian, full of fascinating facts and ideas.

BLAXTER, MILDRED (1981) *The Health of Children: A Review of Research on the Place of Health in Cycles of Disadvantage,* SSRC/DHSS Studies in Deprivation and Disadvantage, number 3, Heinemann. A review of current evidence on the social distribution of health and development; of disease and mortality; of health-related behaviour; and of access to health services at each stage of life from newborn to young adult.

MITCHELL, R.G. (ed) (1980) *Child Health in the Community,* Churchill Livingstone. A useful recent collection of review articles from a primarily medical viewpoint.

MUSGROVE, FRANK (1964) *Youth and the Social Order,* Routledge and Kegan Paul. A major argument about the conditions under which youth conforms and rebels, based on historical and cross-cultural evidence.

TANNER, J.M. (1978) *Foetus into Man,* Open Books. Despite its unfortunate title, this thorough and readable book charts the development of males and females from conception to adulthood.

Chapters 11 to 13

CAMPLING, JO (ed.) (1981) *Images of Ourselves,* Routledge and Kegan Paul. A collection of short accounts by women who suffer from a variety of physical handicaps, revealing the struggle to overcome not only the handicap itself, but also the disabling response of society.

CAVENDISH, RUTH (1982) *Women on the Line,* Routledge and Kegan Paul. The author is a lecturer who gave up her job to work for a year on a factory production line. This book is an account of her experiences.

GRAHAM, HILARY (1984) *Women, Health and the Family,* Harvester. A stimulating account of how women organize the key resources of time, money and energy to promote the health of their family; the author brings together an impressive array of research findings.

HMSO (1984) *Report of the Committee of Inquiry into human fertilization and embryology* (Chairman: Dame Mary Warnock). Chapter 11 deals with the use of human embryos for research and hence the vexed question of when 'fetal rights' begin.

OAKLEY, ANN (1976) *Housewife,* Penguin. A study of the historical development of the housewife's role and the present-day situation of women as housewives — both as society sees them and as they see themselves.

PFEFFER, N. and WOOLLETT, A. (1983) *The Experience of Infertility,* Virago. A valuable and revealing book, based on interviews with couples undergoing investigation for infertility.

WEEKS, JEFFREY (1981) *Sex, Politics and Society,* Longman. A detailed history of public attitudes towards sexuality in Britain since 1800.

WEIDGER, PAULA (1978) *Female Cycles,* The Women's Press. A readable, non-technical account of the interactions of hormones and way of life in menstruation and the menopause.

Chapters 14 to 16

DANNON, D., SHOCK, N.W. and MAROIS, M. (eds) (1981) *Ageing: A Challenge to Science and Society, Volume 1, Biology,* Oxford University Press. Papers based on a conference on ageing in various body systems — fairly high-powered science.

DE BEAUVOIR, SIMONE (1977) *Old Age*, Penguin Books. A seminal work (first published 1970) on attitudes to old age (past and present) and on the idea of the elderly as outcasts.

KINNAIRD, JOHN, BROTHERSTON, SIR JOHN and WILLIAMSON, JAMES (eds) (1981) *The Provision of Care for the Elderly*, Churchill Livingstone. A selection of papers on policies, planning, pensions and care for the elderly.

ROSSITER, CHRIS and WICKS, MALCOLM (1982) *Crisis or Challenge? Family Care, Elderly People and Social Policy*, Study Commission on the Family. A compilation of facts and figures on the financial, housing, health and family status of the elderly.

Chapters 17 to 19

ARIÈS, PHILIPPE (1983) *The Hour of our Death*, trans. Helen Weaver, Penguin Books. A dense, long study of funeral practice and attitudes to death in Europe from early medieval times to the present day. If you can wade through the detail, the conclusions are surprising, and nearly always convincing.

BOWLING, ANN and CARTWRIGHT, ANN (1982) *Life After A Death: A Study of the Elderly Widowed*, Tavistock. A thoughtful and thorough study of bereavement among elderly people – their experiences, responses, difficulties, preoccupations and sources of help.

DUNCAN, A.S., DUNSTAN, G.R. and WELBOURN, R.B. (1981) *Dictionary of Medical Ethics*, Darton, Longman & Todd. Covers a wide-range of ethical problems from legal, moral, and practical points of view.

GORER, GEOFFREY (1965) *Death, Grief and Mourning in Contemporary Britain*, Cresset Press. This is not only the most influential study of attitudes to death in Britain, but is beautifully written with very moving verbatim reports of the respondents' remarks.

PARKES, COLIN MURRAY (1975) *Bereavement: Studies of Grief in Adult Life*, Penguin. A discussion of reactions to bereavement and the natural progression and effects of grief.

Answers to self-assessment questions

Chapter 2

1 (a) In pre-war rural Ireland, 'you can be a boy forever as long as your old man's alive'; and in the UK today women may still be called 'girls' well into their fifties.

(b) It suggests that the terms we use to describe age are also used to describe people's social status. They indicate relative power and authority granted them within a society. This in turn suggests that our social 'age' is not simply a reflection of our biological age, but may be shaped by the economy, by patriarchy (the rule of men over women), by colonialism, and so forth.

2 The following problems emerge:

(i) What is 'normal' is seen differently by midwife and mother. The midwife's judgement is based on measurements of blood pressure and haemoglobin levels which are outside the 'normal' range. However, it is not clear that all such deviations are actually harmful.

(ii) The women is labelled 'anaemic' on the basis of the midwife's judgement, moving her closer to being defined as a medical 'problem'.

(iii) Such detailed antenatal care is a controversial modern phenomenon, as you will see in Chapter 5.

(iv) The woman is being closely monitored because she is pregnant and the health of children is the subject of most medical surveillance.

Chapter 3

1 (a) The proportion of all women in formal employment has risen since the Second World War to almost 50 per cent on average. In the early 1970s the average participation rate of men was closer to 90 per cent, but rising unemployment since then will have pushed these rates down. Women's participation rates fall in the 20s age groups, partly due to their leaving the labour-force to have and care for children. This dip does not occur among men.

(b) Data on participation rates over the life-span are cross-sectional. They therefore exclude the 'cohort effects' experienced by individuals. These could only be examined by means of longitudinal data.

2 (a) 'Pig in the python' effects have been claimed to result in crowding in the education system and the labour market, perhaps leading to greater stress in the 'pig cohort' and consequently higher morbidity and mortality rates.

(b) It has been suggested that the birth rate rises and falls in response to changes in economic conditions that influence such things as numbers of children desired and age of marriage.

Chapter 4

1 The most obvious consequence is the increased life expectancy of women and improvement in their general health, but this in turn improved the health and viability of the children born to them. Smaller families could be fed and housed more adequately than larger ones, with health benefits for all family members. Since child labour had been outlawed, there was no loss of income to families with fewer children.

2 There appear to be two main assumptions underlying this statement, both of which can be challenged on the basis of your knowledge of family diversity. First the authors assume that one-parent families are a homogeneous group, but as you saw there is in fact great diversity among this group in terms of marital status, and this in turn is linked to differences in social, emotional and economic circumstances. The second assumption is that the absence of a parent *per se* will *inevitably* be a bad thing. Family structure is not necessarily a good indicator of the type or quality of roles and relationships within the family. The generally poorer health of those in one-parent families may owe more to poverty than to the absence of a parent.

3 Three areas of 'disintegration' are commonly identified by people who fear the collapse of the family: namely, rising rates of divorce, employment among women with dependent children and the dissolution of kinship ties. An historical perspective reveals that (for example) as many marriages were broken by death 100 years ago as are now disrupted by divorce; marriage is more popular now than ever before — the population contains its highest ever proportion of married women, and most divorced people remarry; female employment was considered 'natural' in the seventeenth and eighteenth centuries, and only began to

be condemned in the nineteenth century, and then only for middle-class women; kinship patterns do not seem to have changed much in the last 100 years, and ties may even have become stronger.

Chapter 5

1 A baby is more likely to die in the perinatal period if its mother comes from social class IV or V — in Oakley's words, from a 'deprived household'. An unhealthy diet is a concomitant of relative poverty (as you should recall from the discussion in Book III, *The Health of Nations*, Chapter 10). Smoking is also more common among working-class women, and can be seen as partly a 'personal' choice, but influenced heavily by the incidence of smoking among family and friends and in response to harsh social circumstances. Deprivation, poor diet (and, possibly, smoking) interact to produce measurable biological effects, in particular, low birthweight, which is in turn a powerful indicator of perinatal mortality. (Note that Oakley's statement stresses the view that factors in the mother's lifestyle are *more* important indicators of perinatal outcome than the antenatal care she receives; as you will know from the discussion in this chapter, this view is not universally accepted.)

2 The statement implies that screening measures applied to *all* pregnant women are: (i) inefficient, for example, in time, money and use of equipment; (ii) ineffective, since they are of benefit to only a few women and have a capacity for detecting pathology where none exists (i.e. false positive results). (iii) inhumane, since many women attend clinics for unnecessary tests, with all the travelling and waiting this entails, and run the risk of being wrongly diagnosed.

However, abandoning such testing altogether would be to the detriment of those few women whose babies are saved by early detection of a treatable condition. The solution suggested by several authorities in this chapter is to use the initial antenatal visit to identify those women for whom further tests would be advisable.

Chapter 6

1 These data show that medical problems suffered by babies born to 'low-risk' mothers were as common as those suffered by babies who should (in the authors' opinion) have been born in hospital. Two rather different conclusions could be drawn from this:

(a) Assessing a women as 'low-risk' does not guarantee an unproblematic birth or neonatal period. Therefore all babies should be born in hospital, where the best possible facilities are available to deal with unpredictable difficulties. (This is the conclusion drawn by the authors.)

(b) Obstetric risk factors are poor indicators of subsequent problems in the baby, therefore it could be argued that the presence of a risk factor is not adequate grounds for refusing a home confinement, since more than 75 per cent of women in both risk groups gave birth to normal babies at home.

2 (a) They agreed that induction reduces perinatal deaths, tends to increase the job satisfaction of obstetricians, and reduces the length of labour.

(b) They agreed that induction tends to increase the rate of Caesarean sections, the development of jaundice in the baby and pain in labour (although note that almost twice as many midwives as obstetricians perceived induced labour to result in increased pain).

(c) Obstetricians, on average, tend to feel that induced labour is a better experience for women, gives midwives more job satisfaction, reduces the use of forceps slightly, and tends to reduce hypoxia in babies. On all these criteria the midwives, on average, held the opposite view. This may reflect the closer contact between midwives and women in labour, resulting in greater sensitivity to the adverse consequences. This view is reinforced by the fact that some obstetricians are out of touch with what makes midwifery satisfying to midwives. The discrepancies may also reflect gender differences since the obstetricians are predominantly male, and may underestimate the disadvantages of induction experienced by women in labour and observed by female midwives.

3 Biological factors are implicated in her tiredness, and in the pain from her 'wound' (episiotomy). Social factors that may have contributed to her depression are, firstly, the episiotomy itself since this is an innovation of the last 20 years; and secondly, the lack of social support for a couple coping with a new baby that is implied by her being 'too damn tired' and by the 'definite tension' between the parents. A personal factor may be the distance at which her mother lives; she might have received more support if the distance was less or transport easier.

Chapter 7

1 (a) Some people have argued that due to the dramatic changes in the childhood mortality rate, contemporary society treats children with far more care and affection than used to be the case. On this account, we have all learned to take Rousseau's injunction to heart. However, evidence from diaries and anthropology suggests that affection between children and parents was always the norm. Even so, the world of childhood and adulthood were once more closely interwoven than they are now. Responsible employment and sexual relationships are now reserved for adults, and the rise of mass education has segregated children from adults in some respects. Associated with this development there has arisen a sentimental cult of childhood which emphasises the difference between adults

and children and lays particular stress on their innocence.

(b) The development of special medical services for children is a relatively recent phenomenon. At the turn of this century, paediatrics barely existed and paediatricians shared the standard medical view that children were merely small adults. Since that time, however, there has been a huge growth of special services for children; indeed, they are now the most closely monitored of all sections of the population. However, it is naïve to assume that this is simply because we are nicer to children than previous ages. Nation-states have powerful economic and military motives for taking good care of the health of their children. In addition, the definitions of 'perfect health' have narrowed so that a large proportion of children are diagnosed as suffering from a condition that would not have attracted medical attention in the past.

2 After the first year of life, mortality falls very sharply and stays at a low level throughout childhood. However, morbidity is relatively high. There is a high accident rate, and infectious diseases, though no longer a great killer in childhood, remain of considerable importance as a source of minor acute illness. In addition, a significant percentage of children are diagnosed as suffering from chronic conditions, both physical and mental. Finally, though, serious handicapping conditions are mostly rare, and the majority of psychiatric conditions do not persist into adulthood.

Chapter 8

1 Clearly, something happens to the relative mathematical ability of boys and girls in the two age-groups. One interpretation would be that boys are genetically superior to girls at maths — a superiority which manifests itself following the hormonal changes at puberty. In fact, you could not conclude any such thing from the data as presented, for three main reasons. First, the two groups were measured at the same time, thus they come from different cohorts, which may have had different educational experiences. Second, there might simply be differences in the rate at which the two sexes develop mathematical skills — perhaps the girls would 'catch up' by the time they were 18? Third, girls might be *expected* to be worse at maths than boys, or not to enjoy it, and so be discouraged in subtle ways by teachers, parents, or fellow students. That is, the *gender* difference may be real without implying an underlying biological *sex* difference in mathematical capacity.

2 From the chart of Figure 8.4, the girl's height falls on the 3rd centile at age 7. Her expected height at age 9 would be 120 cm. As she was only 114 cm the doctor might want answers to the following questions. Were her parents also short? (There is a genetic component to height.) Had she had chronic childhood illness? Was she well fed or showing signs of undernutrition? How did she rate on other developmental tests, for instance, of intelligence? Were there any signs of hormonal deficiencies?

Chapter 9

1 The very sharp decline in accidental deaths in all age groups, but particularly among younger children, since 1950, demonstrates that accident rates cannot be explained solely in terms of biological development. Rates for children in the three age-groups, once widely divergent, have converged in recent years. Small children in 1980 are not more advanced in motor or sensory development than they were in 1950, so the most important determinant of the change in accident rates must be social changes: for example, safety legislation concerning electrical wiring, slum clearance, better awareness of road safety, etc.

2 A remarriage may lead to the deterioration of the child's relationship with the non-custodial parent (for example, visits from the child's 'natural' father tend to decline following the mother's remarriage). The relationship with the custodial parent may also come under strain: for example, he or she may be resented for bringing an 'intruder' into the house to replace the absent parent. There may be conflict between the step-parent and custodial parent about how to treat the child, especially in regard to discipline, and the step-parent may bring children to the remarriage with consequent problems over 'favouritism'. The new marriage may be seen by the partners as a new start and a complete break with the past, whereas children usually want to hold onto aspects of their former family lifestyle. On the positive side, the material circumstances of the child usually improve following remarriage, and better emotional support for the custodial parent may improve life for the child.

Chapter 10

1 The most obvious source of anxiety related to age is that her body is changing very rapidly in response to the biological changes of puberty — this in itself can be unsettling. In addition, the variation in individual development at this age means that the girl probably has friends of her own age who already have the information she seeks because they have begun puberty earlier than she has, so she is anxious about being left out or left behind. Finally, her mother's refusal to talk may be more than embarrassment about the subject, but may reflect the view that a 12-year-old is 'too young to know' about such things. Remember that the age at which girls in industrial countries begin menstruation has become steadily younger during this century, and the mother may well have reached puberty at a later age than her daughter.

2 (i) Even theories that focus on the individual mind maintain that divorce or inadequate parenting, or insensitive handling at school may precipitate problems during this 'vulnerable' phase.

(ii) Cultural expectations about adult behaviour, and in particular the roles ascribed to each gender, may be at fault.

(iii) Adolescents may feel shut out of the adult world by their more powerful elders who make laws that prevent numerous activities before a certain age.

(iv) There has been a historical shift towards lengthening childhood (e.g. by extending schooling) and then rapidly making the transition to adulthood via early marriage — this may itself cause stress especially as each cohort moves at the same rate.

(v) A shortage of employment for adolescents may leave them feeling frustrated and wasted.

3 The motor cyclists on the tape speak about rebelling against their parents' wishes when they bought their first bike, and admit that rebellion was initially part of the thrill. Although they know the dangers and are cautious *some* of the time, they see risk taking as an inevitable consequence of riding a big bike with skill and flair. They consider that their skill makes it 'safe' for them to exceed speed limits, particularly on motorways, and would prefer the choice about whether to wear a crash helmet. They associate being a 'real biker' with being a young man who is prepared to put his life on the line.

Testing your nerve in this way, and joining an elite who have 'made the grade' may also be a part of other forms of risky behaviour that predominantly involve adolescent males — for example, street violence, theft, vandalism, joy-riding in stolen cars, etc. Everyone knows the consequences of getting caught out — but for some boys the prestige of daring and escaping may be worth the risk. However, there is an entirely different set of explanations that locate the prime cause not in gender roles (these merely 'shape' the response), but in social structures that ignore, oppress or belittle young people. And finally, there are reductionist explanations which locate the cause in biological factors such as male hormones.

Chapter 11

1 There are many different factors, but some of the most obvious are:

(i) *Biology* — the state of the woman's health and the condition of the baby are important criteria mentioned in the 1967 Abortion Act; an older woman is more likely to suffer complications during pregnancy and more likely to conceive a malformed child, and therefore more likely to be granted an abortion.

(ii) *Society* — the law pertaining to abortion has changed over time but does not at present directly include a reference to the woman's age. Other factors emanating from society are the regional variations in the likelihood that an abortion will be performed under the NHS — the criteria that differ from region to region might include the mother's age; the pervading cultural attitude to abortions, which has also changed over time and tends to vary with the woman's personal history, e.g. 'careless' youngsters get less sympathy than an older woman who was 'unlucky' to get pregnant.

(iii) *Personal history* — the younger woman is more likely than the older to be facing motherhood alone and in poor financial circumstances; by age 40 there is a greater chance that the woman will be a wage earner or married to one. It is also more likely that at 20 the pregnancy being terminated is the *first* one, whereas at 40 it is probably the last; the 1967 Act allows termination where the health of the woman's *existing* children would suffer if the pregnancy continued.

2 The same scientific data are given a very different interpretation by the two newspapers — especially in their eye-catching headlines. This must add to the confusion felt by women who cannot check the original article in the *British Medical Journal* (in fact it is available in most major public libraries, but most people don't know this). At the time, GPs and Family Planning Clinics were inundated with calls from women trying to discover the truth about any risk they might be running. Freedom to choose a method of contraception must involve access to accurate information about health risks — in this case, a woman may choose on the basis of which newspaper she reads, or whether she reads a newspaper at all.

3 The rise in the abortion rate in this age-group resulted in 7.7 more abortions per 1000 women between the beginning and end of the decade (16.8 minus 9.1). However, the live birth rate to teenagers fell by more than twice this figure (50.4 minus 31.0 = 19.4 fewer births per 1000), therefore the decline in teenage pregnancy cannot be accounted for wholly by more freely available abortions. At least half the decline must be the result of better use of contraception or decreased sexual activity.

Chapter 12

1 (a) Contributory factors may include: unsocial hours; disruption of sleeping or eating patterns; transport problems affecting early or late shift workers; a relentless pace of work; repetitive and boring work; poorly designed workplaces with inadequate ventilation, high noise levels, bad lighting, overcrowding, etc; too much responsibility, or too little (i.e. resulting in a feeling that the work is trivial or low status); excessively long working hours as a result of combining paid employment with family responsibilities; the strain imposed by work which is badly organised for physically impaired employees.

(b) Problems arise in attributing ill-health to such conditions because:

(i) there are no physiological changes that can be taken as reliable indicators of stress;

(ii) physiological changes that *may* be related to stress do not show a consistent association with ill-health.

(iii) factors not related to work may contribute substantially to ill-health, or conversely, aspects of work organisation may exacerbate (rather than cause) existing illness.

2 Men with dependent children are particularly likely to work unsocial hours because rates of pay are higher than for dayworkers. By contrast, most jobs that are predominantly staffed by women do *not* offer extra pay for shiftwork; an adequate workforce during unsocial hours can usually be ensured because many women with dependent children feel able to work only when another family member can take over childcare.

The consequences of this for health in this family will largely depend on how well the husband adjusts to night work and how much work he does in the home. He *may* suffer distress or ill health as a result of disruption to normal sleeping and eating; she *is* suffering as a result of the 'double day' she works, because childcare and housework devolved back onto her despite their agreement.

Chapter 13

1 (i) The doctor may feel that HRT should be prescribed, since there is some evidence that oestrogen supplements help to alleviate hot flushes.

(ii) There is evidence that minor psychiatric problems such as depression may be correlated with the menopause, but there is no strong evidence that these are associated with the decline in oestrogen levels. Depression is sometimes alleviated by oestrogens, but there is also a strong placebo effect when oestrogen has been used in trials.

(iii) There is no evidence that HRT will help, since the woman has not yet had any problems. Since not all women have problems, her fears may be groundless.

2 No. As we noted at the beginning of the chapter, the decline in male fertility and male hormone production occurs very gradually over several decades. Impotence and irritability suddenly occurring at age 50 are unlikely to be due to reproductive changes, but could be responses to other events in this man's life, for example, worries about old age, a lack of advancement or challenge at work, loneliness when children leave home, boredom with his marriage, etc. Note that they could also be due to ill-health which was unrelated to hormone levels.

Chapter 14

1 He loses his *identity*, his *routine*, and his *purpose in life*. Prior to his retirement his identity in society was defined by his work, and his work governed his use of time, and kept him alert. His new identity — of 'Retired, At Leisure' — has no known status and carries with it no purposeful ways of using the day.

2 The writer values her *freedom* to choose how she lives very highly — for her it compensates for the disadvantages she perceives, such as loneliness. Her enjoyment of this freedom depends on factors such as her apparent good health (her eyesight is good enough to read); either she has simple tastes in food, or she has sufficient money to buy exactly what she likes; her love of reading provides a source of pleasure and an occupation that is cheap and readily available.

Chapter 15

1 Diseases of the lung, such as chronic bronchitis, lead to breathlessness on exertion (such as climbing a flight of stairs, or in severe cases just walking a few steps). Heart failure (due to coronary heart disease) also can lead to breathlessness. If the arteries supplying the heart are severely blocked by atheroma, the blood supply to the heart muscle may be inadequate, leading to *angina* (pain from cramp in the heart muscle) on exertion.

2 It depends on the nature of these diseases — whether they cause any *disability*, and whether they are *treatable*. There is little point in uncovering diseases you can do nothing about, or ones which are causing no functional disability.

Chapter 16

1 It is not true. In the UK, more old people get help from relatives than from professionals. There is no evidence that this support has declined recently.

2 The old lady has a considerable say in running her own life — despite needing help physically. However, in getting what she wants, she actually puts demands on her daughter that mean her daughter's life revolves around her mother. This system of care has considerable advantages over professional care for the old lady, but disadvantages for the daughter.

3 The support ratio measures the number of people in the labour force for each old person. It is one way of trying to gauge whether it is becoming easier or more difficult for the working population to maintain those beyond working age. Over the period up to the year 2000 this support ratio is likely to rise, making such maintenance slightly easier. Into the next century, the ratio will start to fall. Of course

many other factors will also affect how the elderly fare in the future, as we noted in the chapter.

Chapter 17

1 It is true in one sense: the life expectancy of a baby at birth has increased. However, the *maximum* life span has not increased.

2 She no longer saw any point to life, and had no reason to keep up standards and ideals. She had lost a companionship that was vital to her enjoyment of people and things. She no longer had the prospect of their plans for the future. She saw no possibility of future happiness.

Chapter 18

1 People rarely talk about death in our culture: it is not usually a 'polite' topic of conversation. There is no well-defined custom or ritual giving guidance on how to approach and talk to someone who has recently been bereaved. Crying in public is discouraged: talking about the death may lead to an embarrassing show of emotion.

Chapter 19

1 This is quite a complicated question. He would probably be influenced by several factors.

(a) His *training* — perhaps he automatically treats *all* chest infections with antibiotics.

(b) His *feelings* — perhaps he so dislikes the idea of death that he cannot decide to let someone die. Alternatively he may be so distressed by the sight of a severely demented old person that he would prefer her to die.

(c) His *ethics* — he may feel that life should be preserved at all cost, and the chest infection must therefore be treated, or he may feel that he must judge her quality of life before deciding how to treat her.

(d) He might know what wishes she had expressed previously — perhaps she had asked to be allowed to die if she ever became unable to care for herself.

(c) He might be influenced by her circumstances. For instance, is she an unbearable burden to her family or are they all coping and want her to live? Is she in a regimented, noisy, impersonal institution or a small, cosy, old people's home?

(f) He might be worried by the fear of legal or professional censure of his actions (though in this particular case he is unlikely either to be sued for inaction or condemned by his colleagues for withholding treatment).

Chapter 20

1 (a) The *biological* influence on his experience is the most obvious — after a lifetime of breathing coal dust and repeated bouts of bronchitis, his lungs no longer function well enough to supply adequate oxygen unless he sits still. (Note that the biological consequences of coal mining are in turn a consequence of social factors — society's requirement for energy, and the failure to protect the men who mine it from dust-related diseases.)

(b) The *social* factors that adversely affect his experience of retirement stem predominantly from his poor financial circumstances, which not only prevent him from enjoying a pint more than once a week but also keep him from the company of his friends in the workmen's institute. There are also hints in the account that he feels less of a 'man' than in the days when he 'supported his family by shovelling coal', reflecting the dominant view of the male gender role in this society.

(c) The *personal history* which may have a bearing on his experience is the fact that he once cut coal by hand and thus felt himself part of a 'special breed of men'; if he feels contempt for young miners who now use machines, what must he feel for himself — a man who can't even make the fire up?

2 (a) The subjects of these studies were all doctors — their reports of episodes of illness may well differ from those that a lay person would consider reporting, or would recall over a period of 10 years. The results are therefore not likely to be generally applicable. Conversely, the scale used to rate their life events into stress categories *was* developed by research on samples of the general population; we do not know if professional people such as doctors would find particular events on the scale significantly more or less stressful than the 'average' person.

Finally, the retrospective study allowed up to 2 years to pass between a life event and a health change deemed to be 'associated' with it. No account was taken of other factors in this period which might affect health, most obviously, contact with sick people!

(b) Given these reservations, no generalisations can be made from the results. However, they show a relationship between the *extent* of life events and the *extent* of episodes of illness: in both the retrospective and prospective studies, doctors with the highest scores of stressful life events also suffered the most illness. The prospective study suggests that the extent of life events in a person's recent past might be used as a basis for *predicting* illness in the near future. Note that the lower percentage of illness associated with life events in the prospective study than in the retrospective one can probably be explained by the much shorter period covered by the prospective study — 18 months as opposed to 10 years. However, it is also possible that the doctors may have made mistakes in recalling their illnesses and life events in the past 10 years, bringing them closer together in time than they actually were, and hence increasing the percentage of associations. No such bias could 'inflate' the results of the prospective study.

Entries and page numbers in **bold type** refer to key words which are printed in *italics* in the text.

Index

Acknowledgements
Grateful acknowledgement is made to the following sources for material used in this book:

Text
W.H. Auden, 'The unknown citizen' in *Collected Poems*, 1969, reprinted by permission of Faber and Faber Ltd.; J. Joseph, 'Warning', reprinted by permission of John Johnson (Authors' Agent) Ltd.

Figures
Figures 3.1, 4.1, 9.1, 10.9 and 11.5 reprinted by permission of the Controller of HMSO; *Figure 3.4* from H. Phelps Brown, *The Equality of Pay*, Oxford University Press, 1979, *Figure 3.6* from R.J. Donaldson, *Essential Community Medicine*, MTP Press, 1983; *Figures 5.1 and 5.2* from P. Huntingford, in S. Kitzinger and J. Davis, *The Place of Birth*, Oxford University Press, © Sheila Kitzinger and John Davis, 1978; *Figure 5.4* from D.W. Smith *et al. The Biologic Ages of Man*, W.B. Saunders, 1978; *Figure 5.6* The Sighthill Maternity Team, 'Community antenatal care: the way forward' in *Scottish Medicine*, April 1982; *Figure 6.7* courtesy Association of Radical Midwives; *Figure 6.8* from R. Caldero-Barcia, 'Physiological and psychological bases for the modern and humanised management of normal labour', in *Recent Progress in Perinatal Medicine and Prevention of Congenital Anomaly*, in Tokyo Ministry of Health and Welfare, 1979; *Figures 7.1 and 7.3* from T.R. Forbes, 'By what disease or casualty' in C. Webster (ed.) *Health, Medicine and Mortality in the 16th Century*, Cambridge University Press, 1979; *Figures 8.2 and 8.3* from E.J. Ebrahim, *Paediatric Practice in Developing Countries*, Macmillan, London and Basingstoke, 1981; *Figures 8.4 and 8.5* from J.M. Tanner and R.H. Whitehouse, *Archives of Disease in Childhood*, vol. 51, 1976 © Castlemead Publications; *Figure 8.6* from W.W. Gruelich, 'Growth of children of the same race under different environmental conditions', in *Science*, vol. 127, March 1958, © 1958 American Association for the Advancement of Science; *Figure 8.7* from J.B. Orr, *Food and Income*, Macmillan, London and Basingstoke, 1936; *Figure 8.8* Institute of Child Health; *Figures 8.9, 10.2 and 10.5* from J.M. Tanner, *Foetus into Man*, Open Books, 1978; *Figure 8.10* from E.M. Widdowson, 'Mental contentment and physical growth' in *Lancet*, 1951; *Figure 10.8* from A.J. Stunkard *et al.* 'The influence of social class on obesity and thinness in children' in *Journal of American Medical Association*, vol. 221, © 1972 American Medical Association; *Figure 11.6* from *Communicable Disease Report*, 8, 1984, PHLS Communicable Disease Surveillance Centre; *Figure 13.1* from S.M. McKinlay and M. Jefferys, 'The menopausal syndrome' in *British Journal of Preventative Medicine*, vol. 28, 1974; *Figure 13.2* from G.T. Bungay *et al.*, 'Study of symptoms in middle life with special reference to the menopause' in *British Medical Journal*, 1980; *Figure 13.3* from Sturdee *et al.* 'Physiological aspects of menopausal hot flush' in *British Medical Journal*, vol. 11, 1978; *Figure 15.1* from R. Passmore and J.S. Robson, *A Comparison to Medical Studies*, vol. 2, Blackwell Scientific, 2nd edn. 1980; *Figure 15.2* from J.F. Fries, 'Aging, natural death and the compression of morbidity', in *New England Journal of Medicine*, vol. 303, no. 3, 1980; *Figure 20.1* from C.M. Parkes, 'Broken heart: a statistical study of mortality amongst widowers' in *British Medical Journal*, vol. 1, 1969.

Tables
Tables 4.2, 6.2 and 16.1 reprinted by permission of the Controller of HMSO; *Table 5.2* from R. Chamberlain *et al. British Births: Vol. 1 The First Week of Life*, Heinemann Medical Books, 1975; *Table 6.3* from M. Klein *et al.*, 'A comparison of low risk pregnant women booked for delivery' in *British Journal of Obstetrics and Gynaecology*, vol. 90, 1983; *Table 6.4* from C.A. Cox *et al.* 'Critical appraisal of domiciliary obstetrics and neonatal practice' in *British Medical Journal*, vol. 1, 1976; *Table 7.1* from J.D. Campbell, 'Attribution of illness' *Journal of Health and Social Behaviour*, vol. 16, 1975; *Table 7.5* from M. Butler *et. al. Education, Health and Behaviour*, Longman, 1970; *Tables 10.1 and 10.2* from D.J. Weatherall *et al.* (eds.) *Oxford Textbook of Medicine*, vol. 1, Oxford University Press, 1983; *Table 10.3* from J.M. Tanner, *Growth at Adolescence*, Blackwell, 1962; *Table 11.2* from I. Reid, *Social Class Differences in Britain*, Blackwell, 1981; *Table 11.3* from C. Farrell, *'My Mother Said . . .' The Way Young People Learned About Sex and Birth Control*, Routledge and Kegan Paul PLC, 1978.